D1135082

THE STRUCTURE OF
PHYSICAL CHEMISTRY

THE STRUCTURE OF
PHYSICAL CHEMISTRY

BY

C. N. HINSHELWOOD

DR. LEE'S PROFESSOR OF CHEMISTRY
IN THE UNIVERSITY OF OXFORD

OXFORD
AT THE CLARENDON PRESS

Oxford University Press, Amen House, London E.C.4

GLASGOW   NEW YORK   TORONTO   MELBOURNE   WELLINGTON
BOMBAY   CALCUTTA   MADRAS   KARACHI   LAHORE   DACCA
CAPE TOWN   SALISBURY   NAIROBI   IBADAN   ACCRA
KUALA LUMPUR   HONG KONG

FIRST EDITION 1951

REPRINTED LITHOGRAPHICALLY IN GREAT BRITAIN
AT THE UNIVERSITY PRESS, OXFORD
FROM SHEETS OF THE FIRST EDITION
1952, 1958, 1965

PREFACE

PHYSICAL chemistry is a difficult and diversified subject. The difficulty can, of course, be overcome by a suitable intensity of application and the diversity dealt with in some measure, by judicious specialization. This is very well as far as it goes, but leaves something to be desired, because there is, it is to be hoped, still room for a liberal occupation with wide studies, and this in a manner which goes beyond the polite interest of the dilettante. In the light of a good long spell of University teaching, however, I have the impression that this aspect of the matter is in some danger of neglect. I thought, therefore, I would like to write a book of moderate compass which, in no way competing with more formal works, should lay emphasis on the structure and continuity of the whole subject and try to show the relation of its various parts to one another. Certain themes or, one might almost say, leitmotifs run through physical chemistry, and these would be used to unify the composition.

The treatment would be neither historical, nor formally deductive, but at each stage I would try to indicate the route by which an inquiring mind might most simply and naturally proceed in its attempt to understand that part of the nature of things included in physical chemistry. This approach I have ventured to designate humanistic. The proper study of mankind, no doubt, is man, but one of the greatest activities of man is to find things out.

Apart from the question of seeing the subject as a whole, there is that of seeing it with a sober judgement. It seems to me specially important in modern physical chemistry to be clear and honest about fundamentals. This is not so easy as it sounds. Some of the current working notions are expressed in words which easily become invested with a more literally descriptive character than they deserve, and many young chemists—this is my impression at least—are led to think they understand things which in fact they do not. Something simple and direct seems to be conveyed by words such as 'resonance' and 'activity', which is not legitimately conveyed at all. By certain descriptions, which it is easy to give, one is reminded of Alice: 'Somehow it seems to fill my head with ideas—only I don't exactly know what they are.' Many of the mathematical equations which serve important technical purposes in the modern forms of theoretical chemistry are of a highly abstract kind, but they have acquired a dangerous seductiveness in that they clothe themselves rather readily in metaphors. Occasionally it is salutary to regard this metaphorical apparel with the eyes of the child who surveyed the emperor's new clothes. I have done my best here and there to help the uninitiated reader keep in mind just what the content of theories amounts to.

On the other hand, I have not attempted any refined analysis of conceptions such as probability, or statistical equilibrium, since these are not difficult to have a working knowledge of, though purists could subject to harassing criticism almost any treatment save a very elaborate one. Excessively detailed analysis however, would have obscured the general plan which I was anxious to try and depict.

Evidently, therefore, my undertaking, although on a fairly modest scale, is a somewhat rash one involving various kinds of compromise, but as the book does not claim in the slightest degree to supersede or replace other sources of information (upon which, of course, it almost wholly depends itself) I hope the boldness is not quite unjustified.

Finally I should like to express indebtedness to various colleagues who have helped me in many ways; to Dr. R. F. Barrow for also reading through the proofs, and to the staff of the Clarendon Press who have given much more help than any author has the right to expect.

C. N. H.

OXFORD
January 1951

CONTENTS

CONTENTS

PART V

THE FORMS OF MATTER IN EQUILIBRIUM

PART VI

PASSAGE TOWARDS EQUILIBRIUM

PART I

THE WORLD AS A MOLECULAR CHAOS

SYNOPSIS

SOME of the ancient philosophers conceived the world to be made up of primordial particles in random motion, but their theories were not very fruitful since they lacked the necessary empirical basis. The formation of this was a long, complex, and far from obvious process.

Quantitative relations between the masses, and in certain cases the volumes, of substances which combine chemically establish the atomic theory as a scientific doctrine, and rather subtle coherence arguments reveal the distinction between atoms and molecules. Developments in physics lead to the recognition of heat as the invisible motion of the molecules themselves, and the kinetic picture of matter emerges.

Even in its first primitive version, this picture gives a satisfying representation of nature in many of its broad aspects. Molecules are envisaged as microscopic masses following the laws which Newtonian mechanics prescribe for macroscopic bodies. They are believed to be in chaotic motion and also to exert forces upon one another at small distances. Their motions tend to scatter them through all space: the forces to agglomerate them into condensed phases. The conflict between these two tendencies governs the existence of material systems in their various states, determines the range of stability of gases, liquids, and solids, and regulates the extent to which various possible combinations of atoms into molecules occur.

Reasonable estimates can be made of the absolute sizes, masses, speeds, and modes of motion of molecules, and coherent explanations can be given of many of the physical properties of matter in its different forms.

At this level of interpretation nothing is yet postulated about the forces, except that they manifest themselves in the measurable energy changes which accompany almost every kind of physical and chemical transformation. It is necessary, therefore, to describe the state of a chaotic system of particles primarily in terms of its energy. Such a description is provided in statistical theory.

In the world of molecular chaos various energy states are regarded as so many boxes occupied by molecules at random, and everything tends to that condition which may be realized in the largest number of ways. This idea leads to the definition of entropy, a function which measures the probability of a molecular assemblage, and to the laws of thermodynamics, which prescribe the conditions of equilibrium and the direction of possible changes in all such processes as expansion and contraction, melting and evaporation, and in actual chemical transformations. These laws themselves are closely related to empirical observations about heat-changes which can be used to provide an independent basis for them.

Given only an empirical knowledge of the energy changes accompanying atomic and molecular regroupings, the dynamical and statistical laws (or the equivalent thermodynamical principles) predict the relations of solids, liquids, and gases for single substances and for mixtures, and also the dependence of chemical equilibrium upon concentration and temperature.

But the representation so made is limited in two ways. First, the forces remain unknown. The energy changes are measurable by experiment, but their nature remains unexplained. Secondly, the actual prescription of the condition of molecular chaos proves on closer inspection to present certain subtle problems which cannot be solved at this stage. If molecules are assigned to states according to the laws of probability, then what constitutes a state ? In the first instance, equal ranges of momentum can be satisfactorily regarded as defining a series of states. But while this idea leads to valuable laws regarding changes in entropy, and the dependence of all kinds of equilibrium upon variables such as concentration and temperature, it leaves quite unsolved the question of the absolute position of chemical and physical equilibria.

Scientific explanations seek to describe the unknown in terms of the known. The first attempt at such an explanation of the material forms and relations of the world works in terms of particles which are themselves small-scale models of grosser objects. It goes a long way, but reaches a boundary beyond which it cannot pass.

I

ATOMS AND MOLECULES

Introductory observations

ADAM and Eve, tradition tells us, ate from a tree of knowledge and though driven forth from Eden were the forebears of a progeny which never lost their taste. Prometheus, we also hear, stole fire from heaven, yet the fate he met has not deterred posterity from emulation. These two old stories are the symbols of two deep desires: the one to understand the essence of the world, the other to achieve the power of dominating nature. It is not inappropriate that the allegories are taken from diverse mythologies, expressing as they do profoundly different attitudes of mind. To some men knowledge of the universe has been an end possessing in itself a value that is absolute: to others it has seemed a means to useful applications. These two divergent views are never reconciled by argument, yet by a strange entanglement the history of the sciences was made not by the one or by the other school of thought but from the interplay of both. The route to mastery has lain indeed through abstract knowledge, yet the path to knowledge by the ways of contemplation has seldom proved a practicable one. Direct solution of the problems which the useful arts present is not infrequently attainable by application of the principles already known and understood, but theories and hypotheses of other than a vague and misty kind are seldom based upon a panoramic survey of the general scene. They rest more often on a detailed searching into matters which a casual view might well dismiss as specialized, recondite, and obscure, and access to the realm of fruitful theories is usually by devious and unexpected ways, found out by men with very different ends in view.

As it is handed down, the outcome of past probings into nature presents a variegated and uneven picture, resembling in some ways those interlocking growths of crystals which have sprung from many centres. By the proper methods such tangles may be induced to recrystallize into uniformly oriented systems, and from the character of its origins any experimental science stands in need from time to time of the treatment which this analogy suggests.

The matter goes deeper even than the metaphor implies. Science is not the mere collection of facts, which are infinitely numerous and mostly uninteresting, but the attempt by the human mind to order these facts into satisfying patterns. Now a pattern or design is not a purely objective function but something imposed by the mind on what is presented to it, as is seen in those pictures of piled cubes which can be made at will to appear in advancing or receding order. The imposition of design on nature is in fact an act of artistic creation on the part of the man of science, though it is subject to a discipline more exacting than that of poetry or painting. Two painters may depict quite differently a given scene, though the canvasses of both may present essential truth. Science has greater objectivity than painting, but the formulation of its laws cannot be rendered wholly independent of the individual mind. The limitation is the greater since knowledge is never absolute and its expression rarely perfect. Much of the content of a growing science is subsumed in working hypotheses, constructions which in the last analysis are not impersonal.

Upon the heterogeneity imparted to science by its multiple and fortuitous origins is thus superimposed another resembling that of a picture whose various parts are painted by artists of different schools. Judgements may often differ as to which of two conceptions is the more fundamental, so that related theories may sometimes start from very varying premisses. The unaesthetic element of variegation can never be wholly removed, but from time to time greater harmony can be introduced by rearrangement. To resort once more to metaphor: in a time of great expansion a museum might fill its galleries with the most disparate works of art, revealing to the scholar, stimulating to the craftsman, and to the man of taste a little disconcerting. But at intervals the acquisitions are regrouped according to a principle—in which the critics may not acquiesce— but which at least is consciously decided. In science, too, this re-arrangement must from time to time be undertaken, and on the writer who describes a field of any breadth there falls the task of making what is practically an artistic judgement.

These more or less philosophical observations would a generation ago have seemed out of place as an introduction to an account of the field which we call physical chemistry. Today, however, they are relevant and serve to suggest what may be expected from the survey and what may not. To realize that the content of the subject is a series of accounts of how human minds have tried to represent their probings into nature, by diminishing unjustified expectation, increases admiration for what in fact has been achieved. What might appear as oddnesses, inconsistencies, and arbitrary assumptions fall into their perspective and no longer disconcert. The best under-standing of the subject is attainable, to return to the metaphor already used, by proceeding from room to room of the gallery and studying the works of various schools with a due realization that values must be adjusted in transit.

It is in this spirit that we shall examine the scope and achieve-ments of physical chemistry, and see what views about the nature of things it reflects. We shall attempt to show the subject in a con-tinuous development which reveals its structure and displays the relation of its parts. We shall therefore not pay much attention to the accidents of history, but we shall be very much concerned with the methods by which an inquiring mind can penetrate the secrets of nature. In this sense the treatment may reasonably be called humanistic.

We shall find it necessary to keep before us what is meant by a scientific explanation: it is in effect the representation of the un-known in terms of the known, but we shall find that the idiom in which the representation is expressible has to suffer some remarkable transformations as we proceed. In the early stages, to employ yet again the metaphor of the picture gallery, we spend some profitable time in a school of primitives: presently we find that more abstract schools command our attention.

Atoms and molecules

Chemistry rests largely upon the theory of atoms and molecules. The idea of an atomic constitution of things was arrived at by the ancients, though the basis of their speculations differed considerably from that of modern chemistry. They thought that there must be a limit to the divisibility of matter, that living creatures must be reproduced from ultimate primordial bodies of the appropriate kind, that various natural phenomena such as the penetration of heat and cold depend upon the hidden motions of tiny particles, and so on. It is hardly conceivable that chemistry as we know it could have arisen directly in this way.

The theory, however, that the sensible qualities of objects could be interpreted in terms of the motion of minute particles of specific kinds was a very great achievement, and itself must have depended upon a long evolution of ideas. We need not enter into this history, but it is important to realize that it must have existed. To distinguish between the material substratum and the qualities for which it is responsible required enlightenment and profound thinking. As far as chemistry is concerned, the process cannot be said really to have been completed until the phlogiston theory disappeared.

The fundamental ideas of matter and motion only acquired their dominance after long processes of trial and error had shown how more and more could be described in terms of them. One accustomed to the ways of thought of science may now find it difficult to realize the elaboration of the analysis by which, for instance, colour came no longer to be regarded as something which a substance contains rather as a fabric contains a dye. Our notions about the scientifically describable substratum of the world are now so familiar that there is some danger of forgetting to what extent it is based upon a working hypothesis, and one which possesses natural limitations.

The basis of chemistry as it grew up in the nineteenth century is *Dalton's atomic theory*. In this the intuitive idea of ultimate particles is applied to explain definite quantitative laws of chemical composition, those, namely, of constant, multiple, and reciprocal proportions. These rules could only have emerged after a long empirical study of diverse and often obscure chemical substances, since many of the things most obviously attracting the attention of the contemplative philosopher—wood, rocks, plants, and the like—would have yielded singularly unfruitful evidence for an atomic theory in its infancy. When, however, the labours of many generations of alchemists, artificers, and craftsmen had provided the necessary facts, when the technique of weighing had been refined and the practice of quantitative measurement had become established, and when the various apt conjunctions of experiment and speculation had at length occurred, there crystallized out the notion that certain specific substances— and not principles such as fire—constituted the chemical elements, and that their union according to quantitative laws gave rise to all the other substances.

The same elements combine in constant and fixed proportions. This suggests that the union of macroscopic quantities is simply an n-fold repetition of the union of indivisible microscopic units of characteristic mass. Other mathematical descriptions of the phenomenon could doubtless be devised, but they could hardly possess the vividness of the atomic conception, which is further strengthened by the facts about multiple and reciprocal proportions. Two elements, which we may call A and B, not infrequently form several compounds with one another, and in these the masses of B which have combined with unit mass of A stand in the ratio of simple integers. This is the *law of multiple proportions*. To each element, further, there may be assigned an equivalent weight, such that it defines the relation of that element not to one other but to every other. The proportions in which any two elements unite are in the ratio of their equivalent weights or in one which is a simple integral multiple of it. This is the *law of reciprocal proportions*. By extending the idea of units to give a coherent set of relationships between all the elements it gives to the atomic theory a still higher status. Some kind of quantitative metric which would satisfy a mathematical physicist could conceivably be devised to embrace the combination of single pairs of elements, but that any other system as simple as that of Dalton could be found to describe the possible relations of every element to every other is unlikely.

A great advance became possible when the technique of making measurements with gaseous substances was introduced. *Gay Lussac's* famous rule states that when chemical combination occurs between gases the volumes of those consumed and of those produced, measured under standard conditions of temperature and pressure, stand in a simple numerical ratio. Since what applies to the masses according to the atomic theory itself now proves to apply to the gas volumes, the conclusion follows that equal volumes of substances in the gaseous state under the standard conditions actually contain, to within a small numerical multiple, equal numbers of the primordial combining units. After various trials and some groping in the dark it proved further that a coherent system requires the *hypothesis of Avogadro*, namely that the numerical multiple in question is unity, but that the primordial particles existing in the free state are molecules which may consist of more than one atom. For many common elements the number of atoms in the molecule was discovered to be two. According to the hypothesis equal volumes of gaseous compounds at equal temperature and pressure possess masses proportional to those of their constituent molecules, a principle of the greatest help in the establishment of chemical formulae and in the assignment of atomic weights to the elements.

The detailed arguments by which the individual atomic weights, after a long process of trial and error, were established need not be enlarged on here, but the principles of the method must be summarized. As many compounds as possible were analysed and the proportions of their elements determined. To a chosen element was arbitrarily given a conventional atomic weight (originally unity to hydrogen, later changed for practical convenience). As many molecular weights as possible were determined from the gaseous densities, and the least weight of a given element which ever appeared in the molecule of any compound came to be accepted as its atomic weight.

The system which was gradually built up, like the hypothesis of Avogadro upon which it was largely based, rested upon arguments of coherence, and could have involved errors of simple numerical multiples—for some time indeed carbon was given the atomic weight six. But the discovery of the periodic system of the elements, and the realization that Avogadro's hypothesis fitted in very well with the kinetic theory of gases, presently showed that the probability of error could be disregarded.

The numerical relations of Gay Lussac's law are only approximate and Avogadro's hypothesis is correspondingly inexact. For this fact the kinetic theory provides a ready explanation. It is, however, only

intelligible in terms of developments which would probably never
have occurred had the inexactitude not been in the first instance
neglected. In science, as in everything else, there is need for courage
to act upon the conviction that more significance may reside in an
approximation to the truth than in the deviations which it for the
moment disregards.

Before passing to consider the alliance of chemistry with physics
we shall try to focus once more the way in which pure chemistry
itself emerges from the complex whole which nature presents to
contemplation. First, this complex is analysed in various tentative
ways until substances are found to be enumerable separately from
qualities, and we realize, for example, that when we say mercury
oxide contains mercury, oxygen, and redness, the first two are
differently significant from the third. Substances commonly existing
in the world are found not infrequently to be separable into parts by
simple means such as distillation. Some which resist this process of
fractionation are classified as pure substances. But these sometimes
change when brought together, and seem to disappear giving rise to
others, often with evolution of heat or light. Such drastic changes
can be reversed by various roundabout ways, and the original participants in what is termed the chemical reaction can be regenerated.
Most substances can be split up into others or made by the union of
others, but some are incapable of further resolution or of synthesis
and become recognized as the chemical elements. Gradually the list
of them is filled, and presently coherent relations between the properties of the individuals emerge. The structure of the periodic
system is revealed and interlopers can be detected and ejected.

In chemical reactions, however spectacular, mass is found to be
conserved within the limits of the sensitivity of chemical balances,
and this is as it should be if the transformations are mere regroupings
of the units of a material substratum. The atoms of ancient speculation fill the roles required. The quantitative laws of chemical combination then follow and permit the development of chemistry in the
form in which it is known today.

It is hard to see how the evolution could have been other than
long and painful, since the commonest objects are among the most
unsuitable for elementary chemical investigation, and the major task
for chemistry in one sense was the discovery of its own tools. Only
by a fortunate disposition of providence has the story not been made

more tangled still, since mass is not really conserved and the elements are only relatively unchanging. But the phenomena of nuclear physics are on such a scale that in chemical reactions they may be neglected, not only in a first but in much higher approximations.

Matter and motion

Chemistry concerns itself with the material substratum of the world. It was once said that the only thing you can do with matter is to move it, and though this statement would probably not sustain detailed analysis in the light of modern physics, it expresses an essential truth with a high degree of approximation. The least that can be said is that it brings into clear relief the need for a kinetic theory of molecules. The atoms of the ancient philosophers were in lively motion, and Lucretius tries to explain in detail how chaotic displacements of minute particles below the threshold of visibility can give the semblance of rest. Facts of common observation, such as diffusion, evaporation, and the like, are readily interpretable by a rudimentary kinetic theory which, however, only attains to the rank of a serious scientific hypothesis when the Newtonian laws are applied to the molecules conceived by chemistry. The laws of motion themselves are based upon the observation of massive bodies, and their application to the invisible, and indeed in the first instance hypothetical, particles of Dalton and Avogadro rests upon an assumption. On the face of it and in the absence of evidence to the contrary there is more reason for making this assumption than for not making it, and the taking of the risk proves to be abundantly justified. But there must be no surprise or concern when the utility of the picture so created turns out to have its limits.

One of the simplest routes to the understanding of the question is, as it happens, that which was followed historically. Observation of common phenomena such as the winds suggests the reasonableness of assuming a material substratum even for the tenuous and invisible parts of nature like the air. The next step consists in making experiments by confining gases in tubes, observing their 'spring', and measuring their pressures in terms of the heights of mercury columns which the spring supports. *Boyle's law* emerges in the well-known form

$$pv = \text{constant},$$

where p is the pressure exerted by a volume v of a gas at a constant temperature.

That the spring or pressure increases as the gas is compressed vividly suggests the picture of a crowd of flying particles seeking to escape and causing pressure on the surface of the containing vessel by their impacts. This idea leads immediately to the first quantitative result.

Gas pressure

Let there be n molecules of a gas in unit volume of an enclosure, and let their motion be random both in direction and in the magnitude of the speeds. Consider those which approach unit area of the surface at an angle of incidence within $d\theta$ of a given value θ and which possess velocities within du of a value u. When they impinge upon the surface they may be supposed to suffer an elastic reflection, the normal component of the momentum of each being changed from $mu\cos\theta$ to $-mu\cos\theta$. The change for each molecule is thus $2mu\cos\theta$. The number of particles which suffer reflection in each second is proportional to n and to u, so that the rate of change of momentum for the type of particle defined is αnmu^2, where α is a numerical multiplier independent of n, m, and u. Averaged over all possible directions of approach and over all permissible velocities, the result becomes $\alpha' nm\bar{u}^2$, where $\bar{u}^2$ is the average value of u^2 and α' is still a numerical multiplier. By Newton's second law the surface will be urged outward with the force necessary to maintain this rate of change of momentum, and the force on unit area constitutes the pressure, p.

Thus
$$p = \alpha' nm\bar{u}^2.$$

A very elementary argument shows that α' is roughly $\tfrac{1}{3}$. If the speeds are fairly closely grouped about the average value all may be taken approximately as $\bar{u}$. Let all velocities be normal to one or other surface. Then in any given direction the number of molecules approaching unit area of the surface and reaching it in unit time is not far from one-sixth of those contained in a prism of unit base and height $\bar{u}$. Thus

$$p = \tfrac{1}{6}n\bar{u} \times 2m\bar{u} = \tfrac{1}{3}nm\bar{u}^2.$$

The more precise evaluation of the multiplier does not in fact make much difference, and for most purposes we shall accept the result

$$p = \tfrac{1}{3}nm\bar{u}^2.$$

It must be emphasized that the parts of the above argument which are stated without proof or sketched in only roughly relate to the value of the numerical multiplier only and not to the proportionality of p and $m\bar{u}^2$.

When a gas is expanded or compressed, n, and consequently p, varies inversely as the volume. This is Boyle's law. No real gases follow it exactly at higher pressures, but many do with a good degree of approximation, and all do at very low pressures.

Temperature

If a gas becomes hotter, the pressure which it exerts increases. In the first instance hotness is gauged simply by sensation. Since p is proportional to $m\bar{u}^2$, that is to the mean kinetic energy of the molecules, the hotness appears to be a function of the invisible translational motion. So rational does this interpretation of the origin of the sensation seem that it becomes expedient to introduce a scale of hotness and to define the degree of hotness, or temperature, as proportional to the pressure which a gas having that degree would exert. For a standard scale the gas must obey Boyle's law. This so-called perfect gas scale is simple theoretically and convenient practically, since the deviations of actual gases from the law are easily corrected for by extrapolation to low pressures.

To define the temperature of a gas we consider one gram molecule of it and write
$$T = pV/R,$$
or
$$pV = RT,$$

where R is a proportionality factor defined by the arbitrary condition that at 760 mm. pressure there shall be 100 degrees of temperature between the freezing-point and the boiling-point of water. What we mean by the temperature of the water, or of any non-gaseous substance, is simply the temperature which a gas would assume if left in contact with it for a long enough time. The idea of thermal equilibrium will require further discussion at a slightly later stage.

In terms of the primary definition of temperature which we have for the time being adopted, Charles's law, which states that gas pressure is proportional to the absolute temperature, would be a tautologous statement. It is not necessarily so, and was not so in its historical setting, since other scales of temperature, notably that based upon the expansion of a mercury column by heat, are possible. The mercury thermometer and the gas thermometer provide scales which in fact correspond rather closely, and it is the former which has been used in practice more than the latter. The approach to the theoretical aspect of temperature which is now being followed thus departs in an important way from the line of historical development.

The statements contained in the equations $p = \frac{1}{3}nm\bar{u}^2$ and $pV = RT$ constitute the simplest possible illustrations of the thesis, established in the course of the nineteenth century, that heat in general is a mode of motion. Since, as in the experiment where Joule warmed up water by the churning action transmitted from falling weights, mechanical energy of a mass is quantitatively convertible into heat, and since all attempts to account for such phenomena in terms of a special kind of caloric fluid prove to be sterile, the identification of heat with the invisible chaotic motion of the molecules is compelling. Mechanical energy becomes apparent when the motions of the invisible parts are so coordinated as to give rise to perceptible motion of the group: it is transformed into heat when the coordination is destroyed and the motion is no longer discernible by any of the senses save that which permits the appreciation of warmth. From the point of view of the individual molecule, nothing has occurred when mechanical energy has become heat, and the *quantitative equivalence of heat and energy* is simply a special example of the conservation of energy. This equivalence is asserted as an empirical principle in the *First Law of Thermodynamics.*

Chemistry gives reason to suppose that molecules, being groups of atoms, should possess shapes, and therefore be capable of rotations. Since, moreover, the union of atoms implies some kind of force to hold them together, there is the further possibility of internal vibrational motions. The existence of liquids and solids, as well as the departure of real gases from Boyle's law, shows that there are forces between molecules themselves, so that there must be potential energy stored up in any collection of them.

We may therefore expect that if we can find appropriate conditions in which to make the comparison, the total energy contents of gram-molecular quantities of various substances should differ greatly according to the specific shapes and structures of the molecules. The possibility of a valid comparison depends upon the principle of thermal equilibrium.

Suppose a portion of substance to be placed in contact with a gas thermometer, or with a mercury thermometer calibrated in terms of one. The reading of the thermometer changes at first and then settles down to a steady value, say, T_1, which is taken as the common temperature of itself and of the substance with which it is now in thermal equilibrium. Suppose now that equal masses of two different substances at temperatures T_1 and T_2 respectively are placed in contact. T_1 and T_2 both alter until a common steady value T_3 is attained. T_3 is not in general the mean of T_1 and T_2. It may, however, be calculated, as elementary physics teaches, by the aid of the assumption that something called heat flows from one body to the other until a common temperature is reached, and that the quantity of heat required to raise a unit mass by one degree varies from substance to substance, each one possessing its own characteristic *specific heat*.

The interpretation which the molecular hypothesis gives of thermal equilibrium and of what constitutes equality of temperature between two bodies with different specific heats is one of the most important chapters of physical chemistry.

Let us begin by supposing that two gases, each of which obeys Boyle's law sufficiently well, are mixed. Initially their respective temperatures are T_1 and T_2. Their molecules interchange energy by collision, and the transfers in any given encounter may be in either direction, but on the average they will occur predominantly from the gas initially at the higher temperature to that at the lower. When the common temperature, T, is reached the interchanges still continue, but now they take place equally in both directions. What is called a *statistical equilibrium* is set up. In this state, for one gram molecule of each gas at a common temperature, pressure, and volume,

$$\tfrac{1}{3}n_1 m_1 \bar{u}_1^2 = \tfrac{1}{3}n_2 m_2 \bar{u}_2^2.$$

If, from the purely chemical evidence to which reference has already been made, we are prepared to believe Avogadro's hypothesis, we assume that $n_1 = n_2$ and infer that

$$m_1 \bar{u}_1^2 = m_2 \bar{u}_2^2.$$

The condition of thermal equilibrium is thus seen to be that the mean translational kinetic energy should be the same for each gas.

This latter result is derivable, as it happens, quite independently of Avogadro's principle and in a form which gives it even greater generality and importance.

The equipartition principle

The establishment of statistical equilibrium is not confined to translational energy. When two substances are in contact or mixed, whether they are gaseous, liquid, or solid, a state must be reached where the gains and losses of each kind of energy, translational, rotational, and vibrational, by the molecules of the two kinds balance. Such a condition corresponds to equality of temperature, and involves a quite definite relation between the different types of energy in the various kinds of molecule.

In a mixture of gases at a uniform temperature the average translational energies of the various kinds of molecule are the same. If some of the molecules present are of more complex structure than others, they will have more possibilities of motion, and the share of the total energy which they take might well be expected to be greater. A detailed investigation, which will be given later, shows in fact that the sharing out is governed by a law known as that of the *equipartition of energy*. The nature of this law is as follows.

Translational, rotational, and vibrational energies may be expressed in terms of vectorial quantities. Translational and rotational velocities may be represented by vectors, that is by lines with definite lengths and directions, which may be resolved into components along three spatial axes of coordinates. Similarly a vibration has an axis and an amplitude, and it is resolvable. Each component of each type of motion is called a *degree of freedom*. To a reasonable degree of approximation the energy may be expressed as a sum of terms in each of which a characteristic molecular constant multiplies the square of a suitable coordinate. Thus kinetic energy of translation is $\frac{1}{2}m(\dot{x}^2+\dot{y}^2+\dot{z}^2)$ where $\dot{x}$, $\dot{y}$, and $\dot{z}$ are the components of velocity along the three axes x, y, and z. Rotational energy may be expressed as a sum of terms of the type $\frac{1}{2}I\omega^2$, where I is the moment of inertia about the axis of rotation and ω is the angular velocity. When the vibrational motion is simple harmonic, which it may often be assumed to be, there is a term for the kinetic energy, $\frac{1}{2}m\dot{x}^2$, and also a term for the potential energy, $\frac{1}{2}\mu x^2$, where x is the displacement of the particle from its equilibrium position and μ is a constant. In so far as the total energy can be represented correctly by a sum of such *square terms*, the equipartition principle states that the average value of each for all types of molecule becomes the same when thermal equilibrium is attained.

The representation of the energy in this way is not really exact: nor are the different kinds of energy in the molecule strictly independent of one another. Thus, for example, as the amplitude of vibration increases the moment of inertia changes, so that the rotational energy is affected. While this complication limits the exactness of the equipartition principle (which is subject to even more important restrictions, as will appear later), it in no way affects the validity of the general conception of a definite functional relation defining the energy distribution in statistical equilibrium. It is the existence of such a relation which gives significance to the ideas of temperature and of heat flow.

The mathematical treatment of equipartition and the general consideration of energy distributions will presently occupy our attention a good deal. For the moment we shall turn to the way in which the simplest form of the principle has helped to deepen our knowledge about the existence of molecules.

Molecular reality and the determination of Avogadro's number

Considerations of the kind which have been so far advanced lay the foundations of a kinetic theory of molecules, which seeks to interpret physical and chemical phenomena in terms of particles and their motions. The conceptions of the ancient philosophers have gained in precision, and the way seems clear for further fruitful investigations. But the atoms and molecules remain, as far as any arguments so far considered go, inferential. They are creations of the mind, inaccessible to the ordinary senses. There was indeed a school of thought about the end of the last century which regarded them as fictions, deplored their excessive use in the theories of physical chemistry, and sought for the description of phenomena in terms of energy and of matter to which no minute structure was attributed. This plea, even in its day, was an extravagance, and it has since been put out of court by the detailed study of such phenomena as the emission of countable particles from radio-active substances and by the application of the techniques of X-ray and electron diffraction to reveal discrete structure in matter. The most direct way in which the challenge can be met is by the analysis of what is called the Brownian motion. This phenomenon provides a means, exploited by Perrin and others, of bridging the vast gulf between the invisible motions of molecules and the visible displacements of macroscopic bodies, of making molecular happenings sensible, and of determining the absolute masses of molecules. It consists simply in this: that certain minute particles still large enough to be directly discernible by the light which they scatter into a microscope are observed to be in rapid random movement.

According to the equipartition principle, the average translational energy of an oxygen molecule at a given temperature is the same as that of a molecule of hydrogen, benzene, or any other substance. No matter how many internal degrees of freedom there are, they do not affect the issue. In the derivation of the principle itself nothing is said about a limit to the size, mass, or complexity of the particle. Thus even a macroscopic lump of lead in thermal equilibrium with the ordinary air is buffeted on all sides by molecules of oxygen and of nitrogen, and acquires translational motion, now in one direction and now in another, such that the time-average of its energy of translation is the same as that for the gas molecules. Its mass being millions of times greater than theirs, its speed is of course imperceptibly small and its displacements quite below the threshold of detection. The question, now, is whether the smallest particles which are still accessible to direct observation may acquire a mean translational energy large enough for their motion also to be perceptible and measurable.

Fortunately this is so, as the existence of the Brownian motion shows. The particles in certain colloidal suspensions fulfil the required conditions. Observation with the ultra-microscope leaves no doubt about their particulate character, and they are seen to be in a state of random motion, darting hither and thither in a manner which gives a vivid impression of irregular impacts first from one side and then from another. These impacts must come from other particles which are themselves invisible, so that the Brownian motion (once the technical difficulty of showing that it is not due to convection currents is overcome) is justly claimed to provide evidence of molecular reality.

The mean kinetic energy of translation of a colloidal particle executing this kind of motion may be written $\frac{1}{2}M\bar{U}^2$ and is equal to that of any gas molecule, that is to $\frac{1}{2}m\bar{u}^2$. Now for the latter

$$p = \tfrac{1}{3}nm\bar{u}^2,$$

and if V is the molecular volume,

$$pV = \tfrac{1}{3}nVm\bar{u}^2 = RT.$$

nV is the total number of molecules in a gram molecule (Avogrado's number), N. Thus

$$\tfrac{1}{3}Nm\bar{u}^2 = RT.$$

Any means of determining $\tfrac{1}{2}M\bar{U}^2$ gives at the same time the value of $\tfrac{1}{2}m\bar{u}^2$ which is equal to it. Since RT is known, N becomes determinable, and thus the individual mass of any kind of molecule may be discovered.

It remains, therefore, to seek such a method of finding the kinetic energy of a particle accessible to observation in the ultra-microscope while it is executing the Brownian motion. There are several such methods. The simplest depends upon a study of the sedimentation equilibrium. Particles heavier than the solution in which they are suspended would if at rest sink to the bottom. Their motion, however, keeps them suspended, though more thickly in the lower layers of the medium than in the higher ones. This sedimentation equilibrium is analogous to the equilibrium of the Earth's atmosphere under gravity and may be similarly treated.

Consider a column of unit cross-section in which small particles are suspended in a medium of some kind. Suppose that the concentration of particles at height h is n and at height $h+dh$ is $n+dn$. In between two horizontal planes at these respective heights there are $n\,dh$ particles and these are urged downwards with a gravitational force $wn\,dh$, where w is the effective weight of each. (w is in fact $g \times$ volume of particle $\times$ difference in density of particle and medium.) This force produces a downward momentum of $wn\,dh$ units in each second. When the suspension is in equilibrium the communication of downward momentum must be balanced in accordance with Newton's second law. Now the motion of the particles renders them capable of communicating momentum and thereby of exercising what is dynamically analogous to a gas pressure. Its value is $\tfrac{1}{3}nM\bar{U}^2$, as in the equation derived on p. 16. Thus $dp = \tfrac{1}{3}M\bar{U}^2\,dn$. $-dp$ must balance $wn\,dh$, and therefore

$$wn\,dh = -\tfrac{1}{3}M\bar{U}^2\,dn,$$

$$\frac{dn}{n} = -\frac{w\,dh}{\tfrac{1}{3}M\bar{U}^2},$$

$$\ln\frac{n}{n_0} = \frac{w(h-h_0)}{-\tfrac{1}{3}M\bar{U}^2},$$

where n is the concentration at height h and n_0 that at height h_0.

$$n = n_0 e^{-\frac{w(h-h_0)}{\frac{1}{3}M\bar{U}^2}}.$$

The scale of the phenomenon is very small and the concentration falls off rapidly as the height increases. It so happens that with suitable colloidal suspensions, by the focusing of a microscope at different depths, $(h-h_0)$ being measured by a micrometer arrangement, counts of the particles (observed by scattered light according to the principle of the ultra-microscope) can be be made, and numbers proportional to n and n_0 conveniently obtained.

The particles being accessible to direct observation by counting and by coagulation, filtration, and weighing, w can be found. The only unknown is $M\bar{U}^2$ which is thus calculable.

Avogadro's number, N, is $RT/\frac{1}{3}M\bar{U}^2$, and the absolute mass of a molecule is the gram-molecular weight divided by N. The value of N is 6×10^{23} (the best measurements being in fact made by a quite different method).

Another method of finding the kinetic energy of the particles in Brownian motion depends upon the observation of their mean displacements: this need not be described, as from the present point of view it introduces no important new principle.

That, in the manner which has just been indicated, a limit to the fine-grained character of matter is determinable by the observation of visible phenomena directly and qualitatively explicable by the molecular hypothesis provides a strong argument for the reality of the entities with which this hypothesis deals.

Some other molecular magnitudes

The speeds of molecules are calculable very simply from the formula for the gas pressure. Since $p = \frac{1}{3}nm\bar{u}^2$, it follows that

$$\bar{u} = (3p/nm)^{\frac{1}{2}}.$$

But $nm = \rho$, the density, so that

$$\bar{u} = (3p/\rho)^{\frac{1}{2}}.$$

If p is expressed in dynes/cm.^{2} and ρ in gram/c.c., then $\bar{u}$ is given in cm./sec. It comes out to be of the order of magnitude of a kilometre a second for simple molecules, and varies inversely as the square root of the molecular weight.

With the reasonable presumption that molecules have a real

existence and ascertainable mass and translational energy, the next step is clearly to seek some means of obtaining information about their size. What precisely is meant by the size of a molecule raises some quite profound questions, the consideration of which, however, is better deferred until the nature of the possible experimental approaches has been surveyed. For a first attempt, a molecule may be envisaged as a small solid elastic sphere obeying the rules of Newtonian mechanics.

With a large number of mass particles in rapid motion the most obvious effect of their finite dimensions will be to cause collisions which interfere with their motion. Instead of pursuing an unbroken trajectory each particle will suffer abrupt changes of direction at each encounter, and will describe a zigzag path. The average length of an uninterrupted straight portion of this zigzag is called the *mean free path* (*l*). A smaller mean free path implies a greater interference of the particles with one another. Thus to find an experimental approach one must turn to a phenomenon which seems to depend upon the mutual obstruction of the moving molecules.

Such a phenomenon is that of viscosity, and the study of this property in gases does in fact provide clear-cut results, though not perhaps in quite the way which might have been expected. The bodily jostling of the molecules, which is more pronounced the bulkier they are, plays the major part in determining the viscosity of liquids, but the treatment of this effect proves to be rather complicated. The viscosity of gases depends not upon a crowding tendency but upon a *transfer of momentum* by molecules as they move from one volume element to another, and the collisions determine it in so far as they regulate the sort of momentum which is available for transfer. The matter may be rendered clearer by a simple calculation.

Suppose that a stream of gas moves in the direction of the x-axis and that there is a velocity gradient dv/dz in the direction z perpendicular to that of the flow. Consider a reference plane of unit area parallel to the flow and thus perpendicular to the velocity gradient. Let the velocity of the stream in this plane be v. In so far as the gas is treated as a continuous fluid one may say that between the faster moving and the slower moving layers there is a frictional force tending to slow down the former and to accelerate the latter until the velocity gradient is destroyed. To maintain this gradient an external force must be applied, and it is the magnitude of this force which measures the viscosity of the medium. The coefficient of viscosity is defined by the simple hydrodynamic relation:

$$\text{force per unit area of reference plane} = \eta\, dv/dz,$$

where η is the coefficient.

In the kinetic interpretation of this effect a distinction is drawn between the streaming velocity, v, the direction of which is common to all the molecules in a given volume element, and the thermal velocity $\bar{u}$, the direction of which for the various molecules is completely random. Molecules move across the reference plane from the faster to the slower layers and equally well in the reverse direction. There is thus a net transport of streaming momentum of a kind which would destroy the velocity gradient unless a force equal to the rate of transport across the reference plane were continuously applied.

The mass of gas moving in one direction perpendicular to unit area of the reference plane in one second is $\tfrac{1}{6}\rho\bar{u}$, by an argument exactly analogous to that used in the derivation of the expression for the gas pressure (p. 10). The streaming momentum carried through the plane in this direction in one second is $\tfrac{1}{6}\rho\bar{u}v_1$, where v_1 is the average value of the streaming velocity for those molecules passing across in virtue of their thermal motion. Now it is the value of v_1 which is determined by the mean free path. This latter represents the distance from the reference plane at which the molecules are last brought into mechanical equilibrium with the stream by mutual collisions. Thus v_1 will be $(v+l\, dv/dz)$. Similarly momentum is carried in the reverse direction and is equal to $\tfrac{1}{6}\rho\bar{u}$ multiplied by $(v-l\, dv/dz)$. The excess of that taken in one direction over that taken in the other is thus

$$\tfrac{1}{6}\rho\bar{u}(v+l\, dv/dz)-\tfrac{1}{6}\rho\bar{u}(v-l\, dv/dz) = \tfrac{1}{3}\rho\bar{u}l\, dv/dz.$$

This represents the viscous force, so that

$$\tfrac{1}{3}\rho\bar{u}l\, dv/dz = \eta\, dv/dz,$$

or

$$\eta = \tfrac{1}{3}\rho\bar{u}l.$$

A simple and obvious modification of the above argument yields an expression for the thermal conductivity of a gas

$$K = \tfrac{1}{3}\rho\bar{u}lc_v,$$

where c_v is the specific heat at constant volume.

According to the above formula, the viscosity of a gas increases with the mean free path. This result may seem a little paradoxical at first sight. The interpretation, however, is that the streaming momentum can be transferred from farther up or down the velocity gradient the remoter from the reference plane is the place at which the molecules last come into equilibrium with the general current. The viscosity does, however, depend upon mutual collisions directly, since without them there would be no hydrodynamic equilibrium at all.

The two equations just derived predict certain quite characteristic, and indeed slightly surprising, phenomena, the experimental verification of which affords good evidence for the essential correctness of the underlying ideas. Thus the viscosity of a gas is independent of the pressure, since ρ and l vary in a compensating way: it increases with rise in temperature, the momentum transfer becoming more lively: and the ratio of viscosity to thermal conductivity is constant and calculable from the specific heat. These results could hardly be explained in any other simple way.

The viscosity coefficient of gases may be determined from measurements of the rate of flow through a capillary tube of known radius under a given pressure difference, and from the result the mean free path, l, may be calculated. For simple gases at atmospheric pressure it is of the order 10^{-5} cm. It varies inversely as the pressure, and long before the highest vacuum given by a modern pump is reached it exceeds the dimensions of ordinary small-scale laboratory apparatus.

From the mean free path the size of molecules may be inferred. $\bar{u}/l$ gives the number of times in a second that the trajectory of a particular molecule has been interrupted and thus measures the number of collisions which it has suffered in unit time. Thus we have

$$Z_1 = \bar{u}/l.$$

The number of collisions is fairly simply related to the size. Let the diameter of a molecule be σ, which may be regarded as an effective value only, since we are not assuming much about the nature of a collision. With this convention two molecules may be regarded as entering into collision whenever their centres approach to within a distance σ of one another.

Let all the molecules in the system save one be imagined frozen into immobility and this selected one be thought to move about among the others with an effective velocity which we will denote by r. r is evidently proportional to $\bar{u}$ and may be written $\alpha\bar{u}$, where α is a numerical factor. If in reality all the molecules possessed the same speed, the directions alone being random, r would be the average value of the relative velocity of two molecules, the average being taken over all possible angles in space between the two directions. α, as a simple geometrical calculation shows, would then have the value 4/3. Correction, however, has also to be made for the fact that the velocities themselves vary according to the distribution law, and when the necessary calculations are made they show that α should be $\sqrt{2}$. Let the stationary molecules further be reduced to points and the selected molecule which moves among them swell so that its radius becomes equal to σ. This process will not affect the number of encounters.

As the selected specimen moves it sweeps out in the course of a second a cylindrical space of cross-section $\pi\sigma^2$ and length $\sqrt{2}\bar{u}$. The volume is $\sqrt{2}\pi\sigma^2\bar{u}$ and is inappreciably affected by the changes in direction which occur at each encounter, the mean free path being, as it turns out, normally very much greater than σ. The number of the point molecules contained in this cylinder is equal to $\sqrt{2}\pi\sigma^2\bar{u}$ $\times$ the number per unit volume, that is, to $\sqrt{2}\pi\sigma^2\bar{u}n$, which must represent the number of collisions made by any given molecule in unit time. Since the same applies to every molecule, the total number entering into collision in a second in one cubic centimetre is $\sqrt{2}\pi\sigma^2\bar{u}n^2$. Each collision involves two molecules, so that the number of collisions is half this. Thus we have

$$Z = \tfrac{1}{2}\sqrt{2}\pi\sigma^2\bar{u}n^2.$$

The viscosity of the gas is comparatively easy to measure, and from it l may be calculated and thus Z may be estimated. For all ordinary molecules, that is to say for those other than the macro-molecules formed by complex polymerization processes, σ is of the order of magnitude 10^{-8} cm. Some typical values are given below.

	$\sigma \times 10^8$ cm.
Helium	2·18
Argon	3·66
Hydrogen	2·72
Oxygen	3·62
Water	4·66
Carbon dioxide	4·66

If the two molecules entering into collision are not of the same species, the above calculation has to be modified, and the result found is of the following form:

$$Z = n_A n_B \sigma_{AB}^2 \{8\pi RT(1/M_A + 1/M_B)\}^{\frac{1}{2}},$$

where n_A and n_B are the respective numbers in unit volume, M_A and M_B the gram-molecular weights, and σ_{AB} the average of the two diameters. A derivation of this formula, by a method which is more precise than that sketched above for the molecules of the same species, will be given at a later stage (p. 384).

Although in the foregoing discussion the molecule was pictured as an elastic sphere, the result retains a good deal of its value even if this simple representation is entirely abandoned and the molecule is regarded, for example, as a mere centre of force which repels similar centres when they approach too closely. What the above calculations have really yielded is information about the average distance between the molecular centres at which transfers of momentum occur. For many purposes this constitutes quite a reasonable definition of the diameter. Ambiguity is, however, avoided if σ is termed the *collision diameter*. In actual fact it corresponds fairly closely to the molecular magnitudes determined by the methods of X-ray and electron diffraction.

The elementary treatment of the mean free path envisages, as it were, a balancing of the molecular accounts at a distance l from any reference plane. It is very useful as far as it goes, but it leaves certain important effects unaccounted for. Its limitations are well illustrated by the phenomenon of *thermal diffusion* (upon which one of the most efficient separations of isotopes depends). If a long vertical tube is heated axially by a wire while the walls remain cold, the heavier constituent of a gas mixture becomes concentrated towards the circumference. Here it sinks towards the bottom of the. tube while fresh gas rises in the warm central region. When a steady state is established the lighter constituent of the mixture predominates at the top of the tube and the heavier at the bottom. The convection effect itself is easy enough to understand, but the initial enrichment of the heavier molecules in the colder region is not explicable in terms of the elementary theory. If pressure is uniform throughout, then, since $p = \frac{1}{3}nm\bar{u}^2$, n is inversely proportional to $m\bar{u}^2$. That is to say that the density is inversely proportional to the absolute temperature, whatever the value of m, since $m\bar{u}^2$ is the same for all types of molecule. Thus no separation of the gases in a temperature gradient seems explicable solely in virtue of the different molecular masses.

This consideration neglects the circumstance that a temperature gradient is only maintainable by a continual transport of heat from one region to another, and furthermore that the assumption of a true equilibrium state established at the end of each free path is only roughly correct. Molecules with a large component of velocity in a given direction tend in general to retain some fraction of it after collision, and the degree of this so-called persistence of velocity is a function both of the mass and of the law of force between the colliding particles. Normally it is such that the lighter molecules outstrip the heavier in penetrating into the warmer regions, so that the concentration of molecules in the cooler regions becomes more pronounced for the heavier than for the lighter. This is a second-order effect which is magnified by the continuous action of the vertical convection currents. With a different law for the intermolecular forces the thermal diffusion could work in the opposite sense and lead to an accumulation of lighter molecules in the cooler parts.

In spite of the importance in certain special circumstances of these subtler phenomena, the achievements even of the rather naïve forms of the kinetic theory are undeniable. They amount to this: that in some major respects the properties of matter are interpretable in terms of the behaviour of sensible objects. Atoms and molecules seem not only to exist, but also to be enumerable and measurable, and representable in some degree as small-scale models of the objects which they themselves build up. This takes us a long step forward in describing the unknown in terms of the known, and this is what really constitutes a scientific explanation. The process can be carried even farther, but we shall soon find that a fresh turn has to be given to it, and that the kinds of known things by which the unknown have to be described become less homely.

II

MOLECULAR CHAOS AND ENTROPY

Molecular chaos

THE quantitative laws of chemical combination provide clear pointers to the molecular theory of matter, which increases progressively in vividness and realism with the application of Newton's laws to the motions of the particles. The interpretation of phenomena such as the pressure and viscosity of gases and the Brownian motion, and the assignment of definite magnitudes to molecular speeds, masses, and diameters render it clear that a continual interchange of energies must occur between the molecules of a material system, a circumstance which lies at the basis of temperature equilibrium and determines what in ordinary experience is called the flow of heat. It is responsible indeed for far more than this, and a large part of physical chemistry follows from the conception of the chaotic motion of the molecules. This matter must now be examined more deeply.

In a sufficiently numerous collection of molecules left to themselves a statistical equilibrium is established, usually, as it proves, with great rapidity. In this state the total quantities of energy in the various forms, translational, vibrational, and rotational, bear definite steady ratios to one another. Each kind of energy in every individual molecule fluctuates with time about a mean value, every kind of motion waxing and waning throughout the system. At a given instant the statistical equilibrium only becomes susceptible of complete definition as the number of molecules under consideration is indefinitely increased, but, even for a few molecules, the average state taken over an extended period of time corresponds to that of the true equilibrium for very large numbers at a single instant.

The state of such a molecular system is obviously chaotic in the sense that some molecules move fast and others slowly: some are in violent vibration or rotation while others are almost quiescent; and the condition of individuals is continually changing. A rough idea of the rapid and irregular variations of motion would be provided by the behaviour of a number of billiard balls propelled in random directions on a table, their translations and spins fluctuating according to the hazards of their mutual encounters.

For an elastic collision of two smooth spheres the laws of mechanics

C

allow the final speeds and directions to be estimated from the initial values, and similar calculations are possible, in principle, for rough spheres, for non-spherical masses, and even for masses which do not collide in the ordinary sense but exercise mutual repulsive forces on close approach. Given the initial state of a mechanical system consisting of any number of particles, the final state is in principle calculable. In the initial state the distribution of motions may not have been random, but may in fact have been governed by definite conditions. For example, in a lead bullet cooled to a very low temperature and possessing a very high translational speed the motions of the molecules are largely ordered in a parallel way. If this bullet is stopped by a stone wall, it grows hot and the movements of the particles become random in the sense that all mass motion disappears and only the irregular invisible motion of the molecules remains. It requires, however, very subtle consideration to decide whether or not the state of motion after the impact can be strictly described as absolutely chaotic. The following reflection shows this problem in a clearer light. If the final motion of every particle in the mass were reversed, then a series of collisions would ensue such that the original initial state would be regained. Now the reversal of a chaotic set of velocities might be said still to leave them chaotic; yet the reversed set in this example would soon be replaced by a highly ordered system.

The original state of all the matter in the world is not known; nor can we predict what would happen if all molecular speeds were reversed. As far as the laws of mechanics go, we cannot assert that existing conditions are unrelated to an earlier condition of order. Whether, therefore, the complete randomness of all microscopic motion can be logically related to the Newtonian laws has in fact been a subject of controversy and no wholly satisfactory answer emerges.

What is undoubtedly true is that for practical purposes the chaos can be regarded at least as very nearly complete. That this is so irrespective of the origin of the present order of things is attested by such simple experiences as the shuffling of a pack of cards, which show how rapidly all vestiges of order become undetectable. While forgoing any attempt at a rigid application of the laws of dynamics to the question, we may therefore introduce as a *specific postulate* the *assumption of molecular chaos* for ordinary systems endowed with thermal energy. In any portion of matter in statistical equilibrium the distribution of motions is taken to be calculable from the laws of probability in conjunction with the appropriate rules of mechanics without any reference to the remote history of the system.

This postulate is broad, clear, and intuitive and quite worthy to serve as the basis of a theory of matter. With its aid wide tracts of physics and chemistry can be illuminated. Its consequences are much more positive than might have been suspected for what sounds at first like a somewhat negative principle.

The distribution law

The first task is to derive some of the important rules of statistical equilibrium among molecules. The state of a given individual at any instant is described by its position coordinates and by other coordinates which define its translational, rotational, and vibrational energy. For the present purpose the different contributions to the total energy of the individual will be taken as independent and expressible by square terms in the way previously outlined (p. 14).

The problem is to define how many molecules out of a very large number are at a particular instant in any given state. Here the definition of what we are to understand by a *state* requires detailed consideration. If the component $\dot{x}$ of the velocity along the axis x is denoted by u, the natural way of formulating the distribution question is to inquire about the number of molecules with velocities in the range from u to $u+du$, with corresponding inquiries about the other coordinates in terms of which the energy is expressed. With the idea, however, of introducing a convenient approximation we might agree to envisage a small arbitrary range in the neighbourhood of u and to consider all the molecules possessing velocities in that range as having the same definite energy ϵ in respect of that coordinate. In this way we should define a discrete series of energy states corresponding to each variable. Thus if the coordinates are p, p', p'',..., there are series corresponding to $p_1, p_2, p_3,..., p'_1, p'_2,..., p''_1, p''_2,...,$ and so on. As will appear, it is best to let the p's represent *momenta*. The contributions to the total energy of the molecule, which are proportional to the squares of these, may be written $\eta_1, \eta_2, \eta_3,..., \eta'_1, \eta'_2,..., \eta''_1, \eta''_2,...,$ etc.

The total energy of a molecule is then $\eta_i+\eta'_j+\eta''_k+...,$ where $i, j, k,...$ can be taken in any combination. The multitudinous values of the total energy which a molecule might have as a result of these different combinations can themselves then be arranged in an ordinal series ϵ_1, ϵ_2, ϵ_3,.... .

It will remain to be decided whether subsequently the intervals in the various series of coordinates or energies are to be made vanishingly small. Later developments will show that this procedure is unnecessary and indeed incorrect, and that a discrete series of states, properly defined by what will be called quantum rules, is what corresponds to nature. For the present, however, the assumption of the series of numerous and fairly closely defined states may be regarded as a convenient simplification.

We envisage, then, a series of energy states like so many compartments into which molecules can be placed, and the distribution among which is to be investigated. The postulate of molecular chaos deliberately assimilates the problem to that of the random partition of a large number of objects among a number of boxes.

Let there be N molecules to be distributed among the states corresponding to the series of energies ϵ_1, ϵ_2, ϵ_3,.... . N may conveniently be taken as the number in a gram molecule. Let there be, in a given distribution, N_1 in state 1, N_2 in state 2, and so on. The number of ways, W, in which such a distribution can be achieved is given by the formula

$$W = \frac{N!}{N_1!\,N_2!\,N_3!\,...},$$

which follows in an elementary way from the principles of permutations and combinations.

The expression may be simplified by the use of Stirling's approximation for the factorials of large numbers, namely that $\ln N!$ tends to the value $N \ln N - N$ when N is large enough. Taking logarithms and making the substitutions for the factorials we obtain

$$\ln W = N \ln N - \sum N_1 \ln N_1. \qquad (1)$$

The principle now to be applied is that in statistical equilibrium W, and thus $\ln W$, will attain a maximum value. N_1, N_2,..., can be subjected to small tentative changes δN_1, δN_2,..., and if the value of $\ln W$ is a maximum, then $\delta \ln W$ will be zero for such processes.

Thus we have as the major condition of our problem

$$\delta \ln W = 0,$$

and from (1), since N is constant,

$$\sum \delta(N_1 \ln N_1) = \sum (1 + \ln N_1) \delta N_1 = 0. \qquad (2)$$

Since the total energy of the whole collection of molecules remains constant and since the total of the numbers in all the states must always add up to N, we have the two auxiliary conditions

$$\sum N_1 = N,$$

so that

$$\sum \delta N_1 = 0, \qquad (3)$$

and

$$N_1 \epsilon_1 + N_2 \epsilon_2 + \ldots = E,$$

so that

$$\delta \sum N_1 \epsilon_1 = \sum \epsilon_1 \delta N_1 = 0. \qquad (4)$$

The solution of (2) subject to the conditions (3) and (4) is a standard problem in conditioned maxima, and what follows down to the result in equation (7) is purely mathematical.

Before we proceed with the solution, however, a word should be said about the use of the Stirling approximation. It has been objected that, although N is large, the number of states is also large, so that some of the numbers N_1, N_2,..., may not be great enough to justify the use of the approximation. If this is so, then one must take N to be much larger still until all the states really do contain enough molecules. The result might apply then only to the time average of any real system of finite size. This is quite all right, because in actual fact there would be a definite distribution law for such a system only if we averaged its condition over a period of time.

We proceed therefore to the solution of (2). (3) and (4) are multiplied by arbitrary constants, α and β, and added to (2) with the result

$$\sum (1 + \ln N_1) \delta N_1 + \alpha \sum \delta N_1 + \beta \sum \epsilon_1 \delta N_1 = 0. \qquad (5)$$

α and β may have any values required by other conditions of the problem, since (5) is an identity based upon three independent equations. Rearrangement of (5) gives

$$\sum (1 + \ln N_1 + \alpha + \beta \epsilon_1) \delta N_1 = 0. \qquad (6)$$

δN_1, δN_2,..., it must be remembered, are small arbitrary transfers made to test whether the condition for a maximum is fulfilled. They are variable and subject only to condition (3). Let α and β, being assignable at will, be given such values that

$$1 + \ln N_1 + \alpha + \beta \epsilon_1 = 0 \quad \text{and} \quad 1 + \ln N_2 + \alpha + \beta \epsilon_2 = 0.$$

Then in (6) the sum of all the terms from δN_3 upwards equals zero. From the nature of δN_4, δN_5,..., they may be chosen, if we so wish, to be zero. Let them be so chosen, but let δN_3 be given a value distinct from zero. Then we have

$$(1+\ln N_3+\alpha+\beta\epsilon_3)\delta N_3 = 0,$$

and since δN_3 itself is not zero its coefficient must be. Thus

$$(1+\ln N_3+\alpha+\beta\epsilon_3) = 0.$$

A repetition of the argument with appropriate modifications shows that in general

$$1+\ln N_j+\alpha+\beta\epsilon_j = 0.$$

Therefore

$$N_j = e^{-1-\alpha}e^{-\beta\epsilon_j}.$$

Since

$$\sum N_j = N,$$

$$N = e^{-1-\alpha} \sum e^{-\beta\epsilon_j},$$

whence

$$N_j = Ne^{-\beta\epsilon_j}/ \sum e^{-\beta\epsilon_j}, \tag{7}$$

the sum in the denominator being taken over all possible states.

This equation is known as the *Maxwell–Boltzmann distribution law*. It rests, as has been seen, on the assumption that the distributions occurring in nature are those which can be achieved by the maximum number of permutations. All possible distributions are, as it were, explored in the course of the blind wanderings of the molecules from state to state, but the condition of real systems for most of their time corresponds closely to that of maximum probability.

The equipartition law

The Maxwell–Boltzmann law is of fundamental importance. We shall begin by applying it to the derivation of the equipartition law, which plays so prominent a part in determining the equilibrium of material systems. ϵ, the energy of a molecule, is the sum of terms η, η', η'',... corresponding to the different coordinates p, p', p'',... which describe the motions. Let attention be fixed upon one particular type of coordinate, p, and for this purpose let (7) be rewritten in the form

$$N_j = \frac{Ne^{-\beta(\eta+\eta'+\eta''+...)}}{\sum e^{-\beta(\eta+\eta'+\eta''+...)}},$$

$$= \frac{Ne^{-\beta(\eta'+\eta''+...)}e^{-\beta\eta}}{\sum e^{-\beta(\eta+\eta'+\eta''+...)}},$$

$$= \frac{Ne^{-\beta(\eta'+\eta''+...)}e^{-\beta\eta}}{\sum e^{-\beta(\eta'+\eta''+...)} \sum e^{-\beta\eta}},$$

the factorization of the denominator being possible since every value of η (that is η_1, η_2,...) is combined in the sum with every value of η', η'',... (that is η_1', η_2',...; η_1'', η_2'',...).

Now let N_j be summed over all possible values of η', η'',..., and the result, which may be written $N_{(j)}$, gives the number of molecules which possess the energy η in the mode of motion corresponding to p, irrespective of the other components.

$$N_{(j)} = \frac{N\{\sum e^{-\beta(\eta'+\eta''+...)}\}e^{-\beta\eta}}{\sum e^{-\beta(\eta'+\eta''+...)}\sum e^{-\beta\eta}}$$
$$= \frac{Ne^{-\beta\eta}}{\sum e^{-\beta\eta}}. \tag{8}$$

Equation (8) might have been obtained intuitively from (7) by imagining the derivation of the latter for the series of η states only, without any consideration of the others.

If $N_{(j)}$ is now summed over the whole series of η states, $\sum N_{(j)}$ will clearly embrace all the molecules, so that it is equal to N.

Consider now the sum $\sum e^{-\beta\eta}$. As it stands it consists of a number of discrete terms, and the law of the series is not defined. One might assume from one term to the next equal increments of the energy itself or equal increments of the coordinate p which determines it. The best assumption, which makes a special appeal to those deeply versed in the science of dynamics, is that the series should be defined by equal increments in *momentum*, that is in general by equal increments of the variables corresponding to p. The basis of this idea is in fact wide experience of the way in which dynamical laws assume their simplest form when expressed in terms of momentum and space coordinates (Hamiltonian coordinates) as the fundamental variables. The successive energy states are then

$$f(p), \quad f(p+\Delta p), \quad f(p+2\Delta p), \quad ....$$

Equation (8) becomes

$$N_{(j)} = \frac{Ne^{-\beta f(p)}}{\sum e^{-\beta f(p)}}.$$

This may be multiplied top and bottom by Δp:

$$N_{(j)} = \frac{Ne^{-\beta f(p)}\Delta p}{\sum e^{-\beta f(p)}\Delta p}.$$

If Δp is made small enough we have for the number of molecules in the state corresponding to $f(p)$, or in the range Δp about it,

$$N_{(j)} = \frac{Ne^{-\beta f(p)}\,dp}{\int e^{-\beta f(p)}\,dp},$$ (9)

i.e.

$$\phi(p)\,dp = \frac{Ne^{-\beta \eta}\,dp}{\int e^{-\beta \eta}\,dp},$$ (9a)

$\phi(p)\,dp$ being for the continuous distribution the equivalent of $N_{(j)}$ for the discontinuous one.

Consider further the integral in the denominator of (9a). It is taken over the whole range of coordinates. A partial integration with respect to p gives the result

$$\int e^{-\beta \eta}\,dp = \left[pe^{-\beta \eta}\right]_{\text{lower limit}}^{\text{upper limit}} + \beta \int pe^{-\beta \eta}\frac{d\eta}{dp}\,dp.$$

The first term on the right is zero at both limits: at the lower limit since $p = 0$ and at the upper limit since $e^{-\beta \eta}$ is a zero of higher order than the infinity of p. Rearrangement of the terms gives

$$\frac{1}{\beta} = \frac{\int \{p(d\eta/dp)\}e^{-\beta \eta}\,dp}{\int e^{-\beta \eta}\,dp}.$$

From (9a),

$$\frac{1}{\beta} = \frac{\int \phi(p)\{p(d\eta/dp)\}\,dp}{N}.$$

The expression on the right is the average value of $p(d\eta/dp)$, so that the equation may be written

$$\overline{\left(p\frac{d\eta}{dp}\right)} = \frac{1}{\beta}.$$ (10)

It is clear from the derivation that the value of $1/\beta$ is the same for all possible momentum coordinates.

Now if the energy is expressible as a square term

$$\eta = ap^2, \quad \text{where } a \text{ is a constant.}$$

$$\frac{d\eta}{dp} = 2ap$$

and

$$p\frac{d\eta}{dp} = 2ap^2 = 2\eta.$$

Thus for all the square terms in the energy the average value is such that
$$2\bar{\eta} = 1/\beta,$$
or
$$\bar{\eta} = 1/(2\beta),$$
the bar signifying as usual an average value.

From the equations for the gas pressure,
$$p = \tfrac{1}{3}nm\bar{u}^2 \quad \text{and} \quad pV = RT,$$
whence
$$pV = \tfrac{1}{3}Nm\bar{u}^2 \quad \text{since} \quad nV = N.$$
Therefore
$$\tfrac{1}{3}m(\dot{x}^2 + \dot{y}^2 + \dot{z}^2) = RT/N = kT,$$
where
$$k = R/N.$$
The average values of $\dot{x}^2$, $\dot{y}^2$, and $\dot{z}^2$ will be equal and thus
$$\overline{m\dot{x}^2} = kT,$$
or
$$\overline{\tfrac{1}{2}m\dot{x}^2} = \tfrac{1}{2}kT.$$
But $\overline{\tfrac{1}{2}m\dot{x}^2}$ is $1/(2\beta)$ by the result just obtained, and thus
$$\beta = 1/kT, \tag{11}$$
and
$$\bar{\eta} = \tfrac{1}{2}kT.$$

The discussion so far has shown that the average energy in each square term is $\tfrac{1}{2}kT$ for a given type of molecule. It remains to show that this result holds good in a mixture of different molecular species.

Let there be N_a molecules of type a and N_b of type b in the same enclosure, and let them be capable of exchanging energy. Let their individual energy states be $\epsilon_{a1}, \epsilon_{a2}, ...$, and $\epsilon_{b1}, \epsilon_{b2}, ...$, and the numbers in these states be respectively $N_{a1}, N_{a2}, ..., N_{b1}, N_{b2}, ...$.

The number of ways of achieving this distribution is
$$W = \frac{N_a!}{N_{a1}! \, N_{a2}! \, ...} \times \frac{N_b!}{N_{b1}! \, N_{b2}! \, ...}, \tag{12}$$
and this must be a maximum. The auxiliary conditions to be observed are
$$\sum N_{a1} = N_a \tag{13}$$
and
$$\sum N_{b1} = N_b, \tag{14}$$
and
$$\sum N_{a1}\epsilon_{a1} + \sum N_{b1}\epsilon_{b1} = E. \tag{15}$$
The problem is solved as before: the logarithm of (12) is trans-

formed by Stirling's formula, differentiated, and equated to zero. (13), (14), and (15) are also differentiated and equated to zero.

$$\delta \ln W = 0, \tag{16}$$

$$\sum \delta N_{a1} = 0, \tag{17}$$

$$\sum \delta N_{b1} = 0, \tag{18}$$

$$\sum \epsilon_{a1} \delta N_{a1} + \sum \epsilon_{b1} \delta N_{b1} = 0. \tag{19}$$

(17) and (18) are multiplied by arbitrary constants α_1 and α_2 and (19) by β. The results are added and the rest of the calculation proceeds as for the case of the single kind of molecule.

There is no need to carry it through in order to obtain the result required at the present juncture. The important thing to notice is that whereas there are now *two* separate constants α_1 and α_2 relating to the total numbers of each species of molecule, there is still only *one* single constant β relating to the constant total energy of the whole system. This expresses the obvious fact that whereas molecules of the types a and b are not interconvertible, energy, on the other hand, is both transformable and transferable from any one type of molecule to any other. Thus β, which plays exactly the same role as in the previous calculation, is the same for both species. The mean energies for a square term are therefore independent of the masses and other physical constants, such as the moments of inertia of the individual molecules.

As will have been seen, the derivation of the equipartition law depends upon certain rather general, and perhaps somewhat abstract, assumptions about molecular dynamics. It is desirable, therefore, to bring the result as soon as possible into relation with experimentally measurable matters. The most striking method of doing this is afforded by the study of specific heats.

Energy content and specific heat

The most obvious test of the validity of the equipartition principle is the attempt to calculate the energy content and thus the specific heat of substances composed of molecules simple enough for a fair guess at their structure and mechanics to be made.

Helium, argon, and the other inert gases might be assumed to consist of small masses devoid of internal motions, and as a first trial one might assume the absence of rotations. They would then possess three translational degrees of freedom only, and the energy of each gram atom would be $N \times 3 \times \frac{1}{2}kT$, or $(3/2)RT$. The increase of this for each degree of temperature is $(3/2)R$, and R being 1·98 cal./degree, the atomic heat should be 2·97, which corresponds exactly to the measured value.

Very stable diatomic molecules such as oxygen, nitrogen, and hydrogen should possess a structure, and might be schematized as objects with a sort of dumb-bell shape, but they might be devoid of vibrational energy, since the two atoms might be imagined to constitute a practically rigid body. If these guesses were correct, there would be three translational degrees of freedom and some rotational degrees. The rotational energy would be referable to three axes, one of which would be chosen to coincide with the geometrical axis of the dumb-bell. Viewed along this axis the structure would be seen in projection in a monatomic form and thus, by analogy with helium, might be supposed to have no rotation about it. Two rotational degrees of freedom would, however, be expected for the two other rectangular axes, making five degrees of freedom in all. These would account for a specific heat of $(5/2)R$ calories per gram molecule. Once again the estimated value is exactly right.

An unstable diatomic molecule, such as iodine, should perhaps be capable of vibration along the axis joining the two atoms, and there would then be an addition to the specific heat of $\frac{1}{2}R$ for the kinetic energy of this motion and (according to the properties of simple harmonic motion) of an equal amount for the potential energy. Thus the total value should be about 2 calories greater than that for oxygen. This, too, is in agreement with experiment.

The application of this method of calculation to crystalline monatomic solids (a category to which many metallic elements would according to a simple view belong) is interesting. Assuming the absence of rotations and translations, and the existence only of three degrees of freedom of vibration, one calculates that the atomic heat of all such solids should be $3(\frac{1}{2}R + \frac{1}{2}R)$ or 6 calories, which is a fairly good approximation to the famous *law of Dulong and Petit*.

There can be little doubt, therefore, that in many respects the equipartition law gives a rather accurate account of what happens. Its successes leave little doubt that when translations, rotations, and vibrations do exist, they are reasonably well describable as sums of independent square terms.

Second thoughts about the whole problem, however, suggest not so much that the equipartition principle is in any very important way inaccurate as that it altogether neglects some factor belonging to the essential nature of things.

The guesses which were made about the modes of motion of various types of molecule seem plausible enough at first sight, but they are strictly speaking inadmissible. There is, in fact, no reason in Newtonian mechanics why helium atoms should not rotate, why oxygen molecules should not have three rotational degrees of freedom, or why all diatomic molecules should not be in vibration. Smooth symmetrical molecules, it is true, are difficult to make rotate, but they are difficult to stop again when once they have been set in rotation. The equipartition law should, in fact, apply whether or not particular modes of motion happen to be difficult to excite. If they are difficult to excite they may acquire energy but slowly: they will also lose energy slowly, and in the equilibrium state they should possess the normal quota. All that can be said is that the dynamical constants characterizing some of the degrees of freedom which do not appear are quantitatively considerably different from those of the modes which do appear. But in the derivation of the law no assumption at all about these magnitudes is made.

Furthermore, detailed experiment shows that all specific heats are functions of temperature, at least over certain ranges, and this is completely inexplicable in terms of the equipartition principle, which makes the energy proportional to T, so that the specific heat, the differential coefficient of the energy with respect to T, should be constant.

The actual mode of variation of the specific heat is such as to suggest that in certain ranges of temperature some of the degrees of freedom pass entirely out of action. The principles so far introduced, then, need amplification by some quite fundamental new rules which provide reasons why sometimes degrees of freedom should be operative and sometimes not. These rules cannot be derived in any way except by the introduction of the *quantum theory*. In the meantime it appears that the equipartition principle is an incomplete statement. If the results it predicted were merely inaccurate in a numerical sense, the discrepancies could be attributed to causes within the framework of ordinary mechanics, for example, to the non-independence of rotations and vibrations, which would spoil the formulation of the energy as a sum of square terms, but the difficulty lies deeper.

There is a complete absence of contributions from modes of motion which according to mechanical principles should exist, a clear-cut qualitative absence, rendered all the more conspicuous by the relative precision with which the contributions of the other modes can be calculated.

At this juncture it is well to remember that the attempt to describe the nature of matter by the application to atoms and molecules of the rules which Newton inferred from the behaviour of massive bodies is no more than an hypothesis to be tested. In the present direction the conclusion about its validity is: thus far and no farther.

But in other directions the simple kinetic theory, without the specific considerations of quantum phenomena, has eminent services to render.

Entropy

We return to the conception of molecular chaos, of statistical equilibrium, and of a partition law defining the thermal balance between the various parts of a material system and making intelligible the idea of a temperature. The obvious task seems now to be the formulation of some quantitative rules about equilibria in systems of many atoms and molecules.

In the solution of this problem a quantity called the *entropy* has come to play a dominant role. What transpires is this: that the conception of molecular chaos, with very little in the way of subsidiary hypotheses except a few very general dynamical laws, goes a long way in explaining many of the major phenomena of physics and chemistry. This being so, it is clearly worth while examining carefully various expressions for the probability of molecular distribution.

We refer once more to the result found for the distribution of the N molecules of a gram molecule among their various energy states. For the present the volume of the system will be taken as constant, and to mark this restriction, which will presently be removed, the number of assignments will be written W_e instead of W. The equation which was derived on p. 28 takes the form

$$\ln W_e = N \ln N - \sum N_1 \ln N_1.$$

W_e measures the number of ways in which the molecules can be assigned to the various energy states for the distribution in question.

The basic principle employed in developing the theory was that W_e, and thus $\ln W_e$, tends to a maximum value.

It is convenient to work generally with $\ln W_e$ rather than with W_e itself, since, if there are two systems characterized by values W_1 and W_2 separately, the number of assignments for the combined system being $W_1 W_2$, the corresponding logarithm is $\ln W_1 + \ln W_2$, and the function describing the state is then formed additively from the values characterizing the individual components. This proves to be a great practical convenience.

$\ln W_e$ defines the degree of probability of the system and gives a quantitative measure of the state of chaos which prevails. Its properties will now be examined. It will be found to be closely related to important thermal magnitudes, and will prove to be one of the most important functions in physical chemistry.

By the calculation already given

$$N_1 = \frac{N e^{-\epsilon_1/kT}}{\sum e^{-\epsilon_1/kT}},$$

where the sum $\sum e^{-\epsilon_1/kT}$ will be written f_e.

For convenience we multiply $\ln W_e$ by k (the expediency of this trivial operation will appear later) and denote $k \ln W_e$ by the symbol S_e.

Thus
$$S_e = kN \ln N - \sum kN_1 \ln N_1.$$

The value of N_1 is now substituted in this expression for S_e, the result being
$$S_e = kN \ln f_e + kNT d\ln f_e/dT,$$
or
$$S_e = R \ln f_e + RT d\ln f_e/dT.$$

The appearance of the differential coefficient of f_e depends upon the relation
$$f_e = \sum e^{-\epsilon_1/kT},$$
$$\frac{df_e}{dT} = \frac{\sum \epsilon_1 e^{-\epsilon_1/kT}}{kT^2},$$
whence
$$\sum \epsilon_1 e^{-\epsilon_1/kT} = kT^2 df_e/dT.$$

Now the total energy, E, of the system is clearly related to f_e. We have
$$E = \sum \epsilon_1 N_1 = \frac{\sum \epsilon_1 N e^{-\epsilon_1/kT}}{f_e} = \frac{N}{f_e} kT^2 \frac{df_e}{dT},$$
whence
$$E = RT^2 \frac{d\ln f_e}{dT},$$
and thus
$$S_e = R \ln f_e + \frac{E}{T}.$$

This relation of the *entropy* to the total energy is extremely important. We shall now throw it into a simple form, in which it will prove to play a quite dominant role. We take the differential coefficient of the entropy, S_e, with respect to the temperature, that is we examine the function which tells us how the degree of disorder changes as the temperature rises and molecules pass into generally higher energy states.

$$\frac{dS_e}{dT} = R\frac{d\ln f_e}{dT} + \frac{1}{T}\frac{dE}{dT} - \frac{E}{T^2}$$

$$= R\frac{d\ln f_e}{dT} + \frac{1}{T}\frac{dE}{dT} - R\frac{d\ln f_e}{dT} = \frac{1}{T}\frac{dE}{dT}.$$

We have supposed the volume of the system to remain constant, so that the last equation is more accurately written

$$\left(\frac{\partial S_e}{\partial T}\right)_v = \frac{1}{T}\left(\frac{\partial E}{\partial T}\right)_v.$$

Now the rate of change of energy with temperature is the specific heat. We thus arrive at the fundamental result that the change of entropy due to an increase of temperature dT at constant volume is given by

$$\boxed{d S_e = \left(\frac{\partial S_e}{\partial T}\right)_v dT = \frac{C_v dT}{T}}$$

As the temperature rises S_e increases according to the relation

$$S_e = C_v \ln T + S_{e0},$$

where S_{e0} may be a function of the volume.

It is important to have an intuitive understanding of the reason why S_e increases with the temperature. It is that as the total energy of the system becomes greater, more and more of the higher energy states become accessible to more and more of the molecules, and that as the distribution so widens, the number of ways of realizing it correspondingly increases. In this sense it is correct to say that when a substance becomes hotter its state becomes more probable.

The question of an analogous treatment of the distribution of molecules in space now arises.

Entropy and volume

If chaotically moving particles are unconfined, they will wander in all directions and fill the whole of any volume accessible to them.

If the temperature is uniform and if the molecules exert no appreciable attractive forces upon one another, they will distribute themselves with a uniform density over all the volume elements, provided that these elements contain numbers great enough for the application of statistical averages. This result could be derived formally by a method similar to that employed in the calculation of the energy distribution, but is itself as obvious intuitively as would be the postulates made in a seemingly more rigorous treatment.

Suppose a gaseous system of total volume V contains N molecules which exert negligible forces upon one another and are of a size negligible in comparison with their average separations. Let the volume be divided into many small elements v, this being a constant standard reference magnitude, entirely arbitrary except in so far as it is supposed small compared with V while being still large enough to contain many molecules. In the equilibrium state the number in each element is Nv/V. The number of ways in which the N individuals can be distributed among the V/v compartments into which the gas is virtually divided so that there are equal numbers in each is given by

$$W_v = \frac{N!}{\{(Nv/V)!\}^{V/v}}.$$

Application of Stirling's formula, $\ln N! = N \ln N - N$, gives the result

$$\ln W_v = N \ln N - N - \frac{V}{v}\left(\frac{Nv}{V}\ln\frac{Nv}{V} - \frac{Nv}{V}\right)$$

$$= N \ln V - N \ln v.$$

Thus
$$k \ln W_v = R \ln V - R \ln v.$$

As the volume increases, therefore, the state becomes more probable. By analogy with the corresponding value of $k \ln W_e$, we may write

$$S_v = R \ln V - R \ln v,$$

and thus, since v is a constant arbitrary magnitude,

$$\left(\frac{\partial S}{\partial V}\right)_T = R\frac{dV}{V}.$$

If we now consider systems in which the temperature and the volume are both variable, we can combine the two foregoing results. The number of ways in which the energy distribution can be realized is W_e; and the number in which the volume distribution is satisfied

is W_v. The number of ways in which both can be satisfied together is expressed by
$$W = W_e \times W_v:$$
then we have
$$k \ln W = k \ln W_e + k \ln W$$
$$= C_v \ln T + R \ln V + \text{arbitrary constant}$$
$$= S.$$

S, which takes into account both the spatial positions of the molecules and their motions, is called the *statistical entropy of the system*.

At the present stage the equation is most useful in the differential form

$$\boxed{dS = C_v \, dT/T + R \, dV/V}$$

This expresses the increase in entropy and probability which accompanies rise in temperature or expansion of volume.

Imperfect gases and substances in general

When there is interaction between the molecules, as in an imperfect gas, and still more in solids and liquids, the form of the volume-dependence becomes too complex to be satisfactorily formulated. f_e, the sum of the terms like $e^{-\epsilon_1/kT}$, is itself a function of the molecular separations. The number of possible energy states becomes indefinitely larger because variable potential-energy terms, each depending upon the proximity of other molecules, are included in the energy of each molecule in any given state.

One relation, however, retains its simplicity: and this fact is of vital importance for the whole of the science of thermodynamics. *However complex the expression for $\partial S/\partial V$ may become, the value of $(\partial S/\partial T)_v$ remains C_v/T.* This crucial result may be seen by inspection of the derivation which was given earlier (p. 38) and where S_e was expressed in the form $R \ln f_e + E/T$, after E itself had been given in terms of f_e. No matter how complex the series of states may become, or how involved a function of volume f_e may become, the relation of E to f_e and of S_e to f_e remains, and hence the relation of S_e to E. Therefore, in a differentiation at constant volume the value of $\partial S/\partial T$ remains C_v/T. Put rather crudely, complex interactions have the same effect on C_v/T as they do on $\partial S/\partial T$. Thus the key relation

$$dS_e = \left(\frac{\partial S}{\partial T}\right)_v dT = C_v \, dT/T$$

holds good.

D

Conditions of equilibrium in molecular systems

At first sight it might appear that the conception of a molecular chaos, though picturesque and affording the opportunity for some ingenious calculations, could hardly bear fruit of a very substantial kind. Nothing could be farther from the truth. It leads directly to the treatment of physical and chemical equilibrium in a manner which is not only illuminating but very useful.

The basic principle to be applied is this: a chaotic collection of molecules will always tend to pass into the state of maximum probability. If it moves nearer to equilibrium from a state in which equilibrium has not yet been established, then the probability increases. If, on the other hand, a completely isolated system moves from one state of equilibrium to an alternative one (as it may on occasion do), the probability does not change.

Molecular systems, however, are not normally found in complete isolation. They are in contact with other systems, and, since the world as a whole is not in equilibrium, they are liable to gain or lose heat by exchange with their surroundings. Moreover, in their blunderings towards a state of maximum chaos the molecules of a given assembly tend to transgress their bounds, and if impeded by obstacles, exert pressure on these, pushing them back in appropriate circumstances and performing mechanical work.

The laws of these interactions determine in a remarkable way the form of many of the phenomena of chemistry and physics.

It is convenient to begin by considering the adiabatic expansion of a quantity of gas, that is, the increase in volume of an assemblage of molecules isolated entirely from their surroundings. The system is supposed to be held in equilibrium throughout the process, the external pressure being always adjusted to the exact value characteristic of the momentary temperature and volume of the gas itself. Thus the system is not to be regarded as moving spontaneously from a given initial state to one of greater probability, but simply as being led successively from one possible equilibrium state to a neighbouring one. In these circumstances $\ln W$ remains constant, and therefore dS is zero. Volume and temperature change, so that we have

$$dS = \left(\frac{\partial S}{\partial V}\right)_T dV + \left(\frac{\partial S}{\partial T}\right)_V dT = 0.$$

If the transition had been, not to the neighbouring state of equilibrium, but towards equilibrium from a less probable state, then dS would have been positive, and we should have had $dS > 0$.

Now we may consider an isothermal expansion, also to a neighbouring state of equilibrium. This may be imagined to occur in two stages. First, the change of volume, dV, takes place adiabatically, the change in entropy being zero, so that

$$\left(\frac{\partial S}{\partial V}\right)_V dV = -\left(\frac{\partial S}{\partial T}\right)_V dT.$$

In this part of the process the system cools. Next a source of heat is found, by contact with which the change of temperature dT may be neutralized, and T restored to its original value. In this stage a quantity of heat must be communicated to the system, the amount required being given by the equation $dQ = C_v dT$. Now by the general result obtained on p. 39, the value of $(\partial S/\partial T)_v dT$ is $C_v(dT/T)$, which is the same as dQ/T. This represents, in fact, the whole entropy change accompanying the isothermal expansion, since that occurring in the initial adiabatic part of the double elementary process was zero. Thus, for an isothermal expansion we have that the entropy change is given by dQ/T.

Next let us consider the general case where V and T both change, the conditions, however, not being adiabatic. Once again the process may be imagined to occur in elementary stages. In the first, which is adiabatic, there is a temperature change dT_1, such that

$$\left(\frac{\partial S}{\partial V}\right)dV + \left(\frac{\partial S}{\partial T}\right)dT_1 = 0.$$

An amount of heat $dQ_1 = C_v dT_1$, is then put in to neutralize dT_1, the change in entropy by the previous argument being dQ_1/T. Finally the temperature is further changed by the prescribed amount dT at constant volume, heat $dQ_2 = C_v dT$ being absorbed and the entropy changing by dQ_2/T. The total change of entropy has been for the various partial steps

$$dQ_1/T + dQ_2/T = dQ/T,$$

where dQ is the total heat taken in.

The argument can be generalized still farther. Let a system as complex as we please, including different chemical substances (which may even suffer interconversions), have a total entropy S, and let it move from a state of equilibrium to an adjacent one, being caused to do so by the change of certain variables, X_1, X_2,..., and T. X_1, X_2,..., may be pressure, chemical composition, or anything that has a physically intelligible meaning in this connexion. Once again let the change take place in stages: first an adiabatic one for which, since the probability remains a maximum,

$$dS = \left(\frac{\partial S}{\partial X_1}\right)dX_1 + \left(\frac{\partial S}{\partial X_2}\right)dX_2 + ... + \left(\frac{\partial S}{\partial T}\right)dT = 0.$$

The change of temperature, dT, is now neutralized by the communication of heat, the amount required being $\sum C_v dT$. The corresponding value of dQ/T represents the change in entropy expressible by

$$\left(\frac{\partial S}{\partial X_1}\right)dX_1 + \left(\frac{\partial S}{\partial X_2}\right)dX_2 ... .$$

Thus we arrive at the fundamentally important result that whenever any system, however complex, or whatever the law of dependence of entropy upon volume or other variables may be, moves from one state of equilibrium to a neighbouring one,

$$dS = dQ/T,$$

where dQ is the heat taken in from outside the system itself.

This result, it should be emphasized once again, depends upon the fact that, however complex $\partial S/\partial X$ may be, $(\partial S/\partial T)_v$ remains C_v/T (or $\sum C_v/T$), and however complex a function of variables C_v itself may be, it is always the measure of the heat required to produce unit rise of temperature.

Since in practical chemistry and physics—not to mention engineering—measurements of heat quantities play a very important part, the equation $dS = dQ/T$ is of great value. It provides a mathematical formulation of a condition of equilibrium.

When a system moves from a condition in which equilibrium does not prevail to one in which it does, the probability increases. The change of entropy will therefore be greater than it would have been in the movement to a neighbouring state of equilibrium. Thus the applicability of the equation $dS = dQ/T$ to a small displacement is a condition that the initial state is one of equilibrium. The important applications of this will appear shortly.

Some of the basic principles of the calculus of molecular chaos may be illustrated in a more direct way by the detailed consideration of the expansion of a perfect gas.

Suppose the volume to increase from V_1 to V_2. No matter how the change is brought about, the last state may be regarded as more probable than the first, since it is that to which the aimless diffusion of the molecules would lead them if they were unconstrained Suppose that they could wander at random through the whole of the volume V_2, then the chance that a given one of them finds itself at a particular instant in a reserved part of the enclosure of volume V_1 is evidently V_1/V_2. The chance that the N molecules of a gram molecule should do so simultaneously is $(V_1/V_2)^N$. This may be regarded as the ratio of two probabilities and written W_1/W_2, where W_2 is an unknown absolute probability of the state of larger volume.

Then
$$W_1/W_2 = (V_1/V_2)^N,$$
$$\ln W_1 - \ln W_2 = N \ln V_1 - N \ln V_2,$$

thus
$$d(k \ln W) = kN d \ln V,$$

or
$$dS = R \, dV/V.$$

In an expansion by dV the entropy increases by $R \, dV/V$ if the temperature remains constant. This result holds good whether the expansion is to a neighbouring state of equilibrium or not.

Suppose first that it is, then the condition of equilibrium implies that the expansive pressure of the gas is held in check by an equal and opposite balancing pressure. This opposing resistance must be forced back as the gas expands and work is done equal in amount to $p \, dV$. If the temperature is to remain constant, this work must be provided for by a flow of heat from without, since in a perfect gas the molecules exert no attraction on one another and the internal energy is independent of the volume. Thus an amount of heat given by $dQ = p \, dV$ is taken in.

$$dQ = p \, dV = RT \, dV/V = T \, dS, \quad \text{since} \quad dS = R \, dV/V,$$

or
$$dS = dQ/T,$$

in accordance with the general law.

If the gas is not in equilibrium but expands, for example, into a vacuum, the change in entropy is still $R \, dV/V$, but no work is done and no heat need be taken in, so that $dQ = 0$, and therefore in this case
$$dS > dQ/T.$$

Now consider a case where the expansion is adiabatic and where it takes place against a balancing pressure, in overcoming which work is done.. Since no heat is taken in, the work of expansion, $p\,dV$, must be balanced by a decrease in the internal energy of the gas, which does in fact cool in the process. Thus

$$p\,dV + C_v\,dT = 0,$$

or $$RT\,dV/V = -C_v\,dT.$$

There is no change in the probability of state in this process: the spatial distribution of the molecules in the expanded gas is more probable, but the energy distribution at the lower temperature is correspondingly less so. The contribution to dS due to the volume change is $R\,dV/V$, so that the contribution due to the temperature drop must, according to the last equation, be $-C_v\,dT/T$. This again agrees with the general statistical result given above.

If the equilibrium conditions were not maintained and if the gas expanded against no opposing pressure, then the entropy would still increase by $R\,dV/V$ in virtue of the volume increase, but since no work would be done, there would be no cooling and no corresponding drop in entropy to compensate the increase. Thus we should have $dQ = 0$ and $dS = R\,dV/V$, so that $dS > dQ/T$.

The kind of transformation which occurs when a system passes from one state of equilibrium to an adjacent one is known as a *reversible change*: that which occurs when it passes from a state farther removed from equilibrium to one less far removed is called *irreversible*.

The condition for equilibrium is that all forces acting upon the system shall be exactly balanced by opposing forces. In a reversible change the maximum resistance is overcome and thus the maximum possible amount of work is done. In an irreversible change the work done is less and may fall to zero.

In a reversible change $dS = dQ/T$: in an irreversible change $dS > dQ/T$.

The condition, then, that a given small displacement should be reversible is also the condition that the system in question starts out from a state of equilibrium.

Thermodynamics and molecular statistics

The ideas outlined in the foregoing pages provide a transition from the notions of molecular statistics to those of heat and work, and thus to the science known as thermodynamics. They have just been illustrated by reference to gases which obey Boyle's law, but the more detailed statistical argument which preceded showed the generality of the law relating dS with dQ/T for equilibrium and non-equilibrium systems respectively.

The exploitation of the idea of molecular chaos, which in turn is based upon the view that molecules are small particles subject to mechanical laws, thus leads to a new point of departure from which wide regions of physical chemistry can be explored.

The entropy principle which has just been developed is susceptible of experimental verification and is equivalent to what is usually called *the Second Law of Thermodynamics.*

Before examining the scope of thermodynamical principles, it may be well to consider the degree of validity and the limitations of the statistical ideas so far developed. In the first place, it has been expedient for the calculations to assume a finite series of discrete energy states, among which the molecules are distributed (p. 27). The number of assignments is then definite, and a calculus of probabilities can be applied. If the spacing of the successive states in the series is made infinitesimally fine, then the number of assignments assumes a large and indefinite value. The absolute magnitude of the statistical entropy, as far as the present discussion has gone, is therefore devoid of significance. That ratios of numbers, both of which tend towards infinity may retain significance is, of course, perfectly possible, so that differences in entropy may be finite and non-arbitrary even when the absolute values are unknown, unknowable, or possibly meaningless. But to assume that this should be so involves something of a working hypothesis.

The positive fruitful results of the foregoing statistical calculations did not in any way depend upon the extrapolation to the case of infinitesimally small differences of energy. The calculations related to small finite differences. If there were a definite law specifying the spacing of discrete energy levels, and if these did not merge into a continuous series, then the number of assignments and the statistical entropy would possess exactly knowable absolute values, and a whole range of possible new applications of the entropy principle might open out.

The series is in fact a discrete one, the laws in question are those of the quantum theory, and the applications of the knowledge which they bring are indeed extensive, as will appear.

To obtain the equipartition law in the form which gave, apart from the mystery of the missing degrees of freedom, the correct form for the specific heat, the finite and discrete spacing of the energy levels had to be given a particular character. The series corresponded not to equal increments of energy but to equal increments of momentum. Even if an extrapolation to a continuous distribution had been made, this hypothesis would have had to be retained. Thus it again becomes apparent that something beyond the normal mechanical laws is needed for a complete solution of the problem.

In the meantime the entropy principle itself has a host of applications which do not involve knowledge of what this something is.

III

THERMODYNAMIC PRINCIPLES

The laws of thermodynamics

THE entropy principle emerges from the conception of the world as a chaos of particles endowed with random motions. It states that when any system undergoes a small displacement from equilibrium the heat taken in, dQ, is related to the entropy change by the equation
$$dQ/T = dS.$$

Such a change is called reversible: for the irreversible change

$$dQ/T < dS.$$

These relations hold whether the molecules exert forces on one another or whether they are nearly independent masses as, approximately, are those of dilute gases. When mutual influences are not negligible, then the internal energy becomes a function of the volume. In general it may also be a function of other external variables.

The difference between dQ, the heat taken in by any system, and dE, the change in the internal energy, is accounted for according to the principle of energy conservation by the performance of external work as, for example, when a gas expands against an external pressure. This available balance is a maximum when dQ itself has its maximum of $T\,dS$ in the reversible transformation. It is then termed the change in *free energy* or the change in *thermodynamic potential*.

The question of the relation between the heat changes accompanying various kinds of natural process and the work which may be performed is one that has been of dominating importance. The conception of the statistical entropy is evidently one which penetrates more deeply into the nature of things, but the idea of deriving work from heat is one which has appealed more strongly to minds bent upon the useful arts such as the construction of steam-engines, and the laws of thermodynamics were discovered independently of the statistical ideas which interpret them.

The first law of thermodynamics states that there is an exact quantitative equivalence between heat consumed and mechanical work generated and vice versa. In the light of the notion that heat is the invisible energy of molecules, differing only from mechanical energy in being disordered rather than ordered, the first law appears as a simple corollary of the principle of the conservation of energy.

What is known as the second law follows from the entropy principle in a fairly direct way. Suppose there are two systems, one of which transfers heat to the other. Let the temperature of the one which loses the heat be T_1, and that of the one which gains it T_2. The former gives up an amount of heat dQ, and the drop in its entropy is dS_1: the latter receives an equal amount of heat, and its entropy increases by dS_2. If the whole transaction is one which takes place spontaneously, the probability increases on balance, so that $dS_2 - dS_1$ will be a positive quantity. In the limit when the transfer of heat is only just possible as a spontaneous process, $dS_2 - dS_1$ just approaches zero. We have

$$dS_1 = dQ/T_1,$$

$$dS_2 = dQ/T_2,$$

$$dQ(1/T_2 - 1/T_1) = \Delta.$$

Δ being positive (or in the limit just zero) and dQ by hypothesis a positive quantity we have

$1/T_2 - 1/T_1$ is positive (or in the limit zero).

Therefore, for a spontaneous transfer, $T_1 > T_2$, or in the limit when the flow just ceases to occur, $T_1 = T_2$.

This is in fact the second law of thermodynamics which states that it is impossible for heat to pass spontaneously from a body at a lower temperature to one at a higher.

An equivalent form of this statement, which relates it more obviously to practical considerations, is that work cannot be derived by the continuous utilization of the heat contained in a system at uniform temperature. An aeroplane, for example, cannot propel itself with the aid of some device which consumes the heat of the atmosphere in which it moves. If it did so, it would leave the surroundings cooler than itself, and the process could only continue if heat flowed against the adverse temperature gradient so created.

The second law in this form denies the possibility of what has sometimes been called perpetual motion of the second kind, just as the first law denies that of the first kind, which is generation of work from nothing at all.

These principles follow from the molecular nature of things, but they have in the past themselves played the part of fundamental laws and, since they are directly relatable to our experience of the sensible world, some people would still prefer to regard them as more satisfactory starting-points than the statistical considerations into which they may be translated. It has been argued that we can be sure of the validity of the two laws of thermodynamics in a way in which we cannot be sure of the molecular theory. Perhaps there is no answer to this, except that the molecular theory might claim greater intelligibility than the laws of thermodynamics by themselves possess.

One claim that is sometimes made is that the laws of thermodynamics are more objective and realistic than molecular-statistical considerations. This purist attitude looks somewhat artificial in the light of the fact that the second law of thermodynamics is really not rigidly true at all, except as a statistical average for large numbers of molecules. For systems small enough to show the Brownian motion it becomes patently false if advanced as a law which takes no cognizance of molecules.

Nevertheless, the adoption of the two formal laws as the starting-point of thermodynamic considerations has many conveniences. Various modes of development are possible, and each has some advantage in yielding a different point of view and clarifying a different set of relations.

Discussion of the second law of thermodynamics

In the first place, by a suitable reversal of the arguments already given, the entropy principle may be derived from the second law. The process is a little cumbrous as traditionally carried out. The following is perhaps the simplest way.

Gases exist which obey Boyle's law nearly enough for the properties of perfect gases to be inferred with some precision. The pressure, volume, and temperature of a perfect gas (for convenience we consider one gram molecule) are connected by the relation $pV = RT$. The temperature which this equation defines is taken as the standard scale. When a perfect gas expands into a vacuum there is no temperature change, so that the internal energy must be independent of the volume. When expansion takes place against an external pressure, work is done, its amount reaching a maximum of $p\,dV$ for an increase of volume dV against a pressure just equal to that exerted by the gas itself. If the temperature is to remain constant, heat, dQ, must flow in, the amount being given by

$$dQ = p\,dV = RT\,dV/V.$$

If the temperature changes by dT, there is an additional absorption of heat, $C_v\,dT$, so that

$$dQ = p\,dV + C_v\,dT = RT\,dV/V + C_v\,dT.$$

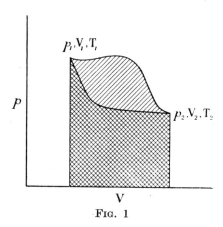

FIG. 1

Now suppose the reversible change is of finite magnitude. The work done is $\int p\,dV$, where p varies in a way which depends upon the course of the temperature change. The total heat taken in can be expressed by the integral of the last equation, namely

$$\int (RT\,dV/V + C_v\,dT),$$

a quantity which cannot be evaluated unless an auxiliary equation is provided giving T in terms of V at every stage. The value of the integral can vary widely according to the nature of this T, V relation, as may be seen in the diagram (Fig. 1). The two curved lines represent two possible paths from p_1, V_1, T_1 to p_2, V_2, T_2 and the two shaded areas correspond to the two different values of $\int p\,dV$, the work done.

On the other hand, the value of $\int dQ/T$ is perfectly definite and depends only upon V_2, T_2 and V_1, T_1.

$$\int dQ/T = \int (RT\,dV/VT + C_v\,dT/T) = \int R\,dV/V + \int C_v\,dT/T$$
$$= R\ln V_2/V_1 + C_v\ln T_2/T_1.$$

If the changes of pressure, temperature, and volume are cyclical, so that the system returns to its original state, the value of $\int dQ/T$ is clearly zero, $(\ln 1 + \ln 1)$, as the last equation shows, though the work done and the total heat absorbed, $\int dQ$, need not by any means be zero, as is seen in Fig. 2, where the area enclosed in the curve is proportional to the work done.

What has just been said is equivalent to the statement that there exists, for a perfect gas, a function, which may be called the thermo-

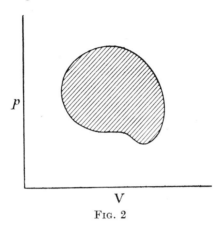

P

V

FIG. 2

dynamic entropy, defined by the equation $dS = dQ/T$ (reversible), and which depends only upon the instantaneous values of the variables describing the state. Had the changes involved in the foregoing argument been irreversible, then the work done in a given expansion would have been less, so that

$$dQ_{(\text{irrev})} < dQ_{(\text{rev})};$$

but $dQ_{(\text{rev})} = T\,dS$, by definition, and therefore

$$dQ_{(\text{irrev})} < T\,dS,$$

or $$dS > dQ/T_{(\text{irrev})}.$$

So far all this has followed merely from the properties of the perfect gas. But the perfect gas has no special status except in so far as it is used to define the normal temperature scale. The important task, therefore, is to show that the entropy principle also applies to other substances.

This is done by a proof that unless the principle applied to all substances the second law of thermodynamics could not be true. The demonstration is as follows.

Suppose there were a substance which could be caused to go through a reversible series of operations and to return to its starting-point in such a way that the value of the function $\int dQ/T$ were greater than zero. One may obviously choose such an amount of this substance that the heat which it requires to take in while traversing some defined small cycle is equal to that taken in by a standard amount of a perfect gas going through a corresponding cycle. That is

$$\int dQ' = \int dQ,$$

where the dash refers to the new substance. By hypothesis, however,

$$\int dQ'/T > 0 \quad \text{while} \quad \int dQ/T = 0,$$

where the letter without the dash refers to the perfect gas.

Now we let the hypothetical substance, in the appropriately chosen amount, traverse its cycle, using any work which it performs to compress the gas, and having any work which must be done upon it done by the gas. The two cycles are in effect coupled together. The integral $\int dQ'/T$ consists of a sum of positive and of negative contributions from different parts of the cycle, and, since for the cycle as a whole it is greater than zero, the positive terms must predominate. In $\int dQ/T$, on the other hand, the positive and negative ones are equal. Thus for the joint system of gas and hypothetical substance the positive contributions must predominate over the negative. But for this joint system the positive and negative contributions to dQ and dQ' cancel, since we chose the amounts of material so that these two quantities were numerically equal, and, in the circumstances prevailing, they are of opposite sign, the new substance forcing the gas to traverse its cycle in reverse. Thus the positive contributions must be associated in general with lower values of T than the negative ones. In other words, the system as a whole must have taken in heat at lower temperatures and rejected it at higher temperatures. This possibility is denied by the second law, and we must therefore conclude that the assumption $\int dQ'/T > 0$ is inadmissible. A similar argument shows that an integral less than zero is equally inadmissible. Hence we must conclude that for all possible substances $dQ'/T_{(rev)} = 0$. It follows by the same argument which was used in connexion with the gas that dS or $dQ/T_{(rev)}$ measures a quantity which is a function of the variables of state only. For an irreversible change, moreover, $dS = dQ/T_{(rev)} > dQ/T_{(actual)}$.

The application of this result to the formulation of conditions of equilibrium follows in exactly the same way as for the statistical entropy.

The principle of Carathéodory

There is yet another method by which the laws of thermodynamics may be derived, and one which exemplifies a completely different attitude towards the interpretation of nature.

The quantity of heat introduced into a system may be expressed as a sum of the quantities going into various separate parts of it, that is,
$$dQ = dQ_1 + dQ_2 + \dots .$$
Each term in the sum is of the form
$$dQ_1 = dE_1 + p_1 dV_1,$$
where dE_1 itself may be expressed in terms of other variables
$$dE_1 = \left(\frac{\partial E_1}{\partial x_1}\right) dx_1 + \dots .$$
Thus dQ is of the general form
$$dQ = X_1 dx_1 + X_2 dx_2 + \dots,$$
where X_1, X_2,..., are functions of the different variables which describe the state of the whole system. For an adiabatic transformation
$$X_1 dx_1 + X_2 dx_2 + \dots = 0,$$
a differential equation of the type known as Pfaff's equation.

Expressions of this kind have of course geometrical interpretations in terms of lines and surfaces, and it is in the light of such ideas that Carathéodory develops the principles of thermodynamics.

First we enter into certain considerations regarding a single substance. Pressure, volume, and temperature are connected by an equation of state, any one of the variables p, V, and T being calculable in principle from the other two. ($pV = RT$ for a perfect gas is the simplest possible example of an equation of state.) It follows that dQ can be expressed as an equation in two variables, and such an equation is in principle always susceptible of integration. The example of a perfect gas will make this point clear.
$$dQ = C_v dT + p dV.$$
Since $pV = RT$, p can be eliminated from the equation for dQ, which becomes
$$dQ/T = C_v dT/T + R dV/V,$$

after division by T. The right-hand side is now immediately integrable and yields

$$S = \int dQ/T = f(V, T).$$

The factor $1/T$ which multiplies dQ is called an *integrating factor*. Now $dQ = T\,dS$, and therefore when $dQ = 0$, $S = $ constant. For an adiabatic change, then, $dQ = 0$ and $dS = 0$.

These results are in no way dependent upon the second law, and follow simply from the existence of an equation of state where two independent variables may be chosen and the third expressed in terms of them.

The following result is also obvious for a single substance. In any adiabatic change all attainable states are represented by points on a curve for which $S = $ constant. There are other points which do not lie on this curve, and which represent states which cannot be reached by an adiabatic transition.

Geometrically the condition that some states are reachable by an adiabatic transition and that others, as near to them as we please, are not, is intimately connected with the existence of an integrating factor for the equation $dQ = X_1\,dx_1 + X_2\,dx_2$. ($x_1$ and x_2 were V and T in the above example.) If there are adiabatically unreachable points, they fill an area bounded by the line of reachable points. This line must be described by an equation of the form

$$f(V, T) = \text{constant},$$

which in turn must be derivable from the equation $dQ = 0$ by a purely mathematical process. Hence the existence of the integrating factor.

The argument thus briefly outlined survives more rigid analysis and, what is important, can be generalized to the case of more than two independent variables. The result which emerges is this: that if in the immediate neighbourhood of any given point, corresponding to coordinates x_1, x_2,..., there are points not expressible by solutions of the equation $X_1\,dx_1 + X_2\,dx_2 + ... = 0$, then for the expression $X_1\,dx_1 + X_2\,dx_2 + ...$ itself there exists an integrating factor. When such a factor multiplies dQ, the product becomes a perfect differential, that is the differential of a function which depends only on the coordinates and not upon the shape of the path connecting two sets of values of these coordinates.

Now, as has been said, the application of this geometrical and analytical result tells us little or nothing about the behaviour of single substances which could not have been inferred directly from the mere existence of the equation of state. But it involves a special condition about the equilibrium between any two substances, and this condition can be used as a basis for a formulation of the second law of thermodynamics.

For two substances in contact

$$dQ = dQ_1 + dQ_2,$$

and to express this we need a three-variable equation of the form

$$dQ = \left(\frac{\partial U_1}{\partial V_1} + p_1\right) dV_1 + \left(\frac{\partial U_2}{\partial V_2} + p_2\right) dV_2 + (C_{1v} + C_{2v}) \, dT.$$

The equations $dQ_1 = 0$ and $dQ_2 = 0$ individually have integrating factors in any case, and may be written $T_1 dS_1 = 0$ and $T_2 dS_2 = 0$ respectively. The equation $dQ = 0$ has an integrating factor only if the assertion is true that in the neighbourhood of any point representing a state of the system there are other points not accessible by adiabatic transformations. If this assertion is in fact true, then geometrical arguments, which are an elaboration of the simple considerations outlined above for the two-variable system, show the existence of an integrating factor for dQ, which can then be written as $T \, dS$.

When this last operation is permissible we have

$$T \, dS = T_1 \, dS_1 + T_2 \, dS_2$$

for the three-variable system.

Further detailed argument of a purely mathematical nature shows that in this case there is one universal factor, T, for the separate systems and for the joint system, and that $dS = d(S_1 + S_2)$, that is, that there is an absolute temperature and an entropy function for all substances. From this point the derivation of the principles of thermodynamics follows the same course as before.

In the orientation given to it by Carathéodory, thermodynamics is made to depend upon the postulate that in the immediate vicinity of any state of a system of more than one body there exist other states which cannot be reached by reversible adiabatic transitions.

That this should be analytically equivalent to the second law may perhaps be seen in a general way by reflecting that if there were no limitation upon the direction of heat transfers, such as the second

E

law asserts, then, even subject to the condition $dQ = 0$, dQ_1 and dQ_2 could assume values corresponding to unnatural transitions, and states could thereby be reached which in reality are unattainable.

Comparison of various methods of formulation of the second law

There are thus three main avenues of approach to thermodynamics. The first is that which starts from the laws of probability, and in its origins is specially associated with the name of Boltzmann. The second is that of Carnot, of Clausius, and of Thomson, and sets out from experience of the flow of heat and of the convertibility of heat into work. The third is that of Carathéodory.

A comparison of these three approaches is of more than historical significance, in that it raises a question which cannot legitimately be evaded, that, namely, of what is meant by a scientific interpretation of the world.

It has been claimed that Carathéodory's method avoids what is alleged to be the unsatisfactory notion of the flow of heat, and dispenses with cumbrous conceptions such as cycles of operations in which heat is utilized and work performed: that it reduces the whole argument to a clean-cut mathematical consideration of the geometry of lines and surfaces, and that it makes only one simple postulate about the possibility of reaching certain states by adiabatic means.

As to the matter of the 'flow of heat', one might ask for a definition of the symbol dQ employed in the development, and it may be suspected that the answer would make a rather thinly veiled use of the notion to which exception is taken. This, however, is a rather unimportant point.

More seriously it can be said that the rigid mathematical development of Carathéodory's arguments is no less elaborate than the alternative mode of discussion, and the question could certainly be raised whether his fundamental postulate would really be of any interest or significance in itself were it not known to be going to lead to the second law of thermodynamics. From one point of view it might be regarded rather as an incidental corollary to the latter, and the derivation of the law from the principle might even be represented as putting the cart before the horse. Moreover, in its primitive form, Carathéodory's postulate is hardly open to confirmation by direct observation.

There is, however, no means of deciding whether the one or the other of these different views about the matter is the more correct one. Something that conforms to a mathematical pattern of an established type will always appeal strongly to some people and there are even parts of science, as will appear, where this mode of description seems to be the only one available. But it is well to remember that this conformity provides a means of description only, and that its significance is partly a matter of aesthetic judgement.

To some men of science such descriptions seem satisfying and to some they do not, just indeed as to certain other people any purely scientific description of the world lacks depth and cogency. Bearing this consideration in mind, we may turn for a moment to the other thermodynamic formulations.

It is in the forms which deal with the flow of heat and the possibilities of obtaining mechanical work that the second law is linked most closely with the everyday experience upon which science partly rests, and with the useful arts to which it owes so much. Here perhaps an objective criterion does exist for giving the traditional formulation precedence over that of Carathéodory. If a major object of science is discovery, then, to that extent, the most satisfactory presentation is that which proceeds by the smallest steps from the known to the unknown. This the methods of the nineteenth-century masters do, whereas those of Carathéodory are more of the nature of a sophisticated commentary on discoveries already made by other means.

The doctrine of molecular chaos, leading to the interpretation of entropy as probability, is in a somewhat different case again. It is based, though not upon direct experiment, upon the primary hypothesis of all chemistry, that of the existence of molecules, and upon the assumption, common to most of physics, that these particles are in motion. It is related very closely to such facts of common observation as diffusion and evaporation, and it takes its place among the major theories about the nature of things. In scope and significance it is of a different order from rather colourless assertions about the geometry of lines and surfaces constructed with the variables of state.

Yet while the geometrical method is self-consistent and, within its limitations, complete, the statistical method is beset with problems. One at least of these, the formulation of what constitutes a molecular state, has already appeared. But it is precisely the examination of this question which leads to fresh realms of discovery.

The geometrical method has qualities about it which might seem to appeal to purists, and as far as the setting forth of the arguments goes, with reason. Yet these qualities are to some extent illusory. No approximation like Stirling's formula is used, yet the very rigidity results in a derivation which ignores in principle the possibility of the Brownian motion, and does not take into account the fact that, in the last analysis, the most interesting thing about the second law of thermodynamics is that it is not absolutely true.

Mode of application of the second law

In its usual form the second law of thermodynamics appears as a negative principle, denying the possibility of certain kinds of change. This being so, it is remarkable how many positive and quantitative results, constituting landmarks throughout physics and chemistry, are built upon it. Some general consideration of the methods by which fruitful conclusions are drawn from the second law is therefore opportune.

All the spontaneous processes which occur in the world are movements from states where equilibrium does not prevail towards those where it does. In these transitions the probability increases. Detailed examination of any individual example reveals that a means can always be devised by which the change could be opposed and the system made to yield work in overcoming a resistance in its passage towards its stabler final state. The greater the opposing influence, the greater is the amount of work which can be obtained, up to a maximum when the system can overcome no greater resistance. When yielding the maximum work the system passes through what is really a series of states of equilibrium between the defined initial and the defined final state, the opposing force being adjusted at each moment to what can just be overcome. The whole process is then carried out in what is called a reversible or quasi-static manner.

These ideas may be illustrated by simple examples. If a concentrated solution is placed in contact with more solvent, molecules of solute diffuse spontaneously until the concentration is uniform throughout. No work is done (provided that there is no volume change on mixture) and the process is irreversible. But there exist what are called semi-permeable membranes, which retain solute while permitting the passage of solvent, and one may imagine a vessel provided with a movable piston permeable to solvent. If solution is placed on the inner side and solvent on the outer, the piston will be urged outwards with a pressure, Π known as the *osmotic pressure*, and can overcome any opposing pressure which does not exceed this in magnitude. If a volume dV of solvent enters the solution, the maximum work which can be performed is $\Pi \, dV$. This in fact is the work of reversible or quasi-static dilution.

This quantity is, of course, of no particular significance in itself and only becomes interesting when compared with the maximum work obtainable in other methods of reversible dilution. Such alternative methods do in fact exist.

Suppose the volume dV of liquid corresponds to dx gram molecules of the substance. Imagine this quantity to be evaporated under its own constant vapour pressure p_0. The volume of vapour generated is $RT \, dx/p_0$, and the work which is performed against the external pressure in the course of its generation is $RT \, dx \, p_0/p_0 = RT \, dx$. This vapour could be condensed into the solution by a compressing force which would expend work $RT \, dx$ in the process, this latter quantity cancelling that obtained in the evaporation. But the vapour pressure, p_1, of the solution is lower than that, p_0, of the pure solvent. Thus, before the condensation is caused to occur, a levy of work can be taken by expanding the vapour against a maximum opposing force as its own pressure drops from p_0 to p_1.

The work obtainable in this process is

$$dx \, RT \int_{V_0}^{V_1} dV/V = dx \, RT \ln V_1/V_0 = dx \, RT \ln p_0/p_1.$$

If this levy is not taken, there is a catastrophic and irreversible condensation of vapour when the solvent is placed in contact with the solution with its lower vapour pressure.

The operation described provides, then, an alternative method of reversible dilution. The maximum work obtainable by the first method is expressible in terms of the osmotic pressure: that obtainable by the second method is expressible in terms of the vapour-pressure ratio. These two quantities of work, as is easily shown, *must be equal*, provided that temperature is constant.

The proof follows in a quite general form from the second law of thermodynamics. Let the maximum amounts of work derivable from two alternative methods of carrying out a given transformation be

A_1 and A_2 respectively. If one of the processes were reversed, say the second, the work done by the system as it returned to the initial state would be $-A_2$. Now let the transformation take place in the forward direction by the first mode and subsequently be reversed by the second, the temperature being maintained constant throughout. The total work derived from this cycle of operations is A_1-A_2. The system returns to its starting-point and its internal energy is therefore unchanged. The amount of work A_1-A_2 must, therefore, have been done at the expense of heat absorbed from the surroundings. The second law denies that work can be obtained in this way, so that the value of A_1-A_2 must be zero. It follows that $A_1 = A_2$.

In the above particular example the two quantities to be equated are the two amounts of work obtained by reversible dilution of the solution. We have therefore the expression

$$\Pi \, dV = dx \, RT \ln p_0/p_1.$$

Certain simple substitutions make this equation more useful. dx gram molecules are equivalent to $M_0 \, dx$ grams where M_0 is the molecular weight of the solvent. $M_0 \, dx$ grams occupy dV c.c., so that $M_0 \, dx/dV = \rho_0$, the density of the liquid solvent. Thus

$$\Pi = \frac{\rho_0 \, RT}{M_0} \ln \frac{p_0}{p},$$

an equation which proves to contain a major part of the theory of dilute solutions.

Free energy and related functions

When a solution is diluted reversibly, work, as has been seen, may be derived from the process. The total volume of liquid, solvent plus solute, may change only negligibly. When the volume can be regarded as constant, it is expedient to represent the maximum work as the decrease, $-\Delta F$, in a potential function, F, which is called the *constant volume free energy*. When, on the other hand, the pressure is constant and the volume changes, the maximum work may be represented as the decrease, $-\Delta G$, in another potential function, G, the *constant pressure free energy*. F and G are called *thermodynamic potentials*, and exist in general for all systems. The idea underlying their use is simply that if the maximum work is independent of the nature of the reversible process by which a system passes from a given initial to a given final state, it represents the decrease in some inherent capacity of the system to do work. Such a capacity is what is normally called a potential.

In the particular example which was quoted in the last section the work is derived partly, or, with a sufficiently dilute solution, entirely from the heat of the surroundings. This is known from the fact that there is no heat change on further irreversible addition of solvent to a solution already dilute, so that the internal energy must be unaffected by the mixing. The inherent improbability of a conversion of heat into work in the reversible dilution is exactly compensated by the increased probability of the spatial distribution of the molecules, which become more randomly scattered as the solute spreads through the larger volume of solvent.

The theorem of the equality of the maximum work derivable isothermally from alternative reversible transformations is applicable in many ways, since, as has been stated, all spontaneous processes can be made to yield work. That is to say, they all occur with diminution of free energy. The exercise of imagination provides means for expressing the maximum work in terms of very varied physical properties, and the equating of the various values leads to connexions between these properties in formulae which are often of great importance.

The scope of the application of these ideas is widened still farther when variation of temperature is brought into the picture. For this extension a preliminary codification of formulae and equations is desirable.

The following quantities are conveniently introduced:

U = internal energy of a substance or system,

$H = U + pV$ = heat content.

Changes in U and H determine the heat taken in or evolved when a change occurs in a calorimeter, at constant volume or at constant pressure respectively, under such conditions that no work is done (other than that of simple expansion).

S = entropy.

If a quantity of heat dQ is added to a system, the balance-sheet is given by

$$dQ = dU + p\, dV,$$

that is to say, the heat supplies the increased internal energy and the work of expansion.

By the second law, if the process is reversible, that is, so long as equilibrium conditions prevail,

$$dQ = T\,dS.$$

Therefore

$$T\,dS = dU + p\,dV. \tag{1}$$

Since in general

$$d(TS) = T\,dS + S\,dT$$

and

$$d(pV) = p\,dV + V\,dp,$$

equation (1) can be written

$$dU - d(TS) = -p\,dV - S\,dT,$$

so that

$$d(U - TS) = -p\,dV - S\,dT.$$

For any small displacement from equilibrium in which dV and dT are zero

$$d(U - TS) = 0.$$

We write

$$\mathbf{U - TS = F,}$$

where F is defined as the constant volume free energy, so that for the small displacement from equilibrium

$$dF = 0.$$

Since, for displacements of systems not in equilibrium, S increases, F must decrease. That is to say, in spontaneous changes at constant temperature and volume, the free energy decreases.

Equation (1) can also be written

$$dU + d(pV) - d(TS) = V\,dp - S\,dT,$$

so that

$$d(U + pV - TS) = V\,dp - S\,dT$$

or

$$d(H - TS) = V\,dp - S\,dT.$$

For small displacements from equilibrium at constant temperature and pressure dp and dT are zero, so that

$$d(H - TS) = 0.$$

We write

$$\mathbf{H - TS = G,}$$

where G is defined as the constant pressure free energy, so that the equilibrium condition becomes $dG = 0$. In spontaneous changes G decreases.

The variations of F and G with temperature are specially important.

In general

$$dF = -p\,dV - S\,dT.$$

When F is expressed as a function of volume and temperature, its total variation is the sum of the partial variations which it would suffer by change of each of these separately. In the notation of partial differentials

$$dF = \left(\frac{\partial F}{\partial V}\right)_T dV + \left(\frac{\partial F}{\partial T}\right)_V dT,$$

where $(\partial F/\partial V)_T$ represents the rate of change of F with V at constant temperature and $(\partial F/\partial T)_V$ that of F with T at constant volume. Comparison of the last two equations shows that

$$\left(\frac{\partial F}{\partial T}\right)_V = -S,$$

but

$$F = U - TS,$$

and therefore

$$\left(\frac{\partial F}{\partial T}\right)_V = \frac{F-U}{T},$$

or

$$\mathbf{F - U = T}\left(\frac{\partial \mathbf{F}}{\partial \mathbf{T}}\right)_V \qquad (2)$$

Similarly

$$dG = V\,dp - S\,dT$$

and

$$dG = \left(\frac{\partial G}{\partial p}\right)_T dp + \left(\frac{\partial G}{\partial T}\right)_p dT,$$

so that

$$\left(\frac{\partial G}{\partial T}\right)_p = -S,$$

but

$$G = H - TS.$$

Thus

$$\left(\frac{dG}{\partial T}\right)_p = \frac{G-H}{T}$$

or

$$\mathbf{G - H = T}\left(\frac{\partial \mathbf{G}}{\partial \mathbf{T}}\right)_p. \qquad (3)$$

The importance of equations (2) and (3) will presently appear in various ways.

Entropy and volume

Another useful equation which may be derived by rearrangement of the fundamental equation (1) is that giving the variation of entropy with volume.

Since

$$dF = -p\,dV - S\,dT,$$

and since in general

$$dF = \left(\frac{\partial F}{\partial V}\right)_T dV + \left(\frac{\partial F}{\partial T}\right)_V dT,$$

it follows that

$$\left(\frac{\partial F}{\partial V}\right)_T = -p \quad \text{and} \quad \left(\frac{\partial F}{\partial T}\right)_V = -S.$$

By the well-known property of partial differentials

$$\frac{\partial}{\partial T}\left(\frac{\partial F}{\partial V}\right) = \frac{\partial}{\partial V}\left(\frac{\partial F}{\partial T}\right),$$

so that

$$\left(\frac{\partial p}{\partial T}\right)_V = \left(\frac{\partial S}{\partial V}\right)_T.$$

Systems of several phases or components

Before embarking on a brief survey of what thermodynamics has to say about the general pattern of physico-chemical phenomena it will be convenient to deal with certain formalities and one or two general principles.

Normally the systems which come under consideration consist of several substances or phases. These may change one into the other by physical or chemical processes, and we are often concerned with the free energy or entropy differences accompanying such trans-formations as solid into liquid, or hydrogen and oxygen into water. Energies, entropies, and free energies are additive, so that in the following chemical reaction, for example:

$$2H_2 + O_2 = 2H_2O$$

the total energy change is:

(energy of two gram molecules of steam) minus (energy of two gram molecules of hydrogen plus energy of one gram molecule of oxygen). This may be written in the following conventional way:

$$2U_{H_2O} - (2U_{H_2} + U_{O_2}) = \sum nU = \Delta U,$$

the reaction products being given a positive sign and the initial substances a negative one. The total change ΔU has a positive sign when the energy of the system is greater after reaction than before, that is, when there is absorption of heat if the reaction takes place in a constant volume calorimeter without performance of any kind of work.

With this convention the equations (2) and (3) of p. 65 can be applied to express the changes of free energy accompanying physical or chemical transformations. They assume the forms:

$$\Delta F - \Delta U = T \frac{\partial(\Delta F)}{\partial T} \qquad (4)$$

$$\Delta G - \Delta H = T \frac{(\partial \Delta G)}{\partial T}, \qquad (5)$$

the Δ referring to the finite increase which occurs in the whole composite system as the result of the change.

Entropy of gas mixtures

Entropy is an additive function, but a special question arises in connexion with the entropies of mixtures of gases. Here, if the gases obey Boyle's law, the total entropy is the sum of the entropies which each gas separately would possess if it occupied the whole volume filled by the mixture.

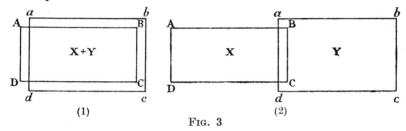

(1)   (2)

FIG. 3

This result follows at once from the fact that the probability of the state is the product of two other probabilities which, in so far as the molecules do not exert appreciable influences on one another, are independent. Macroscopically the result follows from considerations which can be more clearly envisaged if the idea of a semipermeable membrane is introduced (though of course the conclusion implies nothing at all about the real existence of such devices). In Fig. 3 $ABCD$ and $abcd$ are two containers which move with the aid of suitable seals and joints from position 1 to position 2 and back. The wall BC is semipermeable to the gas Y only, and ad to X only. Movement from 1 to 2 and back can occur without performance of work and without absorption or evolution of heat. Thus there is no entropy change in this type of mixing or unmixing. The entropy in condition 1 is the same as that in condition 2, and the principle stated above is evidently true. This case, it is to be noted, is quite different from that where two gases intermingle in such a way that each expands from its own original volume to one which is the sum of the two. In such conditions the entropy would of course increase.

Variation of masses and proportions of components

With a substance in one phase the changes which occur in S, F, G and other thermodynamic quantities are due to variations of temperature, pressure, or concentration. In a system consisting of more than one phase, or of more than one chemical compound, there are further important possibilities.

If a mass, dm, of a solid phase, for example, is transformed into liquid, then there is a gain of $G_2\,dm$ units of free energy on account of the fact that dm of a phase not previously present and contributing G_2 per unit mass appears: and there is a corresponding loss of $G_1\,dm$ units on account of the bodily disappearance of the mass dm of the solid phase with free energy G_1 per unit mass. Thus

$$dG = G_2\,dm - G_1\,dm.$$

Similarly if dn_A gram molecules of a substance A, the free energy of which is G_A per gram molecule, react chemically and are replaced by dn_B gram molecules of B, the value of dG is given by

$$dG = G_B\,dn_B - G_A\,dn_A,$$

provided that A and B themselves constitute phases in which G_A and G_B are independent of concentration terms.

Still more generally we may write

$$dG = \frac{\partial G}{\partial m_1}\,dm_1 + \frac{\partial G}{\partial m_2}\,dm_2 + ...,$$

where $\partial G/\partial m_1$, ... may individually be functions of all the concentrations in any given phase.

Similar expressions of course apply to dF.

It should be observed that when G is written with a subscript, G_1, G_A,..., it refers to the free energy per unit amount of a substance or phase. If we have, for example, a pure solid phase, G_1 means just the same as $\partial G/\partial m_1$, m_1 being the mass of solid present. When concentrations change, $\partial G/\partial m_X$ can still be written G_X as long as one remembers that G_X is a function of concentration.

Activity

The free energy function, G, is defined as $H - TS$. For a perfect gas the entropy is of the form

$$S = C_v \ln T + R \ln V + \text{const.}$$

If the concentration, c, is introduced in the form $c = 1/V$, then at constant temperature S is of the form $(\text{const.} - R \ln c)$. Therefore G is of the form $G = G_0 + RT \ln c$, where G_0 is a constant.

For substances other than perfect gases it is convenient to write

$$G = G_0 + RT \ln a,$$

where a is a function of the concentration which is called the activity. For a perfect gas $a = c$, and for other substances it is a function of c—in general quite a complicated one. Nevertheless, except in special circumstances, a at least varies in the same direction as c, increasing and decreasing with it, though in no simple manner.

Forces and ordered structures

The particles of which the world is assumed to be built up are conceived to be in chaotic motion. But this cannot be the whole story, or everything would consist of rarefied gas. Solids and liquids testify to the existence of ordering and agglomerating forces. At the present stage the nature of these is unknown. The union of atoms to give molecules depends upon attractions of another kind, also unknown. The inquiry into the origin of these mutual influences has to pursue a route other than that of statistics and thermodynamics, but for many purposes the forces are sufficiently characterized, both experimentally and theoretically, in terms of the energy changes which manifest themselves when they operate. As is now known, atoms are composed of electrical particles, molecules of atoms, solids and liquids of agglomerations of molecules (or occasionally atoms). At each level of this hierarchy of structures there is a balance between two tendencies: that, on the one hand, for the random motions to dissipate the constituent particles as widely as possible through the available space, and that, on the other hand, for the forces to order them into patterns possessing a minimum of potential energy.

These two opposing effects are reflected in the two terms of the free energy equations. For displacements from equilibrium, at constant pressure and constant volume respectively, we have, if $\alpha \tau = 0$,

$$dG = d(H - TS) = 0,$$
$$dF = d(U - TS) = 0,$$

so that, S being maximal at equilibrium, G and F are minimal. At a given temperature the influence of H and S or of U and S are opposed to one another.

From what has been said of the nature of the problem and from the character of these thermodynamic functions it is obvious that they will define important properties of physical and chemical equilibria. Among the major problems which confront us in the attempt to see how the world emerges from chaos are three: first, that of the equilibrium between gases, liquids, and solids, and in general of the equilibrium between any number of gaseous and condensed forms; secondly, that of the relations between systems of molecules which pass from states of segregation to states of admixture, in other words, the process of solution; and thirdly, that of the equilibrium between free elements and their compounds, and in general between the reacting substances and the products in any chemical change.

IV

AGGREGATION OF MOLECULES TO SOLIDS AND LIQUIDS

Matter in various states of aggregation

WHEN molecules pass from one phase to another, for example, from the solid to the gas, the intensity of the binding forces changes and the potential energy is altered. As the molecules become freer, energy is absorbed, and constitutes what is measured calorimetrically as latent heat.

For the purposes of a statistical or thermodynamic treatment of phase equilibria the magnitude of the forces themselves is sufficiently characterized by the value of ΔU or ΔH accompanying the transition from one phase to another.

The conditions under which condensed phases are formed from vapour, or one condensed phase is transformed into another, are subject to important general laws. Suppose two phases of a single pure substance coexist and suppose that the first is capable of passage into the second with absorption of energy; that is, ΔU and ΔH are positive. This would apply, for example, to the transition from solid to liquid, where the potential energy increases because the orderly orientation of molecules is destroyed, or to the passage from a condensed phase to the vapour state, where the potential energy increases because the molecules have been separated against the action of the attractive forces.

We may first examine the conditions under which two phases can coexist at constant pressure. Suppose dn gram molecules of substance pass from phase 1 to phase 2. The change in free energy is given by

$$dG = (G_2 - G_1)\,dn,$$

G_2 and G_1 being the respective free energies per gram molecule in the two phases. For equilibrium $dG = 0$, so that

$$G_2 = G_1.$$

$G_2 - G_1$, according to the convention explained above, is written ΔG, so that, under conditions of stable coexistence, $\Delta G = 0$.

From the definition of G itself

$$G_2 - G_1 = H_2 - H_1 - T(S_2 - S_1),$$

or $$\Delta G = \Delta H - T\Delta S.$$

When $\Delta G = 0$, $T = T_{\text{equil}}$.

Thus $$T_{\text{equil}} = \Delta H / \Delta S.$$

Now ΔH and ΔS are both single-valued functions of temperature, and, therefore, ΔH, on the one hand, and $T\Delta S$, on the other, when plotted against temperature are respectively represented by lines. Only at the intersection of these two curves can $T\Delta S = \Delta H$ and $\Delta G = 0$. Thus, for a given pressure, there exists a single equilibrium temperature at which $G_1 = G_2$. At any other temperature these two quantities are not equal and no equilibrium is possible.

If out of one gram molecule of a substance a fraction α exists in phase 1 and $(1-\alpha)$ in phase 2, then we have

$$G = \alpha G_1 + (1-\alpha)G_2,$$

and G reaches its minimum value corresponding to equilibrium either when $\alpha = 1$ or when $\alpha = 0$, according as G_1 or G_2 is the smaller, except of course when $G_1 = G_2$.

If, therefore, we consider a given pressure, molecules of a pure substance will pass all into one phase or all into the other, except at a single temperature where a given pair of phases can coexist, that is at the melting-point, condensation point, or transition point. At this equilibrium temperature, since $G_1 = G_2$, G remains at its minimum for all values of α. Thus the equilibrium does not depend upon the relative amounts of the two phases present.

This result corresponds, of course, with ordinary experience, the temperature of melting of a pure substance, for example, remaining constant so long as solid and liquid are both present.

Variation of pressure: vapour-pressure formula

The question now arises as to what happens when the constant pressure at which the phase transition occurs is altered from one value to another. The influence of variation of pressure may be treated as follows.

Let dn gram molecules of a substance pass from one phase in which the molecular volume is V_1 to another phase in which it is V_2. The volume change is given by

$$dV = (V_2-V_1)\,dn,$$

and the heat absorbed by $\lambda\,dn$, where λ is the molecular latent heat. The change in entropy is dS, where

$$dS = \left(\frac{\partial S}{\partial T}\right)_V dT + \left(\frac{\partial S}{\partial V}\right)_T dV.$$

In this example the temperature stays constant and

$$dS = \left(\frac{\partial S}{\partial V}\right)_T dV.$$

If the system remains in equilibrium, then by the general law

$$dS = dQ/T.$$

Therefore $\quad \left(\frac{\partial S}{\partial V}\right)_T dV = \frac{dQ}{T} = \frac{\lambda\,dn}{T} = \frac{\lambda\,dV}{(V_2-V_1)T}.$

By the result on p. 66,

$$\left(\frac{\partial S}{\partial V}\right)_T = \left(\frac{\partial p}{\partial T}\right)_V,$$

so that $\quad \left(\frac{\partial p}{\partial T}\right)_V = \frac{\lambda}{(V_2-V_1)T}.$

Since at the equilibrium temperature the proportion of the phases is immaterial, we may write simply

$$\frac{dp}{dT} = \frac{\lambda}{(V_2-V_1)T},$$

or $\quad \dfrac{dp}{dT} = \dfrac{\Delta H}{T\Delta V},$

since $V_2-V_1 = \Delta V$, and λ is a special value of what in general is represented by ΔH.

The equilibrium temperature will vary with pressure, and in a direction which depends upon the sign of ΔV.

When liquid or solid passes into vapour, ΔV is positive and p increases with T. With rising temperature the equilibrium pressure becomes higher: this is the well-known increase of vapour pressure with temperature.

The last equation can be thrown into a convenient approximate form with the help of two assumptions, namely that the volume of the condensed phase is negligible in comparison with that of the vapour, and that the vapour obeys the laws of perfect gases. In these circumstances $\Delta V = V_2$ and

$$\frac{dp}{dT} = \frac{p\lambda}{RT^2}; \quad \frac{1}{p}\frac{dp}{dT} = \frac{\lambda}{RT^2},$$

i.e.

$$\frac{d\ln p}{dT} = \frac{\lambda}{RT^2}.$$

If, further, the variation of the latent heat with temperature is assumed negligible in comparison with that of the vapour pressure itself, the last equation may be integrated in the simple approximate form

$$\ln p = C - \frac{\lambda}{RT},$$

where C is a constant. Thus the logarithm of the vapour pressure should be a linear function of the reciprocal temperature. Over moderate ranges this relation is in fact rather well satisfied.

For other phase transitions occurring in the sense for which ΔH is positive, the sign of ΔV may be positive or negative and, accordingly, the equilibrium pressure increases or decreases with rising temperature; or, if the pressure be regarded as arbitrarily controlled, the equilibrium temperature rises or falls with increasing pressure. In the transition from ice to water, for example, there is a contraction, ΔV is negative, and hence the melting-point falls as the pressure increases.

Coexistence of several phases

Most substances can assume the three forms: solid, liquid, and vapour, and we may inquire under what conditions the three can coexist. For any given pair of phases at a selected pressure there is in general a definite equilibrium temperature (with an exception which will be referred to later). For solid and liquid the equilibrium temperature may be plotted as a function of pressure, and yields a definite curve. For liquid and vapour there is a corresponding curve, neither identical with nor parallel to that for solid and liquid. The two lines will in general, therefore, cut at a definite point, representing a fixed temperature and a fixed pressure. Under these conditions the three phases can coexist stably. They can do so nowhere else. The point of coexistence is called the *triple point*.

When there are several components in the system, fresh possibilities open out. We may begin by considering two substances A and B which as solids are immiscible, but which in the liquid state are miscible in all proportions, a behaviour exemplified by many real pairs. For equilibrium of solid A with liquid we have

$$G_{2(A,B)} dn_A - G_{1(A)} dn_A = 0 \tag{1}$$

and for the equilibrium of solid B with liquid

$$G_{2(B,A)} dn_B - G_{1(B)} dn_B = 0, \tag{2}$$

where the subscript 2 refers to the liquid phase and the subscript 1 to the solid phase. dn_A and dn_B represent the amounts of A and B respectively which pass from one phase to the other in the small displacement from equilibrium by which the constancy of G is tested. $G_{2(A,B)}$ is the free energy per gram molecule of A in the mixed liquid at the prevailing composition, and $G_{2(B,A)}$ that per gram molecule of B. Both these latter quantities are functions of the composition of the liquid, but it is to be noted that the fixing of the value of one automatically fixes the value of the other. $G_{1(A)}$ and $G_{1(B)}$ contain no concentration terms and neither depends upon the ratio of A to B in the system as a whole, since each refers to a pure solid phase. Since $G_{2(A,B)}$ has a different value for each proportion of A to B, there will be a whole range of temperatures at which equation (1) can be satisfied. Thus solid A can exist in equilibrium with liquid at temperatures which vary with the composition of the system. Similar considerations apply to the solid B. If a fixed temperature is chosen (within a certain range), a composition of liquid can be found which will permit equilibrium with A, but this composition, though determining $G_{2(B,A)}$, will not in general permit equilibrium with B. For the simultaneous equilibrium of the two solids with the mixed liquid at a given pressure it is necessary to choose from the range of compositions possible for A and B separately that one which suits both together. This being fixed, the temperature is also fixed. Thus the two solids can only coexist with liquid at one particular temperature, which is known as the *eutectic* temperature.

The situation is again changed if the two substances A and B are miscible in the solid state. For equilibrium at constant pressure we now have

$$G_{2(A,B)} - G_{1(A,B)} = 0,$$

$$G_{2(B,A)} - G_{1(B,A)} = 0,$$

where $G_{1(A,B)}$ and $G_{1(B,A)}$ are now functions of composition as well as of temperature. For any given temperature (within a certain range) a composition can be found which corresponds to equilibrium, since now the concentration in the solid phase as well as that in the liquid can adjust itself in such a way that the two equations can be satisfied together. The equilibrium temperature will vary continuously between the melting-points of the separate substances.

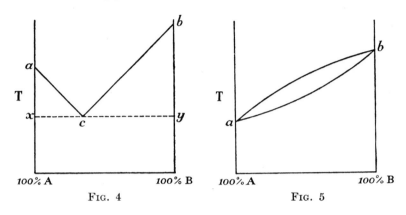

FIG. 4   FIG. 5

The relations between solid and liquid to which these principles lead are shown in Figs. 4 and 5. In Fig. 4 a is the melting-point of pure A, b that of pure B. If there is no miscibility in the solid state, the composition of solid must correspond either to A or to B, except at the eutectic, where it can correspond to any proportion of the two solid phases. Thus composition of solid follows the line $axyb$. That of liquid follows acb.

Where miscibility in the solid phase is complete, the relations are as shown in Fig. 5, where the upper line represents the composition of the liquid phase and the lower line that of the solid in equilibrium with it at a given temperature. Variants of this case are shown in Figs. 6 and 7, and an intermediate case where the miscibility in the solid state is partial is shown in Fig. 8.

Fig. 4 illustrates the fact of common observation that the melting-point of each pure component is lowered by the addition of a second substance. That it should be changed has already been shown: that it should specifically be *lowered* is a matter for more detailed consideration.

The condition for equilibrium of the pure substance is that $G_2 = G_1$.

Also, $\left(\dfrac{\partial G_2}{\partial T}\right)_p = -S_2$ and $\left(\dfrac{\partial G_1}{\partial T}\right)_p = -S_1.$

Now since heat is absorbed when solid changes reversibly into liquid, the entropy of the liquid is the greater, that is, $S_2 > S_1$. Therefore

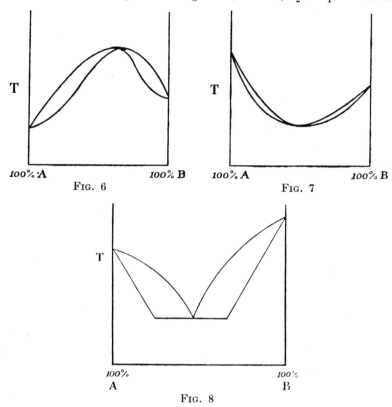

FIG. 6   FIG. 7

FIG. 8

G_2 decreases more rapidly with rise of temperature than G_1. If, then, the temperature *drops*, the free energy of the liquid *increases* relatively to that of the solid. The two phases are in equilibrium at the melting-point, so that as the temperature drops below it there develops a positive tendency for the liquid to change into solid with decrease of free energy. This tendency could be counteracted and the equilibrium could be preserved if the free energy per unit quantity of the liquid were reduced in some compensating way. A simple way is to add a foreign substance to the liquid. Free energy in general is expressible in the form $G = G_0 + RT \ln a$, where a is a function which, except in quite special circumstances, increases with concentration

(p. 69). If the pure liquid phase of A is diluted by a substance B the value of $G_{2(A)}$ is lowered. The addition, therefore, provides the compensating influence which, by decreasing the free energy of the liquid phase, allows equilibrium with the solid at a temperature below the normal melting-point.

General rules of phase equilibrium

Solid, liquid, and vapour of a given substance can, as has been seen, coexist in equilibrium only at a fixed temperature and pressure. Such a system is said to be *non-variant* or to possess no *degrees of freedom*. Solid and liquid can coexist over a range of temperatures, provided that for each temperature an appropriate pressure be chosen. Liquid and vapour can be in equilibrium at a continuous series of pressures, each corresponding to a definite temperature. These systems are called monovariant, and are said to possess one degree of freedom.

The addition of another substance to a given system increases the number of degrees of freedom. For example, with two substances present in the liquid phase, a given solid can exist in equilibrium with liquid over a whole range of temperatures at a given pressure, and not at the normal melting-point only: the pressure can be varied independently. Thus, while in the one-component system there is only one degree of freedom when two phases are present, for the two-component system there are two degrees of freedom. The extra variability is due, as is clear from the foregoing discussion, to the existence of an adjustable concentration in the liquid. In general, we may infer that when the number of components, C, is increased by one, the number of degrees of freedom, F, will be increased by one also. In other words, for a given number of phases in equilibrium we should suspect the relation, $F - C = $ constant.

Furthermore, as was seen above, if there is one solid phase and one liquid phase in the two-component system A, B, the equilibrium is possible over a range of temperatures even at one pressure, whereas, if the two solid phases are separately present, the equilibrium, for a given pressure, is possible at one temperature only. Thus, for a given number of components, the addition of a new phase reduces the number of degrees of freedom by one. This result, too, is general, and we may well suppose that $P + F = $ constant, where P is the number of phases.

Combining these two tentative rules, we obtain

$$P+F-C = \text{constant.}$$

Since for a single substance, three phases coexist in an invariant system,

$$3+0-1 = \text{constant,}$$

whence the constant is evidently equal to 2, and the above induction takes the form

$$P+F = C+2.$$

This is known as the *Phase Rule*.

A more formal derivation is possible and runs as follows. For each pair of phases, as has been seen, there must be an equation expressing the change in free energy which accompanies the virtual transfer of any given component. If there are P phases, the number of independent pairs is $(P-1)$. With C components there will be C equations for each pair of phases, the total number being $C(P-1)$. To define the composition of the whole system the concentrations of $C-1$ components in each phase must be known (the remaining concentration always being calculable by difference). Thus there are $P(C-1)$ concentration variables. To these must be added temperature and pressure, making $P(C-1)+2$ in all. The $C(P-1)$ equations define a corresponding number of variables, leaving

$$P(C-1)+2-C(P-1)$$

to be assigned at will. These assignable variables constitute the degrees of freedom. Thus

$$P(C-1)+2-C(P-1) = F,$$

or

$$P+F = C+2.$$

The Boltzmann potential energy relation

So far the equilibria between phases have been considered in the light of thermodynamic principles. These, of course, are only a formal embodiment of the statistical laws governing the behaviour of large numbers of particles, and the major results which they predict should be interpretable directly in terms of the molecular-kinetic picture. Though sometimes more difficult to carry through in detail, the molecular interpretations are of considerable interest in themselves. All are variations on the familiar theme that the random motions of the molecules tend by themselves to dissipate matter into the state of rarefied gas, while attractive forces tend to collect it into condensed phases. Equilibria result from the opposition of these two tendencies.

The first departure from random distribution is expressed in the Boltzmann potential energy law. If in any region the potential energy of molecules differs by an amount ΔU from that in the rest of space, U_0, the molecules will cluster there more or less densely in the ratio n/n_0 such that

$$n = n_0 e^{-\Delta U/kT}.$$

If ΔU is negative, that is, if the potential energy is lower in the special region, they cluster more thickly.

The proof of the theorem is as follows. From the general statistical law, the relative numbers of molecules in two states of energy ϵ_j and ϵ_k respectively are

$$\frac{N_j}{N_k} = \frac{e^{-\epsilon_j/kT}}{e^{-\epsilon_k/kT}} = e^{-(\epsilon_j-\epsilon_k)/kT}.$$

If the state j differs from the state k only in the value of the potential energy, so that $\epsilon_k = \epsilon_i + U_0$ and $\epsilon_j = \epsilon_i + U_0 + \Delta U$,

$$\epsilon_j - \epsilon_k = \Delta U,$$

$$\frac{N_j}{N_k} = e^{-\Delta U/kT}.$$

The last expression is quite independent of the value of ϵ_i, so that N_j and N_k may, for all internal energy states of the molecules, be replaced by the general values n and n_0.

The existence of attractive forces leads to a certain condensing tendency, since potential energy runs down as attracting molecules approach one another. The average disturbance of density (or orientation) is insignificant as long as ΔU is small compared with kT. When temperature drops there comes a point at which complete condensation or orientation occurs and a phase change results.

The nature of the phase changes and the conditions of equilibrium between matter in different states is a subject for detailed examination.

Kinetic consideration of equilibrium between different phases of matter

In the consideration of actual phase changes evaporation is the simplest case with which to begin. Consider the surface which separates a liquid from its vapour. If there is a condition of equilibrium, the rate of condensation of molecules from the vapour equals the rate of evaporation from the liquid. Since the surface of separation of the two phases is unchanging, the rate of evaporation at a given temperature is constant.

The rate of condensation is, however, proportional to the pressure of the vapour. The latter increases until the rate of condensation equals the rate of evaporation, at which point

$$c_1 = c_2 p,$$

where c_1 and c_2 are functions of temperature only. Thus $p = $ constant at any given temperature. For small changes of temperature c_1 does not change very much, the rate at which molecules return to the surface being proportional to their speeds, which in turn vary as $T^{\frac{1}{2}}$. The rate of evaporation, however, is determined by the fraction of molecules in the liquid which have enough energy to escape from the attractions of their neighbours. This fraction is approximately proportional to $e^{-\lambda/RT}$, where λ is the latent heat.

Thus $\qquad\qquad c_1' e^{-\lambda/RT} = c_2 p$

approximately, or $\qquad p = \text{const.} e^{-\lambda/RT},$

whence $\qquad\qquad \dfrac{d \ln p}{dT} = \dfrac{\lambda}{RT^2},$

the formula which has already been derived (p. 74).

Next we may discuss melting. When the molecules of a liquid orient themselves into regular geometrical arrays, solidification occurs, and the potential energy (which decreases in liquefaction of vapour) runs down still farther. To escape from solid into liquid, molecules require extra energy (derived from their neighbours by the hazards of collision), while to pass from liquid to solid, molecules need to assume special orientations. The two corresponding rates of transfer are separate and independent functions of temperature, and could be plotted as curves. Where the lines cut equilibrium is possible. This is at the melting-point. The rates are separately and independently influenced by pressure, whence the functional relation between melting-point and pressure.

The balance liquid $\leftrightarrows$ solid is affected by pressure, and that of

liquid ⇋ vapour by temperature. By choosing the correct temperature a vapour pressure can be defined which will be equal to the
equilibrium pressure for the system solid ⇋ liquid at that same temperature. This defines the position of the triple point.

The entropy of a solid is less than that of a liquid, a fact which is
reflected in the evolution of heat when the liquid solidifies. It is an
expression of the ordered state of the solid, in which the regular
orientation of the molecules contrasts with the more random configuration of the liquid.

Certain aspects of the phenomena of condensation and crystallization which the thermodynamic discussion ignores are accounted for
by kinetic principles. In the last paragraphs the balancing of the
rates of transfer from phase to phase was assumed to occur at plane
interfaces which do not modify their character as the change of state
proceeds. This assumption is perfectly correct when the equilibrium
involves large amounts of established phases. Such quantities, however, are not present during the first formation of an entirely new
phase; and the conditions become very different, with the result that
special phenomena make their appearance.

If droplets of liquid are to form in the midst of vapour, or minute
crystals in the midst of liquid, they must grow from nuclei which, in
the first instance, have to be produced by the chance encounters of
molecules with appropriate velocities and orientations. The incipient
nuclei are subject to two opposing influences. In virtue of the attractive forces, they tend to grow, and in virtue of the thermal motion
they tend to disperse. These tendencies exist at all temperatures, but
above the point of condensation or crystallization they come into
balance while the agglomerates are still few, minute, and transitory.
The existence of the nuclei amounts to no more than an increased
probability of finding small groups of molecules closer together than
they would be in the absence of attractive forces, and is a direct
consequence of the Boltzmann principle.

As the temperature falls the chance of a considerable gathering
together of molecules increases. Growth of the clusters brings about
two effects. First, the tendency to redisperse becomes greater with
the number of independently moving molecules in the aggregate.
But, secondly, the tendency to capture yet more molecules increases
also, since the decrease in potential energy accompanying capture is,
up to a point, greater the more complete and ordered the central

nucleus has become. Thus, on growth of a nucleus, one factor favours and another antagonizes still further enlargement. At high temperatures the first factor predominates, at lower temperatures the second. There may be a definite size below which a nucleus will redisperse and above which it will grow. The lower the temperature the smaller is the critical size.

The temperature at which spontaneous condensation or crystallization will occur is ill defined. It depends upon the probability that somewhere in the system there is formed by a series of chance encounters a nucleus which exceeds the critical size and is large enough to grow continuously rather than to redisperse. Crystallization or condensation thus becomes more likely the lower the temperature, the longer the time allowed for the consummation of chance events, and the greater the volume in which the chances are awaited. Large quantities of liquid are in fact much less given to supercooling than small ones, and if a considerable number of small tubes of liquid are sealed up and left at a constant temperature somewhat below their melting-point, one can observe a functional relation between the time of waiting and the number which have crystallized at the end of it.

If there is present in the system a foreign body capable of attracting the molecules which are to condense or crystallize, it may constitute a sort of base on which a veneer of the new phase is deposited. Small numbers of molecules then imitate a nucleus which could only have been formed from much larger numbers in the pure substance. Hence the efficacy of dust particles and the like in promoting phase changes.

Principles similar to those which provide the interpretation of phase relations for single substances apply to the equilibria existing in systems of several. They can be illustrated conveniently by reference to the melting of a pair of substances, A and B, for the two cases respectively where these are immiscible and completely miscible in the solid phase, though miscible in all proportions in the liquid. The pressure may be taken as constant.

Pure solid A and pure liquid can coexist at one temperature only, that, namely, at which the rate of melting at the interface equals the rate of crystallization. These opposing rates are functions of temperature and are equal only for a single value of the latter. If a liquid phase of A is diluted by the addition of B, the rate of passage of molecules of A from the solid to the liquid will not be sensibly affected, but the rate of passage from the diluted liquid to the solid will usually be lowered. Thus passage from solid to liquid will come to predominate and melting will occur. In other words, the melting-point of A will be lowered by the presence of B. If the temperature is reduced, both the opposing rates fall, but the rate of passage from solid to liquid falls more than the reverse rate (since it depends upon the probability that molecules should acquire enough energy to escape from the ordered array of the solid state). Thus a new balance can be established at a lower temperature. The greater the reduction of the equilibrium temperature, the greater is the proportion of B required to produce it. As this proportion mounts there comes a point where there is enough in the liquid to hold in check the loss of B molecules from a crystal of solid B itself. Two solid phases now occur in the equilibrium state, and no further adjustments are possible while they persist. The temperature remains set at the eutectic point: A and B can crystallize out together in the proportion which leaves the composition of the liquid constant. A degree of freedom has disappeared. If more B is added to the liquid it occasions too great a rate of deposition on the solid and equilibrium cannot be maintained unless the temperature is raised. If this is done, solid A has to disappear, there being too little A in the liquid to balance its solution.

When, in contrast, A and B are miscible in the solid state, both may exist in each phase over a complete range of temperature. Suppose the rate of passage from solid to liquid at a given temperature balances the reverse rate for each of the two substances. Now let the temperature fall so that the balance is disturbed. Suppose A now crystallizes faster than it dissolves. The liquid becomes depleted of A and the solid enriched until a new steady state is reached in respect of A. This would in general lead to an A/B ratio in the liquid quite incompatible with the existence of pure B, or with any arbitrarily chosen proportion of B in the solid. But, since the concentrations of B both in liquid and solid are now independently adjustable, a new equilibrium for B also is attainable, In brief, any maladjustment of the relative rates in either direction is rectifiable both for A and for B by changes in their proportions in liquid and in solid, while any general disturbance of rate of melting relative to rate of crystallization is rectifiable by change of temperature.

Quantitative discussion of melting-point lowering: illustration of some general principles

It is now desirable to consider quantitatively the influence of a substance B on the melting-point of another substance A. The essential methods are illustrated, and the result assumes a conveniently simple form if attention is restricted to the special case where B is present in small proportion in a large amount of A, B thus constituting a 'solute' and A a 'solvent'. A and B are further assumed to be miscible in the liquid state but not in the solid state.

The principle of the calculation will first be stated. At the equilibrium temperature we have

$$\Delta G = G_2 - G_1 = 0.$$

For pure A, as has been seen, G_2 and G_1 are unaffected by the extent of the transformation, since affluence of fresh molecules of a uniform species to solid or liquid makes no difference to the properties of either. When the solid consists of pure A and the liquid is a mixture, G_1 retains its constant character but G_2 becomes a function of the proportions of A and B. In particular, it will be shown that the contribution to G from A drops as A becomes admixed with B. Addition of B thus lowers G_2 without changing G_1. At the melting-point of pure A, therefore, ΔG will no longer be zero and the equilibrium is disturbed. ΔG in fact becomes negative and there is a decrease in free energy accompanying melting, which thus tends to occur spontaneously. ΔG, however, depends upon temperature, and the departure from zero, which may be written $\delta(\Delta G)$, can be cancelled by a compensating change in ΔG brought about by a reduction in temperature. The change in temperature, δT, required to compensate the disturbance caused by the presence of B, measures the lowering of melting-point.

The detailed calculations fall into several parts, some of which involve results of general importance and validity.

1. We first require to know how the contribution to G from two components of a mixed phase are related. In general we may write

$$G = n_A \bar{G}_A + n_B \bar{G}_B,$$

where n_A and n_B are the respective numbers of gram molecules and $\bar{G}_A$ and $\bar{G}_B$ are the respective contributions per gram molecule.

$\bar{G}_A$ and $\bar{G}_B$ are themselves functions of the *proportions* of A and B, though not of their *absolute amounts*. As long as n_A and n_B are varied in such a way as to keep a standard *ratio*, $\bar{G}_A$ and $\bar{G}_B$ remain constant. Thus

$$dG = \bar{G}_A \, dn_A + \bar{G}_B \, dn_B.$$

On the other hand, as a quite general mathematical relation we have

$$dG = \bar{G}_A \, dn_A + \bar{G}_B \, dn_B + n_A \, d\bar{G}_A + n_B \, d\bar{G}_B.$$

Comparison of the last two equations reveals that

$$n_A \, d\bar{G}_A + n_B \, d\bar{G}_B = 0,$$

whence

$$d\bar{G}_A = -\frac{n_B}{n_A} \, d\bar{G}_B.$$

This relation is important, since for a dilute solution of B there is a simple expression for changes in $\bar{G}_B$, whereas for the purposes of the present calculation it is the corresponding changes in $\bar{G}_A$ which are required.

2. As has already been shown (p. 69),

$$G = G_0 + RT \ln a,$$

where a is the activity, and for a substance obeying the gas laws $a = c$ the concentration.

It will be shown in due course that for a dilute solution also a may be replaced by c. Moreover, apart from a constant which may be transferred to the G_0 term, $\ln c$ is, for a dilute solution, equal to to $\ln x$, where x is the *molecular fraction* of the solute:

$$x_B = n_B/(n_A + n_B) \sim n_B/n_A.$$

Thus for the solute B in the liquid

$$\bar{G}_B = \bar{G}_{0B} + RT \ln x_B.$$

From the result of the previous paragraph,

$$d\bar{G}_A = -\frac{n_B}{n_A} \, d\bar{G}_B = -x_B \, RT d \ln x_B.$$

Thus

$$\bar{G}_A = -RT \int x_B \, d \ln x_B = \text{constant} - RT x_B.$$

Thus the *change* in $\bar{G}_A$ as the molecular fraction of solute increases from zero to x_B is given by

$$\delta \bar{G}_A = -RT x_B.$$

The addition of B does not affect G_1 which refers to the solid. The change in ΔG is thus due to the change $\delta \bar{G}_A$ and for the present purpose the change in ΔG due to B may be written

$$\delta(\Delta G) = -RTx_B.$$

This must be compensated, if equilibrium is to be preserved, by a change of temperature.

3. It now remains to calculate the variation of ΔG with temperature. The result follows from the general equation

$$\Delta G - \Delta H = T\,\frac{\partial(\Delta G)}{\partial T}.$$

Division by T^2 and rearrangement gives

$$\frac{1}{T}\frac{\partial(\Delta G)}{\partial T} - \frac{\Delta G}{T^2} = -\frac{\Delta H}{T^2},$$

or

$$\frac{\partial}{\partial T}\left(\frac{\Delta G}{T}\right) = -\frac{\Delta H}{T^2}.$$

For *small* changes of temperature therefore

$$\delta\left(\frac{\Delta G}{T}\right) = -\frac{\Delta H}{T^2}\,\delta T,$$

or

$$\delta(\Delta G) = -\frac{\Delta H}{T}\,\delta T.$$

4. It now remains to choose δT so that the change in ΔG caused by the presence of B is compensated. Thus

$$-\frac{\Delta H}{T}\,\delta T - RTx_B = 0,$$

or

$$\delta T = -\frac{RT^2}{\Delta H}\,x_B = -\frac{RT^2}{\Delta H}\frac{n_B}{n_A}$$

approximately,

or

$$\delta T = -\frac{RT^2}{L_{\text{fusion}}}\frac{n_B}{n_A}.$$

This formula for the lowering of freezing-point provides the basis for the standard method of determining the molecular weights of dissolved substances.

Kinetic treatment of melting-point lowering

The following kinetic derivation of this same relation, although by no means rigid or complete, throws further light upon the nature of melting-point lowering.

When pure A is in equilibrium with its liquid, the rate of passage of molecules from solid to liquid, r_{12}, is equal to the rate of return, r_{21}. For the passage of a molecule from solid to liquid, energy must be supplied sufficient to detach it from the lattice. Let this be E_1 (calculated for convenience per *gram* molecule). The number of molecules which possess this energy at any moment is proportional to $e^{-E_1/RT}$. Thus

$$r_{12} = \rho_{12} e^{-E_1/RT},$$

where ρ_{12} to a first approximation is independent of temperature. The rate r_{21} may similarly be written

$$r_{21} = \rho_{21} e^{-E_2/RT},$$

where, however, E_2 is less than E_1 (and in fact approaches zero, since a molecule in the liquid does not necessarily require energy to attach itself to the solid). $E_1 - E_2$ is equal to $\Delta H = L_{\text{fusion}}$. Thus at the melting-point

$$\rho_{12} e^{-E_1/RT} = \rho_{21} e^{-E_2/RT},$$

so that

$$e^{-L_{\text{fusion}}/RT} = \rho_{21}/\rho_{12}.$$

Addition of B to the system does not affect ρ_{12}, since B does not enter the solid. On the other hand, the molecular fraction of A in the liquid is thereby reduced to $x_A = 1 - x_B$, and it is reasonable to suppose that ρ_{21} is reduced to $\rho'_{21} = \rho_{21}(1 - x_B)$. Thus in presence of B, r_{21} no longer balances r_{12}. If the temperature is lowered r_{12} falls more rapidly than r_{21} and equilibrium can be restored. At a temperature $T + \delta T$ we have

$$\rho'_{12} \sim \rho_{12},$$

$$\rho'_{21} = \rho_{21}(1 - x_B).$$

Therefore

$$e^{-L_{\text{fusion}}/R(T+\delta T)} = \frac{\rho_{21}}{\rho_{12}}(1 - x_B)$$

$$= e^{-L_{\text{fusion}}/RT}(1 - x_B),$$

$$1 - x_B = e^{-L_{\text{fusion}}/R\{1/(T+\delta T)-1/T\}}$$

$$= e^{-L_{\text{fusion}}(-\delta T)/RT^2}, \text{ approximately.}$$

$$\ln(1 - x_B) = \frac{\delta T \cdot L_{\text{fusion}}}{RT^2},$$

and if x_B is small we find, on expansion of the logarithm,

$$-x_B = \frac{\delta T\; L_{fusion}}{RT^2}.$$

Thus

$$\delta T = -\frac{RT^2}{L_{fusion}}\, x_B$$

$$= -\frac{RT^2}{L_{fusion}}\frac{n_B}{n_A}.$$

Lowering of vapour pressure and related phenomena

A case that has played an important part in the development of physico-chemical theory is that where a solvent A possesses a measurable vapour pressure. This is lowered by the presence of a solute B, as may be inferred from the following argument.

If a gram molecule of A is transferred by distillation from pure solvent to solution the work derivable (p. 61) is $RT \ln p_0/p$, where p is the vapour pressure of the solution and p_0 that of the solvent. Thus the free energy of the solution is seen to be less than that of the solvent by this amount. But by the argument given in a preceding section, the decrease in free energy of A caused by the presence of a small molecular fraction x_B of B is RTx_B. Thus we have

$$RT \ln p_0/p = RTx_B,$$

or

$$\ln p_0/p = x_B = n_B/n_A.$$

But $\ln p_0/p = \ln\{1 + (p_0 - p)/p\}$ and when $p_0 - p = \delta p$ is small the logarithm may be expanded to the first term only, so that

$$\frac{\delta p}{p} = \frac{n_B}{n_A}.$$

What is called the *relative lowering of vapour pressure* is approximately equal, for sufficiently dilute solutions, to the ratio of the number of molecules of solute to the number of molecules of solvent.

This famous rule was first discovered experimentally by Raoult and provides another basis for the determination of the molecular weights of dissolved substances.

In some treatments of the thermodynamics of dilute solutions *Raoult's law* is taken as the fundamental datum, and the other relations concerning change in equilibrium temperatures are derived

G

from it. For example, the elevation of boiling-point which is observed when a non-volatile solute is dissolved in a liquid may be calculated in terms of the relative vapour pressure lowering very simply.

At the boiling-point, the vapour pressure of the solvent attains a standard value equal to the fixed external pressure. The addition of a solute lowers the vapour pressure so that the system is no longer in equilibrium. The change is given by Raoult's law,

$$\delta p/p = n_B/n_A.$$

δp must be compensated by an increase in temperature if equilibrium is to be restored. Since $d\ln p/dT = L/RT^2$, it follows that for small changes

$$\frac{1}{p}\frac{\delta p}{\delta T} = \frac{L}{RT^2}, \quad \text{or} \quad \frac{\delta p}{p} = \frac{L\,\delta T}{RT^2}.$$

The two values of $\delta p/p$ must correspond, so that

$$\frac{L\,\delta T}{RT^2} = \frac{n_B}{n_A}, \quad \text{or} \quad \delta T = \frac{RT^2}{L}\frac{n_B}{n_A}.$$

Depression of freezing-point may be treated in an analogous fashion on the basis of the fact that at the equilibrium temperature of solid and liquid their respective vapour pressures are equal.

Osmotic pressure: dilute solutions and the gas laws

For perfect gases the influence of concentration on the free energy is simply expressed, as has been shown, in the form

$$G - G_0 = RT\ln c.$$

When the system is not a perfect gas the form is preserved by writing

$$G - G_0 = RT\ln a,$$

a being the activity. If from a theory of molecular interaction a can be expressed in terms of c, then all thermodynamic problems can be dealt with simultaneously.

For a binary system in which a molecular species A constitutes the solvent and a species B the solute, there is an important result, of which use has already been made in anticipation, namely that in the limit of sufficiently small concentrations $a_B = c_B$. This may be expressed by saying that in dilute enough solutions B *follows the perfect gas laws*. This statement is worthy of some detailed consideration. It implies that the solvent plays a role which is in certain respects analogous to the vacuum in which gas molecules move. In so far as deviations from the gas laws depend upon interactions of B molecules among themselves, an approach to conformity at infinite dilution is perfectly natural. What effect the mutual influences of solvent and solute, in general powerful, may have requires more careful examination. As we shall see, the analogy between a dilute solution and a gas is valid enough within certain well-defined limits, which, however, must not be transgressed.

The pathway to a clearer understanding of the matter lies through the study of the phenomenon called *osmosis*. Osmosis is sometimes dismissed as an obscure and secondary effect. It is, on the contrary, the most direct expression of the molecular and kinetic nature of solutions. This nature impels the molecules of a solute placed in contact with a solvent to diffuse until the concentration is everywhere the same. The spontaneous tendency towards the equalization of concentration can, according to a quite general principle (p. 60), be harnessed to yield work. If a solution of B in A is separated from pure A by a membrane which is permeable to A but not to B, then a pressure, known as the *osmotic pressure*, acts on the partition, whereby it is urged to move in such a direction that solvent flows in to dilute the solution. The motion of the partition may be opposed by a resistance against which work is done. If Π is the osmotic pressure and dV the volume of solvent which enters, the work done is $\Pi\,dV$.

Such semi-permeable membranes do in fact exist for solutions and solutes, just as they do for gases—warm palladium, for example, lets through hydrogen but no other gas. Their mode of action—and indeed their practical efficiency—is quite irrelevant. Given the specific permeability, the only matter which concerns us at the moment is the pressure which acts upon them.

Experiment shows that for dilute solutions the osmotic pressure of the solute is the same as the pressure which it would exert if it were present at the same concentration in the gas phase. Thus for a gram molecule $\Pi V = RT$. Free energy changes accompanying variation of concentration depend upon $\int \Pi\,dV$, and all the results for gases are transferable to dilute solutions.

While the empirical basis for the laws of dilute solutions is satisfactory as far as it goes, its theoretical interpretation is a matter of some subtlety, and has occasioned a good deal of difficulty in the past.

The problem is best approached by starting with a gaseous system and imagining the concentration to increase steadily until the liquid state is reached.

First let us consider a mixture of hydrogen and nitrogen. The total pressure is equal to the sum of the partial pressures of the two constituents. If the mixture were contained in a palladium vessel at a fairly high temperature, hydrogen inside and hydrogen outside would equalize their partial pressures and exert no resultant effect on the walls. The measured pressure in the vessel would now correspond to the partial pressure of the nitrogen. This would be analogous to the osmotic pressure of a solute. If the partial pressure of hydrogen inside the vessel were low, more hydrogen from outside could flow in to raise it, even though the measured partial pressure of nitrogen were high. (This, of course, is quite natural—though in the past some scepticism has been excited by the idea that solvent could flow into a container 'against the osmotic pressure' of a solute.) With an appropriate membrane the same considerations apply to a liquid mixture of B with A.

Suppose B starts as a gas unmixed with A. There are in each second a certain number of collisions between the molecules, which also make a certain number of impacts on the surface of the container. The calculation of the collision numbers has already been given. Reference to the derivation (p. 21) will show that the result would be in no way affected by the assumption that some foreign molecules, of A, were present. The cylindrical space swept out by the representative molecule of B becomes more and more bent as collisions with A increase, but apart from this these extra encounters of B with A have no relevance either to the collisions of B with B, or to the impacts of B on any surface which it may meet.

What does happen as the concentration of A becomes very high (and this can be shown very clearly with a mechanical model in which metal spheres of different kinds are agitated in a moving tray) is that pairs of B molecules tend to become hemmed in by the surrounding crowd of solvent molecules and caused to pommel one another repeatedly instead of wandering off to collide with new adversaries. But, as both theory and the mechanical model indicate, the total number of B, B collisions remains sensibly constant, although the ratio of repeated collisions to collisions of fresh pairs increases steadily as the state corresponding to that of a liquid is approached. (In the limit, if the concentration of A becomes so high that the system congeals to a glass, some of the B's would be kept locked in a perpetual clinch, but this would *not* be a state where B, B collisions could be said to have ceased.) In the same way the number of impacts of B on a membrane or partition is substantially unaffected by the presence of A, though, here again, in crowded systems the same B molecules make repeated hits, whereas in a gas the same number of hits would be made by a much more rapidly changing series of attackers.

As far, then, as the number of encounters goes, the mere impeding action of the solvent makes no major difference, and B behaves as though it were a gas.

Molecular interaction of A and B will also have little effect. Suppose A and B actually combined to give new molecules, such as BA or BA_4. The average kinetic energy of these would be precisely equal to that of B itself, and hence the kinetic pressure would be the same. If, then, at the two limits of complete independence and of definite chemical union the solute pressure is the same, it does not seem likely that any intermediate degree of attraction between A and B would alter it.

Thus we may reasonably conclude that deviations from the gas laws depend essentially upon solute-solute interactions, and that if the solute is at a low enough concentration it 'obeys the gas laws'.

The range of validity of this statement should now be evident. Osmotic pressure is equal to gas pressure, activity is equal to concentration, and the free energy is expressible by a formula which would apply to a gas. On the other hand, diffusion rates of solute through solvent bear no relation whatever to those of gas molecules through free space. In dynamic problems the strength and the weakness of the gas analogy become specially evident. As regards total numbers of encounters between solute molecules, the gas formula gives an adequate answer, provided that repeated impacts count as effective. If molecules reacted chemically at each collision, there would be no opportunity for repetitions, and the effective rate of reaction would come to depend upon a diffusion rate. For thermodynamic purposes, however, this limitation is not important, and the statement is essentially valid.

With uncharged molecules of ordinary size, activity and concentration converge at dilutions still within experimentally useful ranges. With charged ions, or with very long molecules, such as those of various polymerized substances, allowance for solute-solute interaction can hardly ever be disregarded, even in the most dilute solutions which it is convenient to employ.

V

FACTORS GOVERNING PHYSICAL
AND CHEMICAL EQUILIBRIUM

Further liquid-vapour relations

THE thermodynamic discussion of phase equilibria is based largely upon the principle that the free energy of unit mass of any given pure phase is constant at constant temperature. The corresponding assumption made in arguments resting directly upon the kinetic theory is that the rate of passage of molecules from one phase to another across an interface is independent of the absolute amounts of the phases present. For mixed phases the free energies and the rates depend upon concentrations, with corresponding modification of the equilibrium conditions.

When a new phase is in process of formation, it may be dispersed in droplets, or minute particles, so small that the free energy per unit mass is no longer independent of the state of mechanical division, and the phenomenon of delayed transformation—which is connected with this—may appear.

The transition from gas to liquid, in particular, follows a different course according as there is a continuous vapour-liquid interface present initially or not. If there is, then the liquid phase simply increases and the vapour phase decreases. If there is not, then droplets must form and grow safely past the limit of the region where redispersion is their likely fate.

In Fig. 9 the pressure-volume relations of a gas-liquid system are represented. A corresponds to a dilute unsaturated vapour. On compression at constant temperature the pressure and volume change more or less in accordance with Boyle's law and the curve AB is followed. Imagine the vapour to be tested at various points by being placed in contact with a continuous surface of its liquid. Up to B, the saturation point, it would take up liquid which would evaporate into it. At B there would be equilibrium, and if in presence of the liquid the pressure were infinitesimally raised, complete condensation would occur at constant pressure: the line BC would be followed to the point C. If pressure were raised further, the compression curve of the liquid, CD, would be traversed. The only variable quantity along BC would be the proportion of the two bulk phases, liquid and vapour.

Now suppose the compression from A to occur in complete absence of liquid. This time the point B possesses no special significance. From B to X the average aggregates of molecules in the vapour (formed in conformity with the Boltzmann principle) are too small to grow. Although beyond B the free energy per unit mass of vapour

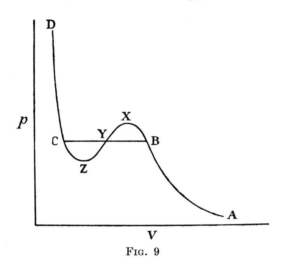

FIG. 9

has become greater than that of massive liquid, it has not become greater than that of the average spontaneously formed clusters. At X, however, these latter acquire the power to grow at the expense of vapour. As they do so they cause condensation. During the course of this process the state of affairs prevailing in the system is unstable with respect to time, but at any given moment there is an instantaneous relation between pressure and total volume such that both drop together, the vapour pressure falling as the vapour condenses to liquid and leaves the space unfilled with molecules. This phenomenon corresponds to the line XY, and though it represents a passage through a series of unstable states, it is none the less characterized by a perfectly definite pressure-volume relationship. The free energy per unit mass of vapour at a point along XY corresponds correctly to that of unit mass of liquid in its instantaneously realized state of dispersion, though this state is one which cannot persist in time. The droplets in fact coalesce to give liquid of lower free energy. If they could by some means be caused to retain their sizes, then the equilibrium represented by a point on XY would also be stable. When Y is reached we practically pass to the case previously considered and the rest of the condensation would follow the course YC.

Next we may consider the process from the other end, starting with liquid at D. The pressure is reduced along DC and the liquid dilates very slightly. At C under some conditions vapour can stream off from the liquid interface and evaporation occurs along CB. Under other conditions in a mass of heated liquid no vapour forms, since the minute bubbles which arise in the midst of the liquid redissolve. Their average size—and they constitute mere invisible holes in the normal texture of the liquid phase—is very small. It increases, however, as pressure drops along CZ. At Z spontaneous increase of these minute holes becomes possible. The pressure and the volume now increase as copious bubble formation occurs. The system passes through a series of states, once again unstable in respect of their permanence in time, but definite enough in that for each liquid–vapour ratio there is an average size of the growing bubble at which the free energy per unit mass of vapour equals that per unit mass of liquid, even though the distribution of sizes is continuously changing, and with it the equilibrium pressure. The curve ZY must be continuous with XY since obviously spontaneous evaporation and spontaneous condensation are reciprocal processes.

At any moment during the traversing of CZ on the one hand or of XB on the other, there is the possibility that a sufficiently large accidental fluctuation in the original phase may give rise to centres of the new one large enough to cause a rapid switch to ZY or to XY respectively, with consequent instability and rapid passage to those states of equilibrium corresponding to the presence of bulk phases. Such transitions correspond to the bumping of a superheated liquid on the one hand and, on the other, to the sudden relief of supersaturation in a vapour.

Van der Waals' equation and other equations of state. Critical phenomena

Somewhat similar relations find expression in equations, such as that of van der Waals, which, starting from the perfect gas laws, modify the expression $pV = RT$ by taking into account both the

finite size of molecules and the existence of attractive forces between
them, and seek to comprehend, at least in a rudimentary way, the
whole fluid state of matter, liquid as well as gas.

Van der Waals' equation itself assumes the form

$$(p+a/V^2)(V-b) = RT.$$

The attractive forces between the molecules lower the momentum
of the impacts which they make on the walls of a container, and
hence reduce the pressure. To correct for this and obtain a value
of p which would satisfy the equation of a perfect gas, van der Waals
added the term a/V^2, where a is a constant. The correction is taken
to be inversely proportional to V^2 since it is a function of the interaction of pairs of molecules and the numbers of close pairs will depend
roughly on the square of the density. b is a correction for the finite
size of the molecules, $(V-b)$ representing the free space in which
movement can actually occur. The equation is approximate, and
indeed of qualitative significance only, so that more elaborate arguments for the form of the correction terms are not worth entering
into. Nevertheless, it gives an overall picture of important phenomena which is extremely valuable.

Rearrangement of the terms gives a cubic equation in V. For
appropriate values of T, the cubic has three real roots. This means
that for certain values of p, V has three values, as shown in Fig. 10,
and indeed in Fig. 9, where the general form of the curve $DCZYXBA$
is just that given by van der Waals' equation in the region where it
has three real roots. For large values of T there is only one root, and
there is a definite transition temperature where the three roots become
identical and above which two of them become imaginary. The
family of curves corresponding to a series of increasing values of T
is as shown in Fig. 10.

At temperatures above that where the three roots coalesce and
the curve assumes the form 3, there ceases to be any region corresponding to XZ of Fig. 9, where unstable conditions prevail, and
which can correspond to the growth of droplets or bubbles. Neither
is there any possibility of a line such as BC short-circuiting the passage
through unstable states when continuous phases are present. Pressure
of vapour increases and volume decreases without any discontinuity,
until the system is dense enough to be regarded as liquid. Conversely
on reduction of pressure the liquid never generates bubbles of vapour,

but thins down progressively till it can be called gas. There exists, in these circumstances, what is called *continuity of state*. The point above which the transformation of liquid to vapour becomes continuous in this way is called the *critical temperature*. Its existence is due to the fact that when thermal agitation is violent enough there is no pressure at which small liquid aggregates begin to grow spontaneously at the expense of vapour. They can grow gradually as the

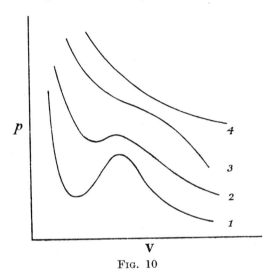

Fig. 10

pressure is raised and as the assembly passes through a series of states of stable equilibrium. At some not well-defined point we may choose to call the state liquid, but the single phase is in a sufficient condition of turmoil to be regarded equally well as highly compressed gas.

The mathematical derivation of the critical temperature in terms of the constants of the van der Waals' equation is simple. p is given as a function of V. Maxima and minima occur where $(\partial p / \partial V)_T = 0$. When there are three roots there are two such turning-points. The three roots coalesce at the critical point and here

$$\left(\frac{\partial^2 p}{\partial V^2}\right)_T = 0.$$

Differentiation with respect to V in the equation

$$(p + aV^{-2})(V - b) = RT$$

gives

$$\left(\frac{\partial p}{\partial V} - 2aV^{-3}\right)(V-b)+p+aV^{-2} = 0,$$

$$\frac{\partial p}{\partial V} = 2aV^{-3} - \frac{p+aV^{-2}}{V-b}$$

$$= 2aV^{-3} - RT(V-b)^{-2} = 0,$$

$$\frac{\partial^2 p}{\partial V^2} = -6aV^{-4} + 2RT(V-b)^{-3} = 0.$$

From the last two equations it follows that

$$V = 3b \quad \text{and} \quad T = 8a/27Rb.$$

These expressions give the critical temperature and the corresponding volume in terms of the constants of the gas equation.

Van der Waals' equation, however, is by no means the only one which yields the critical constants. Values for these are derivable from any analogous formulation which suitably introduces two terms, one favouring further reduction of pressure as the volume increases, that is, expressing the influence of an attractive force, and the other acting in the opposite sense.

The prediction of critical constants made by most equations of state is not very accurate. Comparison of the predicted values with experiment provides rather a good criterion for the degree of approximation of the equations themselves.

The direction of phase changes: range of existence of phases

Phase changes from solid to liquid or from liquid to vapour are accompanied by the absorption of heat. This is because there is more motion in the less constrained phase. There is also greater disorder, that is, higher entropy.

We write

$$\Delta G = G_2 - G_1,$$

$$\Delta H = H_2 - H_1,$$

where the subscript 2 refers to the phase of higher energy content.

Then

$$\frac{\partial(\Delta H)}{\partial T} = \frac{\partial H_2}{\partial T} - \frac{\partial H_1}{\partial T} = \Delta C_p,$$

where C_p is the specific heat measured at constant pressure. Therefore

$$\Delta H = \Delta H_0 + \int \Delta C_p \, dT,$$

where ΔH_0 is the latent heat at the absolute zero.

From the general relation (p. 67),

$$\Delta G - \Delta H = T \frac{\partial(\Delta G)}{\partial T}.$$

Rearrangement and division by T^2 gives

$$\frac{1}{T} \frac{\partial(\Delta G)}{\partial T} - \frac{\Delta G}{T^2} = -\frac{\Delta H}{T^2},$$

i.e.
$$\frac{\Delta G}{T} = -\int \left(\frac{\Delta H_0 + \int \Delta C_p \, dT}{T^2} \right) dT + J,$$

where J is an integration constant.

$$\Delta G = \Delta H_0 - T \int \left(\frac{\int \Delta C_p \, dT}{T^2} \right) dT + TJ.$$

When $T = 0$, $\Delta G = \Delta H_0$.

According to this, at the absolute zero the decrease in free energy will occur always in the direction in which the energy content decreases. That is to say, the molecular arrangements of the minimum potential energy prevail: all vapours will condense and all liquids will solidify.

What antagonizes this tendency and leads ultimately to the reversal of sign of ΔG is the influence of the entropy terms. In general liquids have more molecular freedom than solids, and vapours than liquids. As a result

$$T \int \frac{\left(\int \Delta C_p \, dT \right)}{T^2} dT$$

contains positive terms, and the influence of these in the expression for ΔG becomes more important as the temperature rises. Finally they reduce ΔG to zero. This means that the tendency to pass into a state of minimum potential energy is now opposed by the tendency to attain the more random conditions of the phase of higher energy (we shall return to this matter on p. 141).

The absolute position of the equilibrium point on the temperature scale depends upon the magnitude of the potential energy factor and upon the disparity in degree of randomness between the two phases.

Some interesting consequences follow from this conception. For example, the relative positions of melting- and boiling-points of a given compound vary very markedly with its chemical structure.

When the molecules are very far from spherical in form, rotations about the equilibrium positions are impossible in the solid, but become possible in the liquid. This means that large differences in entropy between liquid and solid exist. With molecules having something which approaches a spherical symmetry, rotations (or at any rate oscillatory angular displacements from the equilibrium orientation) can begin in the solid state without destruction of the ordered

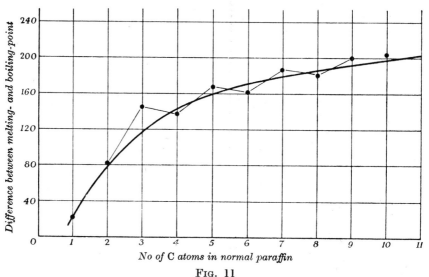

Fig. 11

crystalline lattice. Thus the solid can approach much more closely to the gas in entropy, and the melting process may be deferred until the temperature has risen quite close to the boiling-point. In some examples the range between melting- and boiling-point is extraordinarily small.

In Fig. 11 the difference between the melting-point and the boiling-point is plotted as a function of the number of carbon atoms for the series of the normal paraffins. The range expands steadily as the molecule becomes more elongated and its symmetry departs from that of methane.

The isomeric pentanes form an interesting series. With n-pentane the range is 168°, with the branched 2-methyl butane it is 187°, but with the completely symmetrical tetramethyl methane it falls abruptly to 30°, not very much more than for methane itself. Clearly the symmetrical molecule must possess in the solid state much of the freedom which other molecules only achieve by breaking loose from the crystal lattice.

The compound hexachlorethane has a melting-point and a boiling-point which practically coincide: in fact, at atmospheric pressure it sublimes before it melts. With benzene there is a liquid range of 74°, which rises to 202° in toluene. o- and m-xylene are also less symmetrical than benzene and the ranges are 171° and 193° respectively, but p-xylene achieves a certain measure of symmetry once more and the melting-point rises to within 125° of the boiling-point.

For the understanding of the range of existence of the solid and liquid states the entropy factor as affected by the degrees of freedom is thus of great importance. The position of the boiling-point itself is often to a predominant extent determined by the magnitude of the potential energy factor, as reflected in the latent heat, the other factors for gaseous and liquid states not being so different.

According to Trouton's rule the ratio of molecular latent heat to boiling-point is constant, and this statement is by no means very far from the truth. In so far as it holds it means that the expression

$$\ln p = \int \frac{\lambda}{RT^2} \, dT$$

can be integrated in the form

$$\ln p = C - \frac{\lambda}{RT},$$

with C varying little from liquid to liquid in comparison with λ. λ/T_b is in fact constant within about 10 per cent. for a quite wide range of liquids. (T_b = boiling-point at atmospheric pressure.)

Yet another aspect of this general question of the factors determining phase equilibria is illustrated by the partition of a solute between two solvents. In so far as the activity of a solute in a dilute solution is proportional to its concentration, the equilibrium distribution will be such that the ratio of concentrations in two immiscible solvents in contact is constant at constant temperature and pressure. The same principle will apply to the solution of a gas in a liquid. The concentration of dissolved gas is proportional to its partial pressure above the solution. These statements presuppose that the molecular complexity of the solute is the same in both phases, and that association or dissociation, ionic or otherwise, is excluded.

An interesting illustration of general thermodynamic and statistical principles is provided by the behaviour of very long molecules, such as those of a polymerized substance like rubber. In distribution experiments these substances show a marked tendency to go either wholly into one phase or wholly into the other. The distribution is, as always, determined by the free energy relationships. But a very long molecule, say of n segments, has an interaction energy with a solvent (or with molecules of its own kind) which is n times as great as that of a similar molecule of a single segment. By the equipartition law, however, it possesses only the normal allocation, $(3/2)kT$, of translational energy. Therefore its free energy relationships are determined almost entirely by the potential energy terms, and the concentration of molecules occurs where the potential energy is least. There is an almost complete displacement of the equilibrium in the one direction or in the other, as there would be even with small molecules in the neighbourhood of the absolute zero.

The discussion of these and other interesting matters demands intimate knowledge of the modes of motion of molecules and of the way in which these modes are affected by temperature. This is precisely what the simple conception of molecular chaos and of the kinetic theory cannot yield. As we have seen, these ideas, fruitful as they are, do not account for the variation of specific heats with temperature, nor indeed for the non-operation of certain degrees of freedom. Nor, moreover, do they yield any information about the magnitude of the constant J in the formula for the free energy change.

These limitations are removed by the introduction of the quantum theory. We shall have occasion to return to the whole problem after the quantum laws have been considered.

Chemical changes

The equilibrium in the solid state between such substances as the allotropic forms of tin or sulphur, or between the participants in any other chemical reaction, is governed by principles precisely similar to those which regulate the coexistence of phases such as solid and liquid.

The method of applying thermodynamics to the discussion of chemical equilibria in the gaseous state, or of equilibria in solutions, is also essentially the same. A small displacement of the equilibrium at constant temperature is envisaged, and, according as the pressure or the volume is fixed, dG or dF is equated to zero.

Consider the reaction

$$2H_2 + O_2 = 2H_2O.$$

For this transformation we have

$$\Delta U = 2U_{H_2O} - 2U_{H_2} - U_{O_2} = \sum nU,$$
$$\Delta H = \Delta U + \sum npV.$$

For constant volume and temperature

$$\Delta F = \Delta U - T\Delta S$$
$$= \Delta U - T \sum nS$$
$$= \Delta U - T \sum n(C_v \ln T - R \ln c + S_0).$$

Now let $2\delta x$ gram molecules of hydrogen react with δx of oxygen to give $2\delta x$ gram molecules of steam. The change in free energy is expressed by $dF = \delta x \Delta F$. If the concentrations of all the gases present correspond to an equilibrium state, then $\delta x \Delta F = 0$. Thus

$$\Delta U - T \sum n(C_v \ln T - R \ln c_{eq} + S_0) = 0.$$

In this equation the only terms which, for perfect gases, depend upon the concentrations at all are those contained in the set $\sum nR \ln c_{eq}$.

Therefore, since none of the other quantities could compensate a variation in this group as a whole, it must be constant. Thus, at constant temperature,

$$\sum n \ln c_{eq} = \text{constant}.$$

It may be written $\ln K_V$, where K_V is a function of the concentrations. In the specific example which was quoted above it assumes the form

$$K_V = c_{H_2O}^2 / c_{H_2}^2 c_{O_2}.$$

In general, if the concentrations do not correspond to equilibrium,

$$\Delta F = \Delta U - T \sum n(C_v \ln T - R \ln c + S_0).$$

But from the equilibrium condition itself

$$0 = \Delta U - T \sum n(C_v \ln T - R \ln c_{eq} + S_0),$$

whence by subtraction

$$\Delta F = RT[\sum n \ln c - \ln K_V].$$

If, for example, there were less steam and more hydrogen and oxygen than corresponded to equilibrium, $\sum n \ln c$ would be less than $\ln K_V$ (products being positive and reacting substances negative in the summation). ΔF would thus be negative and the reaction would go forward spontaneously.

H

The equation for ΔF is frequently known as the van 't Hoff reaction isotherm. (It must be noted that ΔF is the free energy change which *would* occur if molecular quantities reacted without change of their existing concentrations.)

The value of ΔF may be inserted in the general thermodynamic equation

$$\Delta F - \Delta U = T \frac{\partial(\Delta F)}{\partial T},$$

giving

$$RT \sum n \ln c - RT \ln K_V - \Delta U = T \left[R \sum n \ln c - R \ln K_V - RT \frac{d \ln K_V}{dT} \right],$$

whence

$$\frac{d \ln K_V}{dT} = \frac{\Delta U}{RT^2}.$$

In a precisely analogous manner, for a reaction at constant pressure, there is found the result

$$\frac{d \ln K_p}{dT} = \frac{\Delta H}{RT^2}.$$

These two equations illustrate a well-known principle of stable equilibrium. Substances formed endothermically become more stable as the temperature rises—a fact shown, for example, by the synthesis of nitric oxide from its elements in the high temperature arc. For such substances ΔU and ΔH are positive, that is, the energy or heat content of the products exceeds that of the starting materials. Thus the sign of $d \ln K / dT$ is positive, $\ln K$ (and hence K) increases with temperature, and, from the manner in which the equilibrium constant is written, this corresponds to a greater concentration of product.

The above equations (known as the two forms of the *reaction isochore*) may be integrated. For example

$$\ln K_V = \int_0^T \frac{\Delta U}{RT^2} \, dT + I.$$

Now

$$\frac{\partial(\Delta U)}{\partial T} = \frac{\partial U_{products}}{\partial T} - \frac{\partial U_{reactants}}{\partial T} = \sum n C_v = \Delta C_v,$$

so that

$$\Delta U = \Delta U_0 + \int \Delta C_v \, dT.$$

Thus

$$\ln K_V = \int_0^T \frac{\Delta U_0}{RT^2} \, dT + \int_0^T \frac{\left(\int \Delta C_v \, dT \right)}{RT^2} \, dT.$$

The corresponding equation for K_p involves ΔH_0 and $\int \Delta C_p \, dT$.

ΔU or ΔH is often large compared with ΔC_v or ΔC_p and then, especially since K varies rapidly in the relatively small range of temperatures where measurements are practicable, it is permissible to write approximately

$$\ln K_V = \text{constant} - \frac{\Delta U}{RT},$$

$$\ln K_p = \text{constant} - \frac{\Delta H}{RT},$$

$\ln K$ being a linear function of the reciprocal of the absolute temperature.

For reactions where ΔU or ΔH are small and ΔC_v or ΔC_p large this ceases to be admissible.

In the formation of steam from its elements ΔU is of the order 10^5 calories and ΔC_v under 10. Thus over a hundred-degree range, for example, the approximation would be a quite good one. In the dissociation of a weak acid in aqueous solution ΔH is of the order 10^3 and ΔC_p may be as much as 50 calories. Neglect of its influence here ceases to be even an approximately justifiable procedure and would lead to gross errors.

For these gaseous systems, as for condensed systems, the thermodynamic formulae provide complete information about the variation of equilibrium constant with temperature. They predict also the manner in which equilibrium is governed by concentration. They do not, however, provide information about the absolute values of the equilibrium constant. Knowledge of this depends upon the introduction of fresh conceptions.

The formulae which have been derived for gases apply also to dilute solutions in which the solute follows the gas laws in the sense which has been discussed previously. When these laws are not valid, the concentrations are formally replaced by activities and K is expressed in the form

$$\ln K = \sum n \ln a_{eq}$$

and the free energy change becomes

$$\Delta G = RT[\sum n \ln a - \ln K].$$

One of the most important cases where activities and concentrations differ very widely is that of equilibria in solutions of ionized substances.

As has been shown, the condition that solutes should obey the gas laws is that the mutual interference of their molecules is negligible to a sufficient degree of approximation. Charged ions, acting upon one another according to the inverse square law of electrostatics, are subject to a mutual interference which only becomes negligible at dilutions far greater than those conveniently employed in ordinary chemical measurements. The calculation or experimental determination of the activity becomes, therefore, of great importance. Once its relation to the concentration has been discovered, it is applicable to all problems which depend upon the free energy, that is to say, to the formulation of chemical equilibria and the phase relationships of solutions.

The calculation of the activity itself is a problem quite independent of thermodynamics and rests upon an adequate theory of interionic forces, or, in general, of molecular interactions (see p. 278).

Achievements of the molecular and kinetic theory: conditions for further progress

From the foregoing pages it is already evident that much illumination about the nature of things does in fact proceed from the simple and easily intelligible assumption of a world of matter consisting of randomly moving particles, whose inherent tendency to dissipate themselves through all space is combated by attractive forces.

The essential character of thermal phenomena becomes clear, the conditions of coexistence of solids, liquids, and gases in systems of any number of chemical components are explained, the dependence of equilibria upon concentrations, upon pressure, and upon temperature is defined. The conceptions of entropy and free energy, of statistical equilibrium and energy distribution, provide quantitative laws which describe the perpetual conflict of order and chaos, and which prescribe in a large measure not only the shapes assumed by the material world but also the pattern of its possible changes.

The power, clarity, and beauty of these ideas are undeniable. Yet, great as is their range, it has its boundaries. It constitutes a brilliantly illuminated circle surrounded by obscurity. This darker region can, however, be penetrated and proves to contain many strange new things.

The first great limitation of what we might perhaps call the neo-Epicurean picture of matter is its lack of information about the character of the forces which hold the primordial motion in check.

They are made manifest by the energy changes which accompany their operation. For the theory these energies constitute the fundamental data, a circumstance which has fortunately proved to be no practical impediment, since in experimental science the direct measurement of them is precisely what has been most expedient.

Nevertheless, the nature of these all-important quantities must be inquired into and inferences made about the modes of interaction of the particles concerned.

But even when we accept the energies as known, there is still no way of understanding what determines the absolute position of an equilibrium, whether of solid and liquid, or of the participants in a chemical reaction. The influence of temperature and other variables can be precisely foretold, but all the knowledge is relative. The reason for this lies deep in the character of the theory.

Equilibria are determined by free energies which depend in turn upon entropies. Entropies are measures of the probability of given conditions, and probabilities are defined in terms of the number of modes in which assignments of molecules to states can be made.

The number of ways in which X molecules can be distributed among Y states depends upon the number Y. The extent of what constitutes an energy state has so far remained indefinite. If infinitesimally small differences in energy are detectable and significant, then the number of possible states is indefinitely large and the assignments are infinite. Thus an absolute entropy would be a meaningless quantity.

While changes in an indefinitely large quantity might themselves possess a relative significance and might possibly govern the behaviour of a single system, they could hardly predict the relations of one system with another. When the conceptual substratum is structureless and indefinite the search for a means of predicting the absolute position of equilibrium appears quite vain.

But if infinitesimally small differences of energy were not significant, and if the states were of finite range, then the number of assignments would become a definite number with an absolute meaning. The probability of one system in a given state could be compared with that of any other in another given state, and absolute prediction of equilibria would become a possibility. The substratum of the conceptual world would acquire a structure, and become, as it were, an atomic system rather than a continuum.

The imparting of this structure is precisely what the quantum theory does.

It has indeed already become obvious that the rules of Newtonian mechanics are insufficient for the full understanding of statistical phenomena. The division of molecular states into ranges of equal probability needed the assumption that equal ranges of momentum rather than of energy should be chosen (p. 31). There was no obvious reason for this. Even more striking is the complete failure of mechanics to account for the non-contribution of certain degrees of freedom to specific heats, and for the variation with temperature of the number of degrees of freedom which do so contribute.

It is the further investigation of this problem which leads most directly and simply into the realm of the quantum theory.

This theory, when established, indicates how the numbers of states may be defined, and it opens the way to a complete understanding of the absolute position of the equilibria between all forms of matter.

This fuller understanding, however, is purchased only by the sacrifice of the primitive and simple picture of a molecular chaos which rather resembles a swarm of bees and which is easy to visualize in a quite naïve fashion. It requires the introduction of abstract statements about a non-material substratum. The new picture loses in appeal to the senses what it gains in appeal to the intelligence.

In the course of the development of the quantum theory further sacrifices will be demanded from the naïve conception of particles. In particular it appears that for the correct calculation of entropies the identity of individual particles may even have to be disregarded. The intervening steps, however, will have so accustomed the inquirer to the shedding of his original ideas that he needs to feel no surprise— though possibly he experiences a slight regret. He does well, however, to remember that what emerges in the end is essentially a construction of the human mind by which various sets of facts are related in the most elegant and helpful way.

What is perhaps most important of all is to keep clear which parts of the construction are closely related to things of direct observation and experience, and how the hypothetical edifice expresses these relations.

PART II

CONTROL OF THE CHAOS BY THE QUANTUM LAWS

SYNOPSIS

As a result of a long series of intricate discoveries a solution is found to the problem of knowing where, in the absolute sense, the equilibrium lies between the different states of aggregation of matter and between the various configurations of atoms concerned in chemical transformations.

The first stage is the emergence of the quantum theory, according to which the energy of atomic or molecular systems varies discontinuously. The laws governing the various discrete series of possible energy states are discoverable from the study of such phenomena as specific heats and radiation. They evolve through different forms and are at length crystallized in rules whereby the energies are defined in terms of the permissible solutions of a semi-empirical differential equation, known as the wave equation.

The foundation of this equation is the discovery that on the scale of electronic or atomic phenomena particles obey dynamical laws which are neither precisely those followed by macroscopic masses nor yet those followed by light waves, but are of a special kind.

The new rules impart to the theory an abstract basis. Atoms and molecules can no longer be regarded as small-scale versions of ordinary objects. Furthermore, we have to conclude that there is no physical sense in treating different permutations of individual atoms or molecules within a given energy state as even theoretically distinguishable systems.

Given these apparent sacrifices of the primitive simplicity, energy states become, in compensation, like so many exactly defined boxes, the allocation of molecules to which can be treated by the laws of probability. Absolute equilibria are now seen to be governed by the interplay of two major factors: on the one hand, the tendency of atoms and molecules to assume a condition of minimal potential energy, and on the other hand, their tendency to fill impartially all energetically equivalent states.

With the equilibrium of solid and vapour, for example, the potential energy factor favours condensation of all the molecules to solid. But in the vapour the range of possible energy levels is much greater and molecules populate states according, as it were, to the housing conditions, quantum levels representing in effect accommodation. Expressed in another way, the atoms and molecules escape from the restraints imposed by the forces acting upon them in so far as they achieve fuller self-realization in conditions where more modes of motion and more quantum levels offer them opportunity. The quantum theory having given exact formulations of the accommodation ranges, these statements can be translated into precise terms which lead to a quantitative treatment of all types of equilibrium.

At this stage the nature of the forces and of the interaction energies still remains unknown.

VI

THE QUANTUM RULES

Specific heats

THE most direct route to an understanding of the rules governing the energy content of substances is by the study of specific heats.

From the formula for the pressure of a perfect gas, $p = \frac{1}{3}nm\bar{u}^2$, and the relation $pV = NkT$, it follows that the kinetic energy in the three translational degrees of freedom is $\frac{3}{2}kT$. The allocation for each is thus $\frac{1}{2}kT$. The equipartition law provides that where the energy is shared between s square terms, the average amount in a molecule is $\frac{1}{2}skT$. The molecular heat, C_v, is therefore

$$N \frac{\partial}{\partial T}(\tfrac{1}{2}skT) = \tfrac{1}{2}sR.$$

The assumptions about s which have to be made to account for observed values of C_v are at first sight not unplausible. For the inert gases, $s = 3$, so that they apparently contain translational energy only. For the stable diatomic molecules such as oxygen, nitrogen, and hydrogen, $s = 5$, while for less stable ones such as iodine, it is closer to 7. It would seem that the extra two square terms appearing with iodine represent vibrational energy (kinetic energy $\frac{1}{2}m\dot{x}^2$ and potential energy $\frac{1}{2}ax^2$, where x is the extension from the equilibrium position, m the effective mass, and a an elastic constant).

The two square terms, other than those for the translational energy, which occur with the diatomic gases are evidently connected with rotation. They are two rather than three, since one of the three axes of reference is that joining the two atoms, and about this particular axis the molecule will possess just the same kind of inertia as if it were monatomic. Given that monatomic substances do not in fact show rotation, there is no reason why diatomic substances should show it about the axis in question.

The three vibrational degrees of freedom reasonably attributable to a monatomic solid should account for a constant specific heat of 6, in fair accord with the law of Dulong and Petit.

In one sense these interpretations of the specific heats of simple substances are very successful. But deeper reflection shows that something fundamental is missing. There is no reason in Newtonian mechanics why all the possible degrees of freedom should not be operative in all cases, three translational and three rotational degrees with monatomic gases, and with diatomic gases these six together with a vibrational degree of freedom. Some extraneous factor must

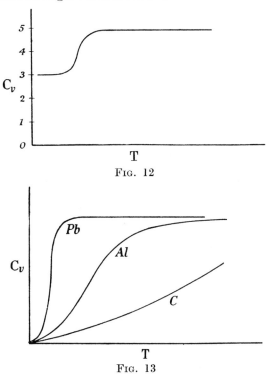

FIG. 12

FIG. 13

dictate whether or not a mechanically possible motion does in fact contribute to the energy.

This factor cannot be connected with permanent structural capacities or disabilities of molecules, since the operation or non-operation of degrees of freedom depends upon the temperature. At low temperatures the specific heat of hydrogen falls from 5 to 3, and that of metals drops to zero. Fig. 12 illustrates the behaviour of hydrogen, Fig. 13, that of some typical solids, and Fig. 14 shows the ideal course of the complete curve for a diatomic molecule.

These phenomena are fully interpreted by the quantum theory. This theory declares that the possible energy states of a molecule, or of a mechanical system in general, form not a continuous but a discrete series.

Suppose the energy of three successive states is 0, ϵ_1, and ϵ_2. At a certain low temperature, δT, the atoms or molecules, which according to the classical theory should possess a quota of less than ϵ_1, possess in fact nothing. Thus the energy content and the specific heat fall below the expected values.

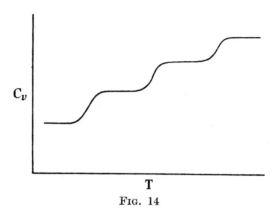

C_v

T

FIG. 14

At a high temperature the proportional difference between ϵ_j and ϵ_{j+1} is quite small because j is large, so that the energy and the specific heat approximate closely to the classically expected values.

These qualitative remarks are rendered clearer by a simple calculation. Suppose that for a solid vibrating in one degree of freedom the energies of the atoms must correspond to 0, ϵ, 2ϵ, 3ϵ,..., that is, the successive values are multiples of a standard 'quantum'. Out of N atoms, the number which would normally possess energy greater than $j\epsilon$ is given by the Maxwell–Boltzmann law to be $Ne^{-j\epsilon/kT}$ (see p. 133). The number with energy between 0 and ϵ is the difference between those with energy greater than 0 and those with energy greater than ϵ, that is to $N-Ne^{-\epsilon/kT}$. These, according to the rules of the quantum theory, contribute nothing. The number with energy greater than ϵ but not greater than 2ϵ is similarly $Ne^{-\epsilon/kT}-Ne^{-2\epsilon/kT}$ and these contribute ϵ only. The sum total of the contributions is thus

$$0(N-Ne^{-\epsilon/kT})+\epsilon(Ne^{-\epsilon/kT}-Ne^{-2\epsilon/kT})+2\epsilon(Ne^{-2\epsilon/kT}-Ne^{-3\epsilon/kT})+...$$

$$= N\epsilon(e^{-\epsilon/kT}+e^{-2\epsilon/kT}+e^{-3\epsilon/kT}+...)$$

$$= \frac{N\epsilon e^{-\epsilon/kT}}{1-e^{-\epsilon/kT}},$$

the series in the brackets being a geometrical progression with the first term $e^{-\epsilon/kT}$ and the common ratio $e^{-\epsilon/kT}$ also. The total energy is in fact contributed by three degrees of freedom, so that

$$E = \frac{3N\epsilon e^{-\epsilon/kT}}{1-e^{-\epsilon/kT}} = \frac{3N\epsilon}{e^{\epsilon/kT}-1}.$$

When $T = 0$, $E = 0$ and the energy vanishes. The behaviour at high temperatures may be seen by expanding the exponential term:

$$E = \frac{3N\epsilon}{1+(\epsilon/kT)+\ldots-1}.$$

When T is large enough this tends to the value

$$E_{\text{limit}} = \frac{3N\epsilon}{\epsilon/kT} = 3NkT = 3RT.$$

If ϵ is small enough, the same result holds for all temperatures, and in the limit when ϵ vanishes, that is, when the series of possible energy states is continuous, the energy is $3RT$ over the whole range and the specific heat is constant with the value $3R$.

In general the value of C_v is given by the relation

$$C_v = \frac{\partial E}{\partial T} = \frac{3N\epsilon e^{\epsilon/kT}\epsilon/kT^2}{(e^{\epsilon/kT}-1)^2}.$$

This is the Einstein specific heat formula.

The course predicted by the equation for C_v as a function of temperature is similar to that shown in Fig. 13. The limiting values are found, as before, by expansion.

$$C_v = \frac{3N\epsilon\{1+(\epsilon/kT)+\ldots\}(\epsilon/kT^2)}{\{1+(\epsilon/kT)+\ldots-1\}^2}.$$

When $\epsilon \to 0$ or $T \to \infty$ this becomes

$$C_v = \frac{3N\epsilon(\epsilon/kT^2)}{(\epsilon/kT)^2} = 3Nk = 3R.$$

When T approaches zero C_v becomes

$$\frac{3N\epsilon^2 e^{\epsilon/kT}}{kT^2(e^{\epsilon/kT})^2} = \frac{3N\epsilon^2}{kT^2\{1+(\epsilon/kT)+(\epsilon^2/2!k^2T^2)+\ldots\}}$$

$$= \frac{3N\epsilon^2}{kT^2+\epsilon T+(\epsilon^2/2!k)+\text{terms in } 1/T,\, 1/T^2\ldots}$$

$$= \frac{3N\epsilon^2}{0+0+(\epsilon^2/2!k)+\infty+\infty+\ldots} = 0.$$

It will be observed that the course of the specific heat-temperature curve is determined by the value of ϵ/T. If $\epsilon = 0$, the specific heat remains $3R$ down to $T = 0$, and the greater the value of ϵ, the higher is the temperature at which C_v first begins to approach its limit. Inspection of Fig. 13 suggests therefore that the values of ϵ vary considerably from one solid substance to another.

The history of the stages by which the rules governing the magnitude of the energy quanta and the spacing of the possible states were discovered is a slightly tangled one. We may begin the elucidation of these rules by stating in a general way that the results regarding the specific heats of solids justify two assumptions: (a) that the successive increments of energy accompanying the passage from one possible state to the next are equal, and (b) that these increments are proportional to the frequency of the vibrational motion with which the energy is associated.

Measuring the energy of a given vibrational degree of freedom from $T = 0$, and taking no account of any which may in one way or another remain stored in atoms or molecules at the absolute zero, we write

$$E - E_0 = n\epsilon = nh\nu,$$

where n is an *integer*.

C_v may be determined as a function of temperature for various solids and may be represented approximately by the Einstein formula from which the size of the quantum may be calculated. This is found to be proportional to the vibration frequency of the solid, which can be estimated in various approximate ways.

A qualitative illustration of this proportionality is easily provided. The frequency of a simple harmonic motion is given by the formula

$$\nu = \frac{1}{2\pi} \sqrt{\left(\frac{restoring\ force\ per\ unit\ displacement}{mass} \right)}.$$

We may compare the three substances whose specific heats are represented in Fig. 13. Diamond is excessively hard, infusible, and involatile, lead soft and fusible, while aluminium is intermediate in character. Thus the frequencies, in so far as they depend upon the strength of the forces holding the atoms in the crystal, will tend to be in the order

$$\nu_C > \nu_{Al} > \nu_{Pb}.$$

Precisely the same order is indicated by the relative masses. If then $\epsilon = h\nu$, we should have

$$\epsilon_C > \epsilon_{Al} > \epsilon_{Pb},$$

and thus, from what has been said, we should expect lead to retain its specific heat of about 6 to much lower temperatures than carbon, and aluminium to lie between the other two. This is precisely what is found, and constitutes a striking verification of the rule relating quantum size to frequency.

The quantitative side of the matter is less definite as far as solid crystals are concerned, because the vibrations of the solid are in reality very complex and can only be described in rough approximation by a single frequency. In fact a complicated spectrum of frequencies must be invoked to do justice to the finer details of behaviour. Nevertheless, the operation of the first of the quantum rules is clearly shown by what has been described.

Radiation and the quantum laws

As it happened, the law that the vibrational energies increase by equal multiples of $h\nu$ had already been much more accurately, though perhaps less simply vindicated by Planck's study of radiation problems. We shall find it expedient to defer detailed discussion of radiation, but enough will be said here to indicate its place in the evolution of the quantum theory.

Matter absorbs and emits radiation, good absorbers being also good emitters, as shown by the fact that a blackened piece of metal glows more brightly when heated to a high temperature than a corresponding piece which has been polished. A cavity surrounded by matter at a given temperature reaches an equilibrium state and becomes filled with radiation of all wave-lengths (as can be shown by spectral analysis of what emerges from an opening in a furnace). The energy per unit volume and the distribution of energy among the various wave-lengths prove to be functions of temperature alone, and spectroscopic examination of the so-called black body radiation escaping through a small opening in an enclosure where thermal equilibrium prevails, reveals the character of this function, which is of great significance. The intensity passes through a maximum at a certain wave-length, and this maximum itself not only becomes higher but is displaced towards shorter wave-lengths as the temperature rises.

The theoretical treatment of the distribution problem is based upon principles analogous to those which determine the partition of molecules among energy states. That average condition is supposed to be realized in nature which can be achieved in the largest number of ways: where many possibilities exist, they contribute largely, where few exist they contribute little.

Radiation contained in an enclosure must satisfy certain relations analogous to those governing, for example, the modes of vibration of the air in an organ pipe, and the wave-lengths of the admissible components are governed by geometrical boundary conditions.

There are many more numerical possibilities for the accommodation of short waves than of long ones, so that the number of admissible frequencies in a given interval $d\nu$ increases rapidly with ν itself. If, then, energy distribution were governed solely by available modes, the intensity should increase continuously with frequency. There should be no maximum, and the actual existence of one reveals the operation of a second factor which discourages the location of energy in the shorter wave-lengths.

If now the quantum law is introduced, specifying that a vibration of frequency ν contains energy in quanta $h\nu$, then for high frequencies the total available energy can provide relatively few quanta only. If these were allocated, the number of ways would be limited. When the frequency is high, therefore, there are too few quanta, while when it is low there are too few states to which they can be allotted. The maximum variety of assignments is possible when an intermediate number of moderate-sized quanta are shared among the modes, that is to say, at a wave-length neither too long nor too short.

As the temperature rises the energy supply increases and more quanta of greater size become available for distribution. The maximum is displaced to higher frequencies. The law of this displacement is

$$\lambda_{\max} T = \text{constant.}$$

It can be shown to define *precisely* the form of the dependence $\epsilon = h\nu$, and this same form also leads to the correct form of curve for the relation of intensity and wave-length at any given temperature. These results will be shown in greater detail later on when Planck's law is considered in the light of still further developments which make possible a derivation far more satisfactory than the original one.

The problem of rotations

The form of the quantum law which makes increments of vibrational energy proportional to frequency deals adequately with the requirements of the specific heat problem. The absence of vibrations in molecules such as O_2 at ordinary temperatures is explained by the tightness of binding of the atoms and the consequent high frequency, which corresponds to a quantum too great for appreciable occurrence. The specific heat-temperature relations of solids are accounted for as has been seen, the difficulties of detail which arise being connected simply with the determination of the true frequency-spectrum.

The question next arises how rotational energy states are to be specified. The proportionality of energy and frequency is here meaningless, since a rotation possesses no natural frequency, but merely one depending upon the energy, and which vanishes as this energy falls to zero.

The obvious course is to throw the formulation of the rule for vibrations into some form which does not involve the frequency explicitly, and to seek to generalize this rule in the modified version. A provisional solution of the problem on these lines was in fact soon found, in a way which came rather naturally to those versed in applied mathematics.

It had long been known that the laws of dynamics assume their simplest and most elegant form when the so-called Hamiltonian coordinates are employed as the fundamental variables. These are position coordinates, usually written q_1, q_3,..., on the one hand, and momentum coordinates, usually written p_1, p_2,..., on the other.

The law $\epsilon_n = nh\nu$ for a simple harmonic motion can be expressed in Hamiltonian coordinates in the form

$$\int_0^T p\, dq = nh,$$

where n is an integer, and $T = 1/\nu$, is the periodic time. This is the Sommerfeld–Wilson equation.

The identification of the two versions is easily made. A particle executing a simple harmonic motion follows the equation

$$x = a \sin 2\pi\nu t,$$

where x is the displacement at time t and a is a constant. In Hamiltonian coordinates

$$p = m\dot{x} = 2\pi\nu ma \cos 2\pi\nu t,$$
$$dq = dx = 2\pi\nu a \cos 2\pi\nu t\, dt,$$
$$\int_0^T p\, dq = 4\pi^2\nu^2 ma^2 \int_0^{1/\nu} \cos^2 2\pi\nu t\, dt = 2\pi^2\nu ma^2.$$

If then we write $\qquad 2\pi^2\nu ma^2 = nh,$

it is the same thing as to put

$$2\pi^2\nu^2 ma^2 = nh\nu,$$

and the expression on the left is none other than the energy. (For, total energy = K.E.+P.E. = constant: when P.E. = 0, K.E. = maximum: therefore, total energy = maximum value of K.E. = maximum value of $\frac{1}{2}m\dot{x}^2 = \frac{1}{2}m(2\pi\nu a)^2 = 2\pi^2\nu^2 ma^2$.)

The formula $\int_0^T p\, dq = nh$ can be applied immediately to a rotation.

Here, $\qquad\qquad p = $ angular momentum

and $\qquad\qquad dq = d\theta,$

where θ is an angular coordinate. For a complete rotation

$$\int_0^T p\, dq = \int_0^{2\pi} \text{ang. mom. } d\theta = nh,$$

whence angular momentum $= nh/2\pi$.

If the moment of inertia is I and the angular velocity ω,

$$I\omega = nh/2\pi,$$

whence the energy is given by

$$E = \tfrac{1}{2}I\omega^2 = n^2h^2/8\pi^2 I.$$

Here, it is to be noted, what increases by equal steps is not the *energy* but the *angular momentum*. This formula does in fact give satisfactory results in the discussion of rotational specific heats. But it does not yet tell the whole story.

The angular momentum rule found its most accurate and striking application in Bohr's interpretation of the hydrogen spectrum, where an analogous postulate was made about the permissible states of an electron circulating around a nucleus, and it may be regarded apart from a trivial correction as established.

Translational energy

The question of translational energy remains. To a superficial view this might appear less urgent than that of rotational and vibrational energy. There is no obvious need to account for any significant departure of the specific heats of monatomic gases from the classical values. Yet a discrete series of translational energies must be postulated if we are to retain the fundamental statistical principle.

If the translational distribution were infinitely fine-grained, and the rotational and vibrational ones were coarse-grained, the infinite increase in entropy which would accompany the passage of energy into the translational form would ensure that this process prevailed to the entire exclusion of the reverse change. Any prospect of defining absolute entropies and of calculating where a chemical equilibrium lies would vanish again. And, anyhow, it seems unlikely that one kind of motion, not differing on close analysis much from the others, should be exempt from what appears to be so fundamental a law of nature.

In the formulation of quantum rules the characteristic of the motion which always enters explicitly is its *periodicity*. The only sense in which a particle executing translational motion can be said to have a period is in relation to its impacts on the sides of a containing vessel. If the particle moves parallel to the x-axis, in a cubical box of side l_x, it repeats its motion each time it completes a path of length $2l_x$. We might try using this fact to determine a periodic time insertion in the Sommerfeld–Wilson equation.

$$\int_0^T p \, dq = \int_0^T mv_x \, dx = \int_0^{2l_x} mv_x \, dx = nh,$$

$$mv_x 2l_x = nh,$$

$$n\left(\frac{1}{2}\cdot\frac{h}{mv_x}\right) = l_x.$$

This gives a form of quantization for translational energy in one degree of freedom, which does in fact agree with that later formulated on the basis of a more general theory.

Wave mechanics

The more general theory of quantum states developed from certain surprising discoveries in physics. These could be summed up in the statement that light, first regarded by Newton as corpuscular and then for a long time believed to consist of some kind of wave motion, possesses a character which is both particulate and undulatory at the same time.

Absorption and emission of light, according to one view, occur in quanta of magnitude $h\nu$. Einstein regarded the quanta themselves as having some of the dynamic properties of particles. For such particles the term *photons* was introduced. By the theory of relativity, the mass and the energy of a particle are connected by the equation:

$E = mc^2$, where c is the velocity of light (see p. 230).

For a photon $\qquad\qquad mc^2 = h\nu$.

Thus $\qquad\qquad\qquad mc = h\nu/c$.

Since photons move with velocity c themselves, mc represents their momentum.

The photon theory achieves many brilliant results.

1. Calculation of the momentum reversal occurring when photons impinge upon a surface gives the pressure exerted by radiation, just as impact of gas molecules accounts for gas pressure. The results are in complete accord with experiment.

2. Consideration of the statistics of photons yields Planck's law of energy distribution in the simplest possible way (p. 155).

3. What is called the *Compton effect* is accounted for. When photons are scattered by matter their momentum is changed, presumably in accordance with the ordinary laws of impact. Since the momentum is $h\nu/c$, a calculable change of frequency is observed in the scattered radiation.

4. An otherwise very difficultly interpretable character of the *photo-electric effect* is explained. When ultra-violet light falls on a metal surface, electrons are emitted. The kinetic energy of these photo-electrons increases with the frequency of the light but is independent of the intensity (though the latter determines the *rate* of emission). The energy of the photon thus appears as though it were concentrated in packets which increase in size with the frequency, and which become more numerous, but no bigger, as the light intensity increases.

But the idea of photons does not dispense with the need for the wave theory of light, which is categorically demanded by the phenomenon of interference. Therefore, a great abnegation of naïve realism is imposed, and it has to be accepted that light behaves in accordance with rules which are unlike those describing the behaviour of bullets on the one hand or of the waves of the ocean on the other. Spatial distribution of light intensities (in interference, diffraction, and so on) follows undulatory laws: intimate interaction of light with matter seems to be governed by the photon properties which are something like those of bullets—though not by any means exactly like.

In the sense of the general thesis that the unknown is to be explained in terms of the known, it appears that the kinds of known things by which the unknown are to be interpreted have advanced a considerable stage in sophistication.

With the blurring of the distinction between waves and particles, the status of what have hitherto been accepted indisputably as particles becomes open to question once more. In a theoretical study L. de Broglie examined the conditions under which singularities in interfering trains of waves might be propagated according to the laws of moving mass points. His considerations led to the view that there could be important correspondences if the wave-length of the hypothetical waves and the momentum of the hypothetical particle were related by the equation

$$\lambda = h/mv.$$

This led rapidly to the discovery that beams of electrons are in fact subject to interference and that they behave in respect of this phenomenon as though an electron possesses, not indeed a constant wavelength, but one related to its momentum in precise accordance with the above equation.

If this result is extended to particles of macroscopic mass, the predicted wave-length is so small that the divergence from rectilinear propagation of a stream of such masses is quite negligible.

A mass moving with one degree of freedom in an enclosure of length l_x must, to be in a steady state, possess such a momentum that an integral number of half wave-lengths fit into l_x. Thus

$$n\lambda/2 = l_x \quad \text{or} \quad nh/2mv_x = l_x,$$

which is just the relation for the quantization of translational motion inferred from the tentative application of the Sommerfeld–Wilson equation.

Beams of electrons having many of the properties of minute masses (p. 164), but being capable of diffraction in a manner only describable by the equations of wave motion, the assumption of a general duality of behaviour is evidently worth exploring. Since a rule for the specification of possible translational states can be guessed from that which defines vibrational and rotational states, and since the same rule follows also from the ascription of a wave-length h/mv to the moving mass, it is fairly evident that all the consequences of the Sommerfeld–Wilson equation should be derivable from some form of wave theory.

Such a theory is embodied in the wave equation of Schrödinger. The propagation of a wave in three dimensions is represented by the expression

$$\frac{\partial^2 \psi}{\partial x^2}+\frac{\partial^2 \psi}{\partial y^2}+\frac{\partial^2 \psi}{\partial z^2}+\frac{4\pi^2 \psi}{\lambda^2} = 0,$$

where ψ is the quantity which varies periodically in space and time.†

If for the wave-length is substituted the value h/mv, then this equation describes the motion of free particles of momentum mv, subject to interference after the manner of electrons.

The meaning of ψ will be considered more closely in a later section. At the present juncture it suffices to say that it is of the form

$$\psi = \psi_0 e^{2\pi i \nu t},$$

† The following considerations show how this equation represents a wave.
$\psi = \psi_0 \sin 2\pi(x/\lambda - \nu t)$ is periodic in x when t is constant (instantaneous picture of a wave) and periodic in t when x is constant (each point vibrates). If the eye is kept fixed on a point such that $x/\lambda - \nu t = 0$, then ψ remains constant: thus the eye is following a disturbance which travels at a rate given by $x/t = \lambda\nu = v$. This is the characteristic of wave propagation along the x-axis.
Partial differentiation of the first equation gives

$$\frac{\partial^2 \psi}{\partial x^2} = -\frac{4\pi^2}{\lambda^2}\,\psi.$$

For the three-dimensional problem the wave may be represented by the expression

$$\psi = \psi_0 \sin 2\pi\left\{\frac{(x^2+y^2+z^2)^{\frac{1}{2}}}{\lambda} - \nu t\right\}$$

$$= \psi_0 \sin R.$$

Then

$$\frac{\partial^2 \psi}{\partial x^2} = -\frac{4\pi^2}{\lambda^2}\,\psi_0(\sin R)x^2(x^2+y^2+z^2)^{-1}+\frac{2\pi}{\lambda}\,\psi_0(\cos R)[(x^2+y^2+z^2)^{-\frac{1}{2}}-x^2(x^2+y^2+z^2)^{-\frac{3}{2}}]$$

$$\frac{\partial^2 \psi}{\partial x^2}+\frac{\partial^2 \psi}{\partial y^2}+\frac{\partial^2 \psi}{\partial z^2} = -\frac{4\pi^2}{\lambda^2}\,\psi_0(\sin R)[(x^2+y^2+z^2)(x^2+y^2+z^2)^{-1}]+$$

$$+\frac{2\pi}{\lambda}\,\psi_0(\cos R)[(x^2+y^2+z^2)^{-\frac{1}{2}}-(x^2+y^2+z^2)^{-\frac{1}{2}}]$$

$$= -\frac{4\pi^2}{\lambda^2}\,\psi_0 \sin R = -\frac{4\pi^2}{\lambda^2}\,\psi.$$

where ψ_0 is a function of the spatial coordinates only, the periodic variation with time being represented in the conventional way by the term $e^{2\pi i \nu t}$.† ν is the frequency, and i has the usual meaning of $\sqrt{(-1)}$. If one writes

$$\bar{\psi} = \psi_0 e^{-2\pi i \nu t}, \quad \text{then} \quad \psi\bar{\psi} = \psi_0^2.$$

ψ_0^2 is the square of a wave amplitude which in any wave phenomenon expresses the intensity. Thus ψ_0^2 is the density of distribution of particles in an interference experiment, or the probability of finding a given particle in the region specified by the spatial coordinates of ψ. For the present we only need to bear in mind that if $\psi = 0$ there are no particles.

If masses are contained in an enclosure, then solutions of the equation are only possible for certain integral relations between the wave-length and the linear dimensions of the container itself. For example, if the motion is confined to the x-axis, then

$$\frac{\partial^2 \psi}{\partial x^2} = -\frac{4\pi^2}{\lambda^2} \psi, \quad \text{whence} \quad \psi = A \sin \frac{2\pi x}{\lambda},$$

where A is a constant. Since there is no particle outside the container, ψ must be zero when $x = 0$ and when $x = l_x$. The value of $\sin(2\pi x/\lambda)$ is zero whenever $2x/\lambda$ is integral, that is when $2l_x/\lambda = n$ or $n\lambda/2 = l_x$: thus the permitted values of the wave-length and of the momentum are defined.

The relations are not quite so easily understandable for vibrating and rotating systems, but Schrödinger made the remarkable discovery that the wave equation is applicable quite generally if handled according to the following prescription.

From the total energy E of the particle under study is subtracted the potential energy U which it may possess in virtue of its presence in any field of force. The balance $E - U$ is the kinetic energy, which is $\frac{1}{2}mv^2$. Thus

$$m^2 v^2 = 2m(E - U),$$

and since

$$1/\lambda^2 = m^2 v^2 / h^2 = 2m(E - U)/h^2,$$

---

† The appropriateness of the form $\psi = \psi_0 e^{2\pi i \nu t}$ to represent the time variation is seen by differentiation.

$$\frac{\partial^2 \psi}{\partial t^2} = -4\pi^2 \nu^2 \psi,$$

or

$$\frac{\partial^2 \psi}{\partial t^2} + a\psi = 0.$$

This is the simplest representation by a differential equation of a quantity vibrating in time.

it follows from the general equation that

$$\frac{\partial^2\psi}{\partial x^2}+\frac{\partial^2\psi}{\partial y^2}+\frac{\partial^2\psi}{\partial z^2}+\frac{8\pi^2m(E-U)}{h^2}\,\psi = 0.$$

This semi-empirical equation has become famous in virtue of the many remarkable properties which it possesses. Only certain of these concern us at the moment. The first set is connected with the possibilities of solution. The differential equation only possesses finite, single-valued solutions for certain quite definite values of the energy, E. These values, known as characteristic or proper values (German, *Eigenwerte*), specify the possible quantum states of the system.

The quantization of translational energy has already been considered. For vibrational systems the equation is found to yield physically admissible solutions only for values of E defined by the relation $E = (n+\frac{1}{2})h\nu$. The successive energy levels differ by $h\nu$ as required. The lowest value occurs when the integer n is zero, so that $E_0 = \frac{1}{2}h\nu$. Schrödinger's equation, unlike the quantum rule which it has superseded, predicts the existence of a so-called *zero-point energy*. The assumption that there is such a thing is in fact required for the explanation of certain phenomena, so that in this respect the new equation possesses an important advantage.

For a rotating system with a moment of inertia I, the permitted energy states are given by the relation

$$E = \frac{n(n+1)h^2}{8\pi^2I}.$$

The previous rule was expressed by the equation

$$I\omega = \frac{nh}{2\pi}, \quad \text{so that} \quad E = \frac{1}{2}I\omega^2 = \frac{n^2h^2}{8\pi^2I}.$$

The new one replaces n^2 by $n(n+1)$. We may write

$$E = \frac{n(n+1)h^2}{8\pi^2I} = \frac{(n+\frac{1}{2})^2h^2}{8\pi^2I}+\text{constant}.$$

Thus the succession of states according to the Schrödinger rules is governed by the values of $(n+\frac{1}{2})^2$ instead of n^2. In the interpretation of certain spectroscopic phenomena this also proves to be an essential emendation.

Before proceeding we may illustrate the manner in which the specification of the quantum states occurs.

Succession of vibrational states

For a simple harmonic motion the acceleration is related to the displacement from the equilibrium position by the equation

$$\ddot{x} = -\mu x,$$

so that
$$U = m \int_0^x \mu x \, dx = m\mu x^2/2.$$

Also
$$x = A \sin \sqrt{\mu} t = A \sin 2\pi \nu t,$$

so that
$$\mu = 4\pi^2 \nu^2 \quad \text{and} \quad U = 2\pi^2 \nu^2 m x^2.$$

The Schrödinger equation thus becomes

$$\frac{\partial^2 \psi}{\partial x^2} + \frac{8\pi^2 m}{h^2} (E - 2\pi^2 \nu^2 m x^2)\psi = 0. \tag{1}$$

This may be thrown into the form

$$\frac{\partial^2 \psi}{\partial X^2} + (a - X^2)\psi = 0 \tag{2}$$

by the substitutions

$$X^2 = \frac{4\pi^2 m \nu}{h} x^2 \quad \text{and} \quad a = \frac{2E}{h\nu}.$$

The equation (2) has finite, single-valued solutions only for values of a which are of the form $(2n+1)$, n being a positive integer. Thus, for acceptable solutions,

$$2E/h\nu = (2n+1),$$

or
$$E = (2n+1)\frac{h\nu}{2} = (n+\tfrac{1}{2})h\nu.$$

The method of proving these statements belongs to the standard theory of differential equations and will be quoted as an example.

In (2) let
$$\psi = e^{-\frac{1}{2}X^2} v,$$

where v is an appropriate function. Then

$$\frac{\partial \psi}{\partial X} = v' e^{-\frac{1}{2}X^2} - v e^{-\frac{1}{2}X^2} X,$$

$$\frac{\partial^2 \psi}{\partial X^2} = v'' e^{-\frac{1}{2}X^2} - v' e^{-\frac{1}{2}X^2} X - v' e^{-\frac{1}{2}X^2} X - v(e^{-\frac{1}{2}X^2} - X^2 e^{-\frac{1}{2}X^2})$$

$$= e^{-\frac{1}{2}X^2}(v'' - 2v'X - v + X^2 v),$$

where v' and v'' are the differential coefficients of v with respect to X. Substitution in (2) and division by $e^{-\frac{1}{2}X^2}$ gives

$$(v'' - 2v'X - v + X^2 v) + (a - X^2)v = 0,$$

or
$$v'' - 2v'X + (a-1)v = 0. \tag{3}$$

Now, further, let v be represented by the general power series

$$v = \sum b_n X^n. \tag{4}$$

Substitution gives for the coefficient of X^n in (3) the values

$$(n+2)(n+1)b_{n+2} - 2nb_n + (a-1)b_n.$$

(It will be seen that in v'', for example, the term in X^n has been derived by differentiation twice of the term in X^{n+2}.) For (3) to be general the coefficient of X^n, and that of any other power of X in it, must equal zero, so that we have

$$\frac{b_{n+2}}{b_n} = -\frac{(a-1-2n)}{(n+2)(n+1)}.$$

If v is to constitute a finite series, the coefficient of some power of X in (4) must become zero, so that

$$a - 1 - 2n = 0,$$

or
$$2n + 1 = a,$$

which establishes the required result.

Rotational states

The general case of the rotator free to move in three dimensions is more complicated, but is treated according to similar principles. The Schrödinger equation is first expressed in spherical polar coordinates, r, θ, and ϕ. For the rotation of a rigid body about its centre of gravity, r is constant and is included in a term representing the moment of inertia, I. The conditions for physically admissible solutions lead to the result

$$E = \frac{h^2}{8\pi^2 I} n(n+1),$$

where n is a positive integer.

A new factor enters here. The function ψ itself begins to assume considerable direct importance. For each admissible value of E there proves to be not a single value of ψ, but a *set of $2n+1$ values*. This is expressed by saying that the *statistical weight* of the nth energy level is $2n+1$, and, in accordance with the general principle, it is supposed that the population of this level will be correspondingly dense.

The factor $(2n+1)$ comes, in this present mode of calculation, from the conditions for solution of the differential equation. In the more primitive form of the quantum theory it may be arrived at by considerations which, if less general and indeed in a certain sense less precise, are easier to relate to a more naïve picture of molecular events. The body is imagined to rotate on its axis, and the axis is conceived to possess not an indefinite number but a finite number of possible *spatial orientations*. n is, in fact, supposed to represent a vector the projection of which on a given axis must also be a whole number. This projection may, according to the angle between it and the vector, possess any value from $+n$ to $-n$, including zero (when the vector and the line of projection are perpendicular). Thus there are $2n+1$ possible values altogether.

The orientation does not normally affect the energy, so that the nth rotational level is, as it is called, a $(2n+1)$-fold *degenerate* one.

Degenerate states: statistical weight

The dependence of the whole statistical theory upon the idea that natural phenomena are largely determined by the possible ways of filling molecular states has already been abundantly illustrated. It is evident, therefore, that if several states of equal energy exist, they really should be regarded as multiple. Their availability does depend upon their number and not upon the accident that they are associated with energies which are quantitatively the same. The case of the orientations of the molecular axis was specially simple to visualize, since one can see clearly that if there are many possible orientations, then the chance that molecules possess motions which avail themselves of this freedom is correspondingly greater.

The example is important, since it shows also that the number of solutions of the ψ equation, which correspond to a given value of the permitted energy value E, is the expression for the statistical weight in the wave-mechanical formulation.

Conclusion

The need for defining the range of individual energy states arose as a logical necessity in the consideration of statistical problems. The discoveries which have been made in the study of specific heats, radiation, and various other matters have shown how the range can be defined.

The formulation of the rules has gone through various phases, the most comprehensive statement being that based upon the wave equation. This expresses the possible energy levels for any kind of system, and provides information about their multiplicity. The equation is not itself based upon any explicit theory of the nature of things, except in so far as it contains a general implication of the wave-particle duality in systems of minute enough dimensions.

The duality referred to, while cutting us off completely from the possibility of describing the invisible in terms of the visible, has the great simplicity that translational motion becomes subject in a not wholly unexpected way to the quantum rules. All kinds of molecular states fall, as a result, into discrete series, and the calculation of absolute probabilities acquires a meaning. There is thus a prospect of answering the fundamental question as to what determines the forms, physical and chemical, into which atoms and molecules eventually settle down.

VII

THE ABSOLUTE POSITION OF EQUILIBRIA

Further statistical considerations

THE great principle which governs the domain of equilibria and which so largely determines the nature of things is that states of equivalent energy are occupied in proportion to the accommodation they afford. Before, however, chemical and physical equilibria can be calculated from the fundamental energy data there is still an important problem to be solved about the assessment of this accommodation.

According to the principle which has already been invoked, the number of ways in which N molecules can be assigned to a series of energy levels, so that the occupation numbers are N_1, N_2,..., respectively is given by

$$W = \frac{N!}{N_1!\,N_2!\,\ldots}.$$

The entropy, which we shall now write more specifically as $S_{\text{Boltzmann}}$, or S_B is given by

$$S_B = k \ln W.$$

Replacement of the factorials in W by Stirling's approximation, $\ln N! = N \ln N - N$, gives

$$S_B = k(N \ln N - \sum N_1 \ln N_1).$$

The condition that W shall be a maximum subject to the two conditions

$$\sum N_1 = N \quad \text{and} \quad \sum N_1 \epsilon_1 = E$$

gives

$$N_1 = \frac{N e^{-\epsilon_1/kT}}{\sum e^{-\epsilon_1/kT}} = \frac{N e^{-\epsilon_1/kT}}{f} \quad \text{(see p. 30)}.$$

Substitution of this value for N_1 leads to the expression

$$S_B = kN \ln f + kNT\, d\ln f/dT.$$

In making the substitution it is to be noted that since

$$f = \sum e^{-\epsilon_1/kT}, \qquad \frac{df}{dT} = \sum \frac{\epsilon_1 e^{-\epsilon_1/kT}}{kT^2},$$

so that

$$\sum \epsilon_1 e^{-\epsilon_1/kT} = kT^2\, df/dT.$$

Thus

$$E = \sum N_1 \epsilon_1 = \sum \frac{\epsilon_1 N e^{-\epsilon_1/kT}}{f} = kNT^2 \frac{d\ln f}{dT}.$$

The entropy, total energy, and free energy are thus given by

$$S_B = kN \ln f + kNT d \ln f / dT,$$

$$E = NkT^2 d \ln f / dT,$$

$$F_B = E - TS_B = -kNT \ln f.$$

The sequence of quantum states being known, f can be calculated in absolute terms. S_B, E, and F_B are thus known.

Although the resulting formulae are correct enough in so far as they are applied to the calculation of *changes* of entropy or free energy, for example, in consideration of shifts of chemical equilibrium with temperature, they still prove to be wrong in absolute magnitude.

The error lies not in the calculation of f, nor in the identification of S with $k \ln W$, but in the way in which W itself is computed.

What is called the Boltzmann statistics must be replaced by a new form which is naturally enough called quantum statistics. This new method of computation leaves the form of S unchanged, but makes a considerable difference to the constant term in the entropy formula, that is, to the absolute value of the entropy. It will be considered in more detail in the following section.

Before proceeding to investigate the need for a change in the definition of the probability, we shall find it convenient first to formulate some values of f, the partition function, in various simple cases.

The total partition function is represented by

$$f = \sum e^{-\epsilon/kT},$$

the sum being taken over all possible states.

In a given state the vibrational, rotational, and translational energies can often be regarded in a sufficient degree of approximation as independent, so that

$$\epsilon = \epsilon_V + \epsilon_R + \epsilon_T.$$

Moreover, each kind itself is represented by a whole series of states, and partial partition functions may be defined as follows:

$$f_V = \sum e^{-\epsilon_V/kT}, \quad f_R = \sum e^{-\epsilon_R/kT}, \quad f_T = \sum e^{-\epsilon_T/kT}.$$

The total partition function, f, is simply the product of the factors

f_V, f_R, and f_T, as may be seen by inspection of the following formula, in which, for brevity, $1/kT$ is written β.

$$f_V f_R f_T = (e^{-\beta \epsilon_{V_1}} + e^{-\beta \epsilon_{V_2}} + ...)(e^{-\beta \epsilon_{R_1}} + e^{-\beta \epsilon_{R_2}} + ...)(e^{-\beta \epsilon_{T_1}} + e^{-\beta \epsilon_{T_2}} + ...)$$

$$= e^{-\beta \epsilon_{V_1}} e^{-\beta \epsilon_{R_1}} e^{-\beta \epsilon_{T_1}} + e^{-\beta \epsilon_{V_2}} e^{-\beta \epsilon_{R_1}} e^{-\beta \epsilon_{T_1}} + ...$$

$$= e^{-\beta(\epsilon_{V_1} + \epsilon_{R_1} + \epsilon_{T_1})} + e^{-\beta(\epsilon_{V_2} + \epsilon_{R_1} + \epsilon_{T_1})} + ...$$

The quantities multiplying β in the final series represent every combination of every possible value of the energies in the partial series. They therefore include every possible state. The final sum is therefore, by definition, f.

By an analogous argument the translational partition function itself may be split into three factors, each representing the contribution of a single degree of freedom. Thus

$$f_{T_{xyz}} = f_{T_x} f_{T_y} f_{T_z}.$$

For the series of energy levels characteristic of a single vibrational degree of freedom $\epsilon = (n + \frac{1}{2})h\nu$. The absolute zero may be taken as the energy reference point, so that the successive energies on the new scale are $nh\nu$ and thus

$$f_V = \sum_0^\infty e^{-nh\nu/kT},$$

a geometrical series of which the sum is

$$f_V = \frac{1}{1 - e^{-h\nu/kT}}.$$

The number of molecules in the nth and higher states, that is, the number with energy greater than ϵ_n is given by

$$\frac{Ne^{-nh\nu/kT}}{f_V} + \frac{Ne^{-(n+1)h\nu/kT}}{f_V} + ... = \frac{Ne^{-nh\nu/kT}}{f_V}(1 + e^{-h\nu/kT} + ...)$$

$$= \frac{Ne^{-nh\nu/kT}}{f_V} f_V$$

$$= Ne^{-\epsilon_n/kT}.$$

The correct treatment of rotations is somewhat difficult and gives rise to series which have no simply expressible sum. For a rigid rotator which is a solid of revolution of moment of inertia I and which, for reasons which will emerge later, must not consist of two identical atoms, the following simple treatment is possible.

The successive energy levels are represented by the formula

$$\epsilon_n = n(n+1)h^2/8\pi^2 I.$$

For the nth level there are $(2n+1)$ possibilities corresponding to $(2n+1)$ orientations of the axis. Thus

$$f_R = \sum (2n+1)e^{-n(n+1)h^2/8\pi^2 IkT}.$$

If the levels are fairly close and n is considerable, this sum may be expressed approximately by an integral

$$\int_0^\infty (2n+1)e^{-An(n+1)}\,dn \quad \text{where} \quad A = h^2/8\pi^2 IkT.$$

Let $n^2+n = x$, then the integral becomes

$$\int_0^\infty e^{-Ax}\,dx = 1/A.$$

Thus for this simple case

$$f_R = 8\pi^2 IkT/h^2.$$

Translational states are defined by the equation

$$nh/2mv_x = l_x \quad \text{so that} \quad \tfrac{1}{2}mv_x^2 = n^2h^2/8ml_x^2.$$

The unidimensional partition function is given by

$$f_{T_x} = \sum e^{-n^2h^2/8ml_x^2 kT}.$$

Since the energy steps are small the sum can be fairly well represented by an integral

$$\int_0^\infty e^{-B^2n^2}\,dn = \sqrt{\pi}/2B.$$

Thus
$$f_{T_x} = \frac{(2\pi mkT)^{\frac{1}{2}}l_x}{h}.$$

For the three degrees of freedom we have

$$f_{T_{xyz}} = \frac{(2\pi mkT)^{\frac{3}{2}}}{h^3}l_x l_y l_z = \frac{(2\pi mkT)^{\frac{3}{2}}V}{h^3},$$

where V is the volume.

The translational partition function unavoidably involves the volume, since only by relating the motion of the particle to the dimensions of the container in which it moves can any formulation of the quantum states be reached. This necessary connexion exists both in the older quantum theory and in the wave mechanical theory which replaced it.

For future reference it will be convenient here to tabulate the partition functions so far calculated.

Vibrational energy in one degree of freedom

$$f_V = 1/(1 - e^{-h\nu/kT}).$$

Rotational energy, rigid rotator, solid of revolution

$$f_R = 8\pi^2 IkT/h^2.$$

(This is a two-dimensional case.)

Translational energy in three degrees of freedom

$$f_{T_{xyz}} = \frac{(2\pi mkT)^{\frac{3}{2}}V}{h^3}.$$

The use of partition functions of the type just derived, or in appropriate cases more complex ones, in the calculation of absolute entropies, leads to incorrect results. The fault lies, as has been stated, with the mode of definition of the probability. The question of a modified definition and a reconsideration of what constitutes the number of assignments to states must now be considered.

Quantum statistics

The treatment of particles by the principles of wave mechanics results in a complete blurring of their identity as individuals. The calculation of statistical probability is profoundly modified thereby and a reformulation of Boltzmann's rules for calculating entropy becomes necessary.

So long as molecules were conceived as distinguishable units, the number of ways in which a given distribution over a series of energy states may be realized could be given by the expression

$$\frac{N!}{N_1!\,N_2!\,...},$$

where N_1 is the number in the first state, N_2 the number in the second, and so on. When, however, identity is lost, the permutations of individuals within a given state becomes meaningless, and this formula becomes unsuitable as a measure of the probability. It may, however, be replaced by another which defines the possible numerical types of assignment of molecules to various states, no distinguishable characteristics being attributed to individuals.

The reason for this renunciation lies in the wave-like nature ascribed to the particle, which is defined as regards its quantum state by its relation to the whole of the vessel in which it is located. This applies to all particles which, whatever they may possess of definite localization in respect of phenomena such as molecular collisions, have lost it in respect of the application of the quantum rules. Therefore there is, at any rate for the purposes of this problem, no way of distinguishing them, and the operation of working out permutations of individuals in a sort of box loses its sense. There will be further opportunity of pondering on this principle as the subject develops.

In the new formulation different assignments are represented by the statements that there are N_1 molecules in state 1, N_2 in state 2, and so on, on the one hand, or, on the other hand, that there are N'_1 in state 1, N'_2 in state 2, and so on. But it makes no difference how for these two assignments, N_1, N_2,..., or N'_1, N'_2,..., are selected and which individuals constitute these groups.

The detailed calculations proceed along lines which differ in the earlier stages from those followed previously. In each possible state the energy of a molecule is determined by the sum of translational, rotational, and vibrational contributions. The translational quantization involves three-dimensional space coordinates as well as momentum coordinates and leads to the existence of very large numbers of closely spaced levels, many of the states being in fact of equal energy. Thus there will be in general g_j states of energy ϵ_j, and the N_j molecules which possess this energy will be shared among the g_j states. The problem is to know how many numerical types of allocation there are when N_j molecules are distributed among g_j states, permutations among the individuals being not only undetectable but assumed to be of no interest, and even meaningless.

The problem is that of sharing N_j objects among g_j boxes. To solve it we consider this procedure: place one box on the left, and then to the right of it in line place in any order the N_j objects and the remaining g_j-1 boxes. There are $(N_j+g_j-1)!$ orders possible. For any one arrangement, sweep up all the sets of objects and place each set in the box immediately to its left. This experiment may be done in any of the $(N_j+g_j-1)!$ ways. But although variations in the number of objects in a box are of interest, the orders of them among themselves, as of the boxes among themselves, are irrelevant. The total number of significant results of the experiment therefore is

$$(N_j+g_j-1)!/(N_j!)(g_j-1)!$$

Thus we have g_j states of energy ϵ_j with N_j molecules, g_k states of energy ϵ_k with N_k molecules, and so on. The combined probability of the complete distribution is given by

$$P = \frac{(N_1+g_1-1)!}{N_1!(g_1-1)!} \cdot \frac{(N_2+g_2-1)!}{N_2!(g_2-1)!} \cdots$$

Neglecting unity in comparison with $N_1, \ldots$ and applying Stirling's approximation, we obtain

$$\ln P = \sum_j \left[(N_j+g_j)\ln(N_j+g_j) - N_j \ln N_j - g_j \ln g_j \right].$$

The entropy may now be defined as

$$S = k \ln P.$$

For the state of greatest probability we now have the relations

$$\delta \ln P = 0, \qquad \sum \delta N_j = 0, \qquad \sum \epsilon_j \delta N_j = 0.$$

These are combined by the method explained on p. 29 and the rest of the calculation proceeds as before, yielding the result

$$N_j = \frac{g_j}{e^\alpha e^{\beta \epsilon_j} - 1}.$$

This differs from the Boltzmann expression only in the presence of the -1 in the denominator, and for low densities becomes indistinguishable from it.

We now proceed to a direct comparison of the two types of expression for the entropy itself.

That already derived is of the form

$$k \ln W = k(N \ln N - \sum N_1 \ln N_1).$$

This, however, is not based upon quite the same distribution as that we have just envisaged in calculating P. The number of molecules in each possible state is specified in the value of W, states which happen to be of equal energy being considered separately. In the expression for P all the molecules with energy ϵ_j are taken together. What must be compared with P is not the W previously calculated but W', a larger quantity. For W' we have in fact instead of

$$\frac{N!}{N_1! N_2! \ldots} \quad \text{the expression} \quad N! \frac{g_1^{N_1}}{N_1!} \frac{g_2^{N_2}}{N_2!} \ldots,$$

since each of the N_1 molecules with energy ϵ_1 has a choice of g_1 subcompartments, these extra options giving rise to $g_1^{N_1}$ fresh possibilities.

When N_j and g_j are large

$$\ln W' = N \ln N + \sum N_j \ln g_j - \sum N_j \ln N_j.$$

We may now compare $k \ln P$ with $k \ln W'$. In general, they are different in form and in magnitude. But in one important special case they approximate closely in form, while remaining of quite different absolute value. If the density is low, that is for gases, g_j is much greater than N_j, the number of translational states being enormous because of the fine-grained nature of the quantization. When $g_j \gg N_j$

$$\ln P = \sum (N_j + g_j) \ln g_j - \sum N_j \ln N_j - \sum g_j \ln g_j$$
$$= \sum N_j \ln g_j + \sum g_j \ln q_j - \sum N_j \ln N_j - \sum g_j \ln g_j$$
$$= \sum N_j \ln g_j - \sum N_j \ln N_j.$$

Thus
$$\ln W' = \ln P + N \ln N,$$
$$k \ln W' = k \ln P + k N \ln N,$$

or
$$S_{\text{Boltzmann}} = S_{\text{quantum}} + k \ln(N!).$$

This result is important. It shows that, for gases at least, the newly defined entropy possesses all the properties of the old except that its absolute magnitude is different.

When this absolute value is required, it may be obtained from the Boltzmann entropy by subtraction of $k \ln(N!)$. It is lower in so far as it is based upon neglect of distinctions which a non-quantum theory might have regarded as valid.

All previous conclusions about equilibria in gases and in dilute solutions retain their applicability, but the convention now adopted will affect assessments of the absolute entropy. The distribution law itself is not appreciably affected. When the density is such that g can no longer be regarded as large compared with N further complications enter which will not be dealt with at this stage.

Absolute calculation of equilibria

With expressions for partition functions appropriate to various special cases, the calculation of absolute values of equilibrium constants becomes possible. The most important step in creating this possibility was, of course, the defining of what constitutes a molecular state. For some purposes the more correct idea of absolute probability is also essential.

Four examples of major importance will cover in principle a large part of the physico-chemical nature of things. They are:

1. The integration constant of the vapour-pressure equation.
2. The transition temperature for a reaction taking place in a condensed phase: for example, an allotropic change, or the melting of a solid phase.
3. The equilibrium constant of a chemical equilibrium in the gas phase.
4. The equilibrium of radiation and matter.

The first shows in the simplest way how a balance is established between order and chaos when molecules endowed with a primeval tendency to roam all space are impelled by attractive forces to agglomerate. The second and third illustrate the subtle interplay of factors which governs the transformation from one possible atomic pattern to another; and the fourth defines the sharing of energy between atomic and molecular systems and what was once called the ether, but later came to be regarded, for some purposes, as space containing photons.

As a first step we proceed to the calculation of the absolute entropy of a perfect gas.

Absolute entropy of a monatomic gas

$$S_{\text{Boltzmann}} = kN \ln f + kNT \, d\ln f/dT, \tag{1}$$

where

$$f = \frac{(2\pi mkT)^{\frac{3}{2}} V}{h^3}, \tag{2}$$

since there is no energy to be considered except that of the translational motion.

$$S_{\text{quantum}} = S_{\text{Boltzmann}} - k \ln(N!) \tag{3}$$

$$pV = kNT. \tag{4}$$

Insertion of (1), (2), and (4) into (3) gives

$$S_{\text{quantum}} = \tfrac{5}{2}kN \ln T - kN \ln p + kN \ln \frac{(2\pi m)^{\frac{3}{2}} k^{\frac{5}{2}} e^{\frac{5}{2}}}{h^3}.$$

All the quantities in this expression are known, so that the entropy is calculable in absolute measure.

Absolute calculation of vapour pressures

What is perhaps the first and simplest task to attempt in the light of knowledge of the absolute entropy is the calculation of the equilibrium between the gaseous and the solid phase for a monatomic substance. This equilibrium expresses the first departure of matter from the state of random dispersion and the first emergence of the forms of things we meet in the ordinary world.

For the equilibrium of solid and vapour,

$$G_1 = G_2 \quad \text{(p. 71)},$$

where G_1 is the free energy for a gram molecule of the solid and G_2 that for one of vapour.

$$G_1 - H_1 = T \frac{\partial G_1}{\partial T},$$

whence
$$G_1 = -T \int_0^T \frac{H_1}{T^2} dT + TJ \quad \text{(see p. 101)}.$$

Since
$$\frac{\partial G}{\partial T} = -S,$$

$$\frac{\partial G_1}{\partial T} = -S_1 = J \quad \text{when } T = 0$$

(see also later, p. 145).

With a condensed phase, it is by no means unreasonable to assume that at the absolute zero $S_1 = 0$. With the disappearance of molecular identities there will be only one way in which particles can be assigned to their lowest state, unless, for some special reason connected with geometrical or other molecular characteristics, the ground level can be regarded as multiple.

With this reservation, to which further reference will be made, J may be set equal to zero.

Then
$$G_1 = -T \int_0^T \frac{H_1}{T^2} dT.$$

For the vapour
$$G_2 = H_2 - TS_2,$$

where
$$S_2 = \tfrac{5}{2}kN \ln T - kN \ln p + kN \ln \frac{(2\pi m)^{\frac{3}{2}} k^{\frac{5}{2}} e^{\frac{5}{2}}}{h^3} \quad \text{(p. 139)}.$$

When $G_1 = G_2$, $p = \pi$, the vapour pressure. Thus

$$-T \int_0^T \frac{H_1}{T^2} dT = H_2 - \tfrac{5}{2}kNT \ln T + kNT \ln \pi - kNT \ln \frac{(2\pi m)^{\frac{3}{2}} k^{\frac{5}{2}} e^{\frac{5}{2}}}{h^3}.$$

But
$$H_2 = U_2 + p_2 V_2 = \tfrac{3}{2}kNT + kNT = \tfrac{5}{2}kNT,$$

and therefore

$$\ln \pi = - \int_0^T \frac{H_1}{kNT^2} \, dT - \tfrac{5}{2} + \tfrac{5}{2} \ln T + \ln \frac{(2\pi m)^{\frac{3}{2}} k^{\frac{5}{2}} e^{\frac{5}{2}}}{h^3}$$

$$= - \int_0^T \frac{H_1 \, dT}{kNT^2} + \tfrac{5}{2} \ln T + \ln \frac{(2\pi m)^{\frac{3}{2}} k^{\frac{5}{2}}}{h^3}, \quad \text{since} \quad \ln e^{\frac{5}{2}} = \tfrac{5}{2},$$

or if we write

$$\ln \pi = \phi(T) + i,$$

$$i = \ln \frac{(2\pi m)^{\frac{3}{2}} k^{\frac{5}{2}}}{h^3}.$$

This gives the absolute value of the integration constant of the vapour-pressure equation

$$\ln \pi = \int \frac{\lambda}{RT^2} \, dT + i.$$

For monatomic substances, then, the vapour pressure is determined by λ and by i, where the latter appears from this discussion to be a function only of the atomic weight and of universal constants.

Calculated and observed values for various monatomic vapours are in general agreement and sometimes correspond very closely.

A certain reservation must be made about the possible multiplicity of the lowest states of the molecules or atoms. If this is taken into account, the formula becomes

$$i = \ln \frac{(2\pi m)^{\frac{3}{2}} k^{\frac{5}{2}}}{h^3} \frac{g_0}{g_c},$$

where g_0 is the so-called statistical weight of the ground level in the gas and g_c that of the ground level in the crystal.

An analogous discussion for diatomic molecules leads to the formula

$$i = \ln \frac{(2\pi m)^{\frac{3}{2}} k^{\frac{7}{2}}}{h^5} \frac{8\pi^2 I}{\sigma} \frac{g_0}{g_c},$$

where I is the moment of inertia of the molecule and σ is the symmetry number, a geometrical characteristic which determines what orientations count as separate states.

Factors determining the balance of solid and vapour

It is now possible to form a general picture of the factors which determine the tendency of a given substance to exist as solid or to escape as vapour. The equation for the vapour pressure is

$$\frac{d\ln\pi}{dT} = \frac{\lambda}{RT^2} = \frac{\lambda_0 + \int \Delta C_p\, dT}{RT^2},$$

i.e.
$$\ln\pi = -\frac{\lambda_0}{RT} + \int \frac{\left(\int \Delta C_p\, dT\right)}{RT^2}\, dT + i.$$

λ_0 measures the potential energy of attraction. The greater this attraction, the lower the vapour pressure. Neither thermodynamics nor statistics vouchsafes any information about the magnitude of λ_0.

ΔC_p may be written in the form $\alpha + \beta T + ...$, and its contribution to the second term on the right of the above equation depends upon the signs of α and β. As long as ΔC_p is positive λ increases, since $d\lambda/dT = \Delta C_p$. The energy of the vapour is then increasing more rapidly than that of the solid, and thus still more energy runs down when condensation occurs. But other influences are at work: consider, for example, a negative value of β. A negative β means that C_p of the vapour increases less rapidly than that of the solid. Increase of C_p means that fresh degrees of freedom come into operation (or that existing ones come more fully into operation). If this happens less rapidly in the vapour than in the solid then, from the point of view of entropy, the solid is gaining in disorder relatively to the vapour. Additional possibilities for existence in the solid state are thus opening up, and the further rise in vapour pressure with increasing temperature is antagonized. Some of the facilities previously offered by vapour only are now offered by existence in the solid state.

An increase of energy of the solid relatively to the vapour has thus two opposing effects. In so far as it represents an increasing facility of escape from the attractive forces it favours evaporation: in so far as it leads to a more disordered state in the solid it favours condensation, or at any rate lessens the tendency to evaporate.

The influence of the constant term i is connected purely with the entropy. If i becomes larger, the vapour pressure becomes greater also. Scrutiny of the formulae reveals several points of interest. As the mass of the molecules or atoms increases, the vapour-pressure constant increases also. This is because a greater mass leads to a more fine-grained quantization of the translational energy in the gas phase. There are thus relatively more possibilities of existence as vapour for the heavier than for the lighter particles. The effect of this factor itself is to favour the existence of heavier molecules in the gaseous state. The fact that the vapour pressure itself usually *decreases* with increasing mass is due to the influence of λ, acting in strong opposition to that of i.

A large ratio g_c/g_0 lowers i, and thus operates in the direction of diminishing the vapour pressure. If there are multiple ground states in the crystal which are not possible in the gas, then the solid phase is thereby favoured. But the question of these relative statistical weights is not very well understood.

For diatomic molecules and polyatomic molecules generally, the moment of inertia appears in the integration constant of the vapour-pressure equation, because the existence of rotations in the gas, while there are usually none in the solid, favours the evaporation of molecules by offering more possibilities of distribution in the gas phase. The greater the moment of inertia, the smaller the rotational quantum and the more numerous the levels. Hence the increase of i with I revealed in the formula.

This whole subject illustrates in a very interesting way how what might metaphorically be called the tendency of matter to achieve self-realization in the dynamical sense opposes the discipline of the attractive forces and determines the partition between different states of aggregation. Quite a vivid mechanical picture can be formed of this conflict, though it must be remembered that the principles underlying the dynamical behaviour are in fact highly abstract.

Transition temperatures

The equilibrium between two solid phases, whether the same in chemical composition or not, is governed by the condition

$$\Delta G = 0.$$

As shown on p. 101,

$$\frac{\Delta G}{T} = -\int \frac{\Delta H}{T^2}\, dT + J.$$

ΔH may be expressed as a power series in the following manner:

$$\Delta H = \Delta H_0 + aT + bT^2 + ...,$$

$$\frac{\partial(\Delta H)}{\partial T} = \Delta C_p = a + 2bT + ...$$

Since at the absolute zero the specific heats of solid phases vanish, a must be zero. Thus

$$\Delta G = -T \int \frac{\Delta H_0 + bT^2 + \cdots}{T^2} \, dT + TJ$$

$$= \Delta H_0 - bT^2 + \ldots + TJ,$$

$$\frac{\partial(\Delta G)}{\partial T} = -2bT + \ldots + J.$$

When $T = 0$, $\qquad \dfrac{\partial(\Delta G)}{\partial T} = J.$

But $\qquad \dfrac{\partial G}{\partial T} = -S \quad$ and $\quad \dfrac{\partial(\Delta G)}{\partial T} = -\Delta S.$

If, therefore, the change of entropy vanishes at the absolute zero, the integration constant J is zero.

In many solid substances the entropy probably does vanish when $T = 0$. Permutations of individual molecules, as has been seen, do not count in the world of quantum mechanics, and at the absolute zero all molecules occupy the lowest possible levels, which they can do in one way only. If the entropy is proportional to the logarithm of unity it of course vanishes. The lowest energy levels may possibly be multiple for one reason or another, and if they are so to different extents for the initial and final phases of a given transformation, J may in fact not be accurately zero. Nevertheless, in many cases it will be.

The original arguments of Nernst on this subject were based upon the view that ΔG and ΔH are equal not only at the absolute zero itself (as they must be from the general thermodynamic equation) but also in the immediate vicinity of this point, so that $\partial(\Delta G)/\partial T$ and $\partial(\Delta H)/\partial T$ vanish when $T = 0$. From these conditions it follows that J will be zero. Nernst put forward the hypothesis about the temperature coefficients as a fundamental thermodynamic principle (sometimes spoken of as the *third law of thermodynamics*). While there are reservations about the complete validity of this view, it is certainly one which is always nearly true, and may often be accurately so.

In so far as the Nernst postulate may be accepted,

$$\Delta G = -T \int \frac{\Delta H}{T^2} \, dT.$$

If ΔH is known from experimental observations and is represented as a function of temperature, then ΔG may also be so expressed with the aid of the same data.

For example, if experimentally determined heat quantities are given by

$$\Delta H = \Delta H_0 + bT^2 + ...,$$

the free energies will be given by

$$\Delta G = \Delta H_0 - bT^2 + ...$$

When G is plotted as a function of T, the point at which it becomes zero can be read off from the graph. This point is the transition temperature at which one solid phase would be transformed into the other.

The nature of the factors which cause ΔG to drop from the value ΔH_0 at the absolute zero to nothing at the transition temperature has already been partially discussed (p. 140). As is now evident, the omission of any reference in the previous account to the influence of the term TJ was immaterial. Its influence is unimportant since it usually vanishes. The sign of b is important. Suppose in the transition $I \rightarrow II$, ΔH_0 is positive. When $T = 0$, $\Delta G = \Delta H_0$ and I is stable. If b is positive, ΔG gradually falls to zero as the temperature rises, and II now becomes stable in spite of its higher potential energy.

Now

$$\frac{\partial(\Delta H)}{\partial T} = 2bT + ...$$

$$= C_{p_{II}} - C_{p_I}$$

$$= \Delta C_p$$

and

$$2b + ... = \frac{\partial(\Delta C_p)}{\partial T}$$

$$= \frac{\partial}{\partial T}(C_{p_{II}} - C_{p_I}).$$

If b is positive it means that the specific heat of the second phase *increases* with temperature more rapidly than that of the first. In other words, the second phase develops new degrees of freedom more rapidly, and offers relatively more accommodation in the way of molecular energy states. This, essentially, is why it eventually becomes the preferred form.

Chemical equilibrium in gases

We may now turn to the further consideration of gaseous equilibria. Thermodynamic principles lead to the equations

$$d \ln K_V / dT = \Delta U / RT^2$$

and

$$d \ln K_p / dT = \Delta H / RT^2.$$

We may take the latter as typical and integrate it thus:

$$\ln K_p = \int \frac{\Delta H}{RT^2}\, dT + I.$$

Knowledge of the absolute magnitude of K_p depends upon the evaluation of I.

The first important step in this direction depends upon a theorem due to Nernst which shows that

$$I = \sum ni,$$

where the i's are the integration constants of the respective vapour-pressure equations for the various substances participating in the equilibrium,

$$\ln \pi = \int \frac{\lambda}{RT^2}\, dT + i.$$

The proof is simple and depends upon the fact that $J = 0$ for a transformation in the solid state.

As shown on p. 105 for a gaseous reaction,

$$\Delta F = RT(\sum n \ln c - \ln K_V),$$

and similarly

$$\Delta G = RT(\sum n \ln p - \ln K_p).$$

If the corresponding chemical change occurred between substances in the solid state we should have

$$\Delta G_{\text{solid}} = -T \int \frac{\Delta H_{\text{solid}}}{T^2}\, dT + \text{zero}.$$

Now suppose all the solids participating in the reaction to be in equilibrium with their respective vapours. There is no change in free energy when evaporation occurs at the saturated vapour pressure. Consequently the value of

$$\Delta G_{\text{sat vap}} = \Delta G_{\text{solid}},$$

but

$$\Delta G_{\text{sat vap}} = RT \sum n \ln \pi - RT \ln K_p$$

and

$$\ln \pi = \int \frac{\lambda}{RT^2}\, dT + i.$$

Therefore

$$\Delta G_{\text{sat vap}} = RT \sum n \int \frac{\lambda}{RT^2} dT + RT \sum ni - RT \ln K_p = \Delta G_{\text{solid}},$$

and thus

$$RT \sum n \int \frac{\lambda}{RT^2} dT + RT \sum ni - RT \int \frac{\Delta H_{\text{gas}}}{RT^2} dT - RTI$$

$$= -T \int \frac{\Delta H_{\text{solid}}}{T^2} dT + 0.$$

The integrals contain no terms independent of T except the integration constants which have been written explicitly. Moreover, the above equation must be identically true for all values of T, and one may therefore equate coefficients of like powers of T on the two sides. The coefficients of the first powers are seen to be the various integration constants themselves, so that

$$R \sum ni - RI = 0$$

or

$$I = \sum ni.$$

Thus

$$\ln K_p = \int \frac{\Delta H}{RT^2} dT + \sum ni.$$

Similarly

$$\ln K_{\text{p}} = \int \frac{\Delta U}{RT^2} dT + \sum ni_0.$$

i_0 differs from i by a constant, the logarithm of the saturated vapour *concentration* differing from that of the pressure in a way calculable from elementary theory.

The two constants i and i_0 are, in principle, calculable in terms of the absolute entropies, so that these two formulae define the equilibrium constants themselves in terms of known quantities.

Gaseous equilibrium constants from partition functions

Before the significance of the various factors expressed in the equations for $\ln K$ is discussed further, an alternative method of deriving the equilibrium constant will be considered. In this it is related to the partition functions of the various molecules taking part in the reaction. It will suffice to deal with K_V.

In simple examples the problem is accessible to frontal attack. The following derivation applies in the first instance to an equilibrium between free atoms and diatomic molecules of a single species formed from them, but the conditions for generalizing the proof are fairly evident.

Let there be in all M atoms of one species and N of another, and let the numbers which exist in the free state be X and Y respectively. Let there be Z molecules formed by the union of one atom of each kind. Then we have the balance-sheet

$$X + Z = M,$$
$$Y + Z = N.$$

There is only one way in which all the atoms could be free and only one in which they could all be combined, but there are many ways in which some can be free and some combined. The total number of permutations by which the balance-sheet specified above can be realized is given by the expression

$$W_0 = \frac{M!\,N!}{X!\,Y!\,Z!}.$$

This follows from the fact that the total number of permutations of the two kinds of atom is $M!\,N!$. For each of these, the first X of one kind and the first Y of the other kind could be detailed for the free state and the residual Z of each sent to form molecules. But the order within the groups X, Y, and Z is immaterial.

The atoms of the two species and the molecules are now assignable to their several energy states, and this process leads to additional combinations

$$\frac{X!}{X_1!\,X_2!\,...}, \qquad \frac{Y!}{Y_1!\,Y_2!\,...}, \qquad \frac{Z!}{Z_1!\,Z_2!\,...},$$

where X_1 is the number of atoms of the first kind in the first of their possible energy levels, and so on.

The probability of the whole assignment—atoms to the free or combined conditions, atoms and molecules to their various energy states—is given by

$$W = W_0 W_x W_y W_z = \frac{M!\,N!}{X_1!\,X_2!...Y_1!\,Y_2!...Z_1!\,Z_2!...}.$$

Stirling's approximation gives

$$\ln W = M \ln M - M + N \ln N - N - \sum X_1 \ln X_1 + \sum X_1 -$$
$$- \sum Y_1 \ln Y_1 + \sum Y_1 - \sum Z_1 \ln Z_1 + \sum Z_1. \quad (1)$$

We also have
$$\sum X_1 + \sum Z_1 = M, \quad (2a)$$
$$\sum Y_1 + \sum Z_1 = N, \quad (2b)$$

for the constancy of the total numbers of atoms, and for the constancy of the total energy we have

$$\sum \epsilon_1 X_1 + \sum \eta_1 Y_1 + \sum u_1 Z_1 = E, \tag{3}$$

where ϵ, η, and u are the energies of the corresponding atoms and molecules in the levels denoted by the subscripts.

The condition that W shall be a maximum subject to $(2a)$, $(2b)$, and (3) is

$$-\delta \ln W = \sum (1 + \ln X_1) \delta X_1 + \sum (1 + \ln Y_1) \delta Y_1 +$$
$$+ \sum (1 + \ln Z_1) \delta Z_1 - \sum \delta X_1 - \sum \delta Y_1 - \sum \delta Z_1 = 0,$$
$$\sum \delta X_1 + \sum \delta Z_1 = 0,$$
$$\sum \delta Y_1 + \sum \delta Z_1 = 0,$$
$$\sum \epsilon_1 \delta X_1 + \sum \eta_1 \delta Y_1 + \sum u_1 \delta Z_1 = 0.$$

The last four equations are, according to the method of undetermined multipliers illustrated already on p. 29, multiplied separately by unity, α_x, α_y, and β, and are then added and rearranged. The result is

$$\sum (\ln X_1 + \alpha_x + \beta \epsilon_1) \delta X_1 + \sum (\ln Y_1 + \alpha_y + \beta \eta_1) \delta Y_1 +$$
$$+ \sum (\ln Z_1 + \alpha_x + \alpha_y + \beta u_1) \delta Z_1 = 0.$$

By an argument similar to that used before, the separate coefficients of δX_1, δY_1, and δZ_1 are therefore equal to zero. Thus

$$\ln X_1 = -\alpha_x - \beta \epsilon_1.$$
$$\ln Y_1 = -\alpha_y - \beta \eta_1,$$
$$\ln Z_1 = -\alpha_x - \alpha_y - \beta u_1,$$

whence

$$X_1 = e^{-\alpha_x} e^{-\beta \epsilon_1},$$
$$Y_1 = e^{-\alpha_y} e^{-\beta \eta_1},$$
$$Z_1 = e^{-(\alpha_x + \alpha_y)} e^{-\beta u_1}.$$

It follows that

$$X = \sum X_1 = e^{-\alpha_x} \sum e^{-\beta \epsilon_1} = e^{-\alpha_x} f_x',$$
$$Y = \sum Y_1 = e^{-\alpha_y} \sum e^{-\beta \eta_1} = e^{-\alpha_y} f_y',$$
$$Z = \sum Z_1 = e^{-(\alpha_x + \alpha_y)} \sum e^{-\beta u_1} = e^{-(\alpha_x + \alpha_y)} f_z',$$

and thus

$$\frac{Z}{XY} = \frac{f_z'}{f_x' f_y'} \frac{e^{-(\alpha_x + \alpha_y)}}{e^{-\alpha_x} e^{-\alpha_y}} = \frac{f_z'}{f_x' f_y'}.$$

As before, $\beta = 1/kT$.

The functions f'_x, f'_y, and f'_z are of the form of ordinary partition functions except in so far as they require adjustment in respect of the energy zeros.

When a molecule is formed from its constituent atoms there is a release of energy, q, of which equation (3) took no account. That expression rests therefore on the convention that the levels belonging to the u series are measured from a zero which is uniformly q higher than the normal molecular level. If we wish to drop this tacit convention and to use normal partition functions, we must increase the values u_1, u_2,... by q. Thus

$$f_z = \sum e^{-(u_1 + q)/kT} = f'_z e^{-q/kT}.$$

Therefore
$$f'_z = f_z e^{q/kT}.$$

But q is the energy released and is thus $-\Delta U_0/N$, where ΔU_0 is the conventional increase of energy per gram molecule. Thus

$$f'_z = f_z e^{-\Delta U_0/RT}.$$

f'_x and f'_y may be replaced by f_x and f_y since there is no adjustment of the reference levels to be undertaken. We therefore have

$$\frac{Z}{XY} = \frac{f_z}{f_x f_y} e^{-\Delta U_0/RT}.$$

Reference to the formulae on p. 135 reminds us that all the partition functions will contain V, the volume, once for each species (from the translational quantization). We may conveniently extract it from f by writing $f = f_0 V$. Transposition of the last formula then gives

$$\frac{(Z/V)}{(X/V)(Y/V)} = \frac{f_{0z}}{f_{0x} f_{0y}} e^{-\Delta U_0/RT}.$$

The last equation may be written

$$K_N = \Pi(f_0) e^{-\Delta U_0/RT},$$

where $\Pi(f_0)$ represents products and quotients of partition functions (with V omitted) built up on precisely the model of the equilibrium constant. For example, for the equilibrium $2H_2 + O_2 \rightleftharpoons 2H_2O$ the value of $\Pi(f_0)$ would be

$$f^2_{0(H_2O)}/f^2_{0(H_2)} \cdot f_{0(O_2)}.$$

K_N denotes an equilibrium constant in which concentrations are expressed not in the usual way as numbers of gram molecules per unit volume but as numbers of molecules per unit volume.

An inspection of the steps of the above derivation reveals what changes will be introduced by a modification in the form of the chemical equation. If the reaction were of a type where two atoms of the first species and one of the second entered the molecule, we should have for the balance-sheet of the total numbers of atoms

$$X + 2Z = M,$$
$$Y + Z = N.$$

Equation ($2a$), which is differentiated and multiplied by α_x, would then contain $2 \sum Z_1$ and give rise to a term $2\alpha_x$ in the coefficient of $\sum \delta Z_1$. The cancellation of the α terms then requires the presence of X^2 and of f_x^2 in the final expression.

It will be noted that the above calculations, like those given on p. 28, amount to the derivation of a distribution law. The result is therefore unaffected by the question of the constant defining the absolute entropy.

More formal consideration of the foregoing theorem

As shown on p. 132, the Boltzmann free energy is related to the partition function by the equation

$$F = U - TS = -RT \ln f.$$

The quantum-mechanical requirement gives for the absolute entropy a value less by $k \ln(N!) = k(N \ln N - N)$ so that $kT(N \ln N - N)$ must be added to F.

Since, moreover, chemical changes are to be taken into account, and since these involve releases or uptakes of energy in forms which do not constitute part of the ordinary thermal energy—being in fact changes in the internal electronic energy, a term U_0 will be added to F. U_0 represents the non-thermal energy which changes only when the chemical nature of the molecule is altered.

Thus $\qquad F = U_0 - RT \ln f + RT \ln N - RT.$

f, the complete partition function, contains a factor V, the volume occupied by a gram molecule, and may be written $f_0 V$.

Thus $\qquad F = U_0 - RT \ln f_0 + RT \ln(N/V) - RT.$

In a chemical change, with the usual meaning of $\sum n$,

$$\Delta F = \sum n(U_0 - RT \ln f_0 + RT \ln c - RT + RT \ln N),$$

since $1/V = c$, the concentration of the gram molecule occupying the volume V.

If the gases are in equilibrium and if a small chemical transformation takes place such that dx times each of the quantities represented in the chemical equation reacts, then

$$(\Delta F)\,dx = 0,$$

$$(\Delta F)\,dx = \sum n(U_0 - RT\ln f_0 + RT\ln c - RT + RT\ln N)\,dx +$$

$$+\frac{d}{dx}\left(\sum nRT\ln c\right)dx.$$

The last term must be added, since it is in fact impossible to conduct the small virtual displacement without slight changes in c. But

$$\frac{d}{dx}\left(\sum nRT\ln c\right)dx = RT\sum n\left(\frac{1}{c}\frac{dc}{dx}\right)dx = RT\sum n\,dx$$

since $dc/c = dx$, dx being the fraction of each gram molecule which reacts, and therefore the fractional change in concentration. Therefore

$$(\Delta F)\,dx = \sum n(U_0 - RT\ln f_0 + RT\ln c + RT\ln N)\,dx = 0,$$

$$\Delta F = \sum nU_0 - \sum nRT\ln f_0 + \sum nRT\ln(N/V) = 0,$$

whence
$$\sum n\ln\frac{N}{V} = \sum n\ln f_0 - \frac{\Delta U_0}{RT},$$

since $\sum nU_0 = \Delta U_0$, the heat of reaction at $T = 0$.

$\sum n\ln(N/V) = \ln K_N$, where K_N is the equilibrium constant with concentrations expressed as number of molecules in unit volume. (V is the volume of one gram molecule, while N, Avogadro's number, is the number of molecules in one gram molecule.)

This formula is that arrived at in the last section, $\ln\Pi(f_0)$ being identical with $\sum n\ln f_0$.

General discussion of the factors determining the position of a gaseous equilibrium

In the light of the formulae derived in the preceding sections we may once more make a general survey of the competing factors which determine the chemical make-up of things.

We begin by collecting together the relevant equations: they are

$$\ln K_P = \int \frac{\Delta U}{RT^2}\,dT + \sum ni_0, \tag{1}$$

$$\ln K_N = \sum n\ln f_0 - \frac{\Delta U_0}{RT}, \tag{2a}$$

$$K_N = \Pi(f_0)e^{-\Delta U_0/RT}. \tag{2b}$$

K is written, as usual, with the reaction products in the numerator. Thus in (1) a large value of ni_0 favours completeness of reaction. The influence of this term might be roughly but vividly expressed by saying that those molecules which have the greatest inherent tendency to escape from the solid state into the vapour have also the greatest tendency to be formed in chemical transformations in the gas phase. The reason is that such molecules have open to them the widest range of states and that populations in general increase with the number of available states.

The operation of the same principle is revealed in a slightly different way in $(2a)$. Other things being equal, K increases in proportion as the partition functions of products exceed those of the initial substances, and they may do this in so far as the selection of available states offered to them is wider.

(1) and (2) both express the powerful influence exerted by $\sum n$ itself. Values of i_0 and values of f_0 vary, of course, considerably from one substance to another, but not so much that the sign of $\sum ni_0$ or of $\sum n\ln f_0$ will not usually be positive or negative according as there are more molecules of product or more molecules of the initial substances in the chemical equation. In other words, products formed with an increase in the number of molecules are favoured, while those formed with a decrease in this number are not. That is to say, that there is a factor rendering decomposition reactions essentially more probable than synthetic reactions. The interpretation of this is obvious. The latter require the fortuitous encounter of a larger number of particles to unite to a smaller number, a process of comparative rarity compared with the spontaneous break-up of a more complex structure into chaotically dispersed fragments.

As T approaches infinity, the factor $e^{-\Delta U/RT}$ tends towards unity and the two influences which have just been considered, namely the relative numbers of available states open to reactants and products on the one hand, and on the other, the relative probabilities of congregation or dispersal, dominate the situation entirely. Conversely, as T drops, the relative effect of these factors declines until at very low temperatures the influence of ΔU_0 becomes paramount.

ΔU_0 represents the amount by which the potential energy of the structures formed in the reaction exceeds that of the original ones. K increases as $(-\Delta U_0)$ becomes numerically greater, that is, as the running down of potential energy accompanying the reaction grows

L

larger. In a static world everything would tend to be in a state of minimum potential energy and this condition is more nearly realized as the absolute zero is approached, the formative tendencies of the attractive forces being here less and less combated by the disruptive action of molecular motions and the blind urge to explore all possible states of existence.

It is interesting to observe the form in which the potential energy factor is expressed in $(2\,b)$. Consider the simple example of a reaction $A \rightleftharpoons B$. The equilibrium constant $K = [B]/[A]$ contains a term $e^{-\Delta U_0/RT}$. The chance that a molecule of B is in its jth energy state is normally $e^{-\epsilon_j/kT}$ or $e^{-E_j/RT}$, counting on a gram-molecular basis. If, however, B is formed from A in a reaction, it receives, as it were, a bonus of energy E_0 and only needs $E_j - E_0$ to attain its jth state, the chance of which now becomes $e^{-(E_j - E_0)/RT}$. Thus every single state of B increases in probability by $e^{+E_0/RT}$ and, since $E_0 = -\Delta U_0$, by $e^{-\Delta U_0/RT}$.

There is still another matter illustrating the interplay of energy and entropy factors which the equations (1) and (2) reveal. (1) may be written

$$\ln K = -\frac{\Delta U_0}{RT} + \int \frac{\left(\int \sum nC_v \, dT\right)}{RT^2} \, dT + \sum n i_0 \qquad (3)$$

since

$$\frac{\partial(\Delta U)}{\partial T} = \sum nC_v$$

so that

$$\Delta U = \Delta U_0 + \int \sum nC_v \, dT.$$

Thus

$$\frac{d \ln K_V}{dT} = \frac{\Delta U_0}{RT^2} + \frac{\int \sum nC_v \, dT}{RT^2}.$$

Differentiation of $(2\,a)$ gives (since the temperature variations of K_V and K_N are the same)

$$\frac{d \ln K_N}{dT} = \frac{\Delta U_0}{RT^2} + \sum n \frac{d \ln f_0}{dT}.$$

From the result on p. 132 the final terms of the last two equations are seen to be consistent. The thermal energy E is $RT^2 d \ln f/dT$, so that $\sum n d \ln f_0/dT = \sum nE/RT^2$. $\sum nE$ is the amount by which ΔU will differ from ΔU_0, and so is $\int \sum nC_v \, dT$.

Equation (3) brings one factor more clearly to light. If the specific heats of products increase with temperature more rapidly than those of the reactants, the formation of products is favoured (cf. p. 142).

$\int \sum nC_v dT$ in these circumstances contains *positive* terms in the higher powers of T and in the integral these give other terms which are also positive. If the products are formed with increase in energy, ΔU_0 is positive and $(-\Delta U_0/RT)$ operates against their formation, but the positive terms just referred to neutralize this influence and favour the products. Specific heats increase with temperature because new degrees of freedom make increasing contributions. If this applies more to the products than to the initial substances, then the states available for the former increase more rapidly than those available for the latter: hence the favourable displacement of equilibrium.

To cite a few specific cases in exemplification of these principles: hydrogen and oxygen combine almost completely except at very high temperatures, in virtue chiefly of the favourable heat of reaction: the influence of the $\sum n$ term is adverse. The equilibrium amount of saturated hydrocarbons formed in synthetic reactions is small for any except methane, and chiefly because of the highly adverse $\sum n$ term. Attempts at a thermal synthesis of ozone would always be relatively disappointing: both energy and $\sum n$ factors are unfavourable. The more subtle factors which the foregoing discussion has brought to light interplay in a complex manner, and this explains why no simple general rules, such as the Berthelot principle (which related equilibrium to heat of reaction), can have more than restricted validity.

Once again the situation can be summed up by the statement that the chemical balance of the world is determined by the interaction of three principal factors: forces which tend to impose order, probabilities of encounter and departure, and the numbers of states available for occupation by molecules in their various chemical forms.

Equilibrium of radiation and matter

Having studied the material equilibrium of particles, it will be advantageous to turn attention briefly to the equilibrium of matter itself with the radiation which bathes it.

In an enclosure containing radiation the role of the matter is to define the temperature. At a given temperature the energy and wave-length relations of the radiation are governed by statistical considerations of a rather general character.

The energy of a photon corresponding to the frequency ν is $h\nu$.

According to the principle of relativity (p. 230) the photon behaves as though it possessed a mass m such that

$$mc^2 = h\nu,$$

where c is the velocity of light. The momentum is therefore given by

$$p = mc = h\nu/c.$$

In a quite general way particles or photons moving in an enclosure must conform to certain boundary conditions. If the motion is confined to the x-axis, the condition for a steady state is

$$n\lambda/2 = a_x,$$

n being a positive integer and a_x being the length of the enclosure in the x direction. Since in general $\lambda = h/p$ (for photons in particular since $h/p = c/\nu$ and $c = \lambda\nu$) we have

$$nh/2p_x = a_x, \qquad p_x a_x = nh/2.$$

Up to a given maximum value, $p_x a_x$, of this product, there would be n possible values spaced at intervals of $\frac{1}{2}h$. As far as energy states go there is a similar set with p reversed, so that there are n states each spaced h apart in units of the product *momentum and length*. In other words, the texture of what is called the *phase space* is such that $dp\,dx = h$.

Similarly the volume of the phase space which constitutes a state for the three-dimensional motion is h^3. If desired this last statement can be taken as the fundamental postulate.

Suppose the volume of the enclosure is V and the resultant momentum in three dimensions is p. Let p be represented as a function of p_x, p_y, and p_z, giving a vector. Now consider all the vectors corresponding to momenta between p and $p+dp$. Their terminal points lie in a region bounded by two spheres of radii p and $p+dp$ respectively. The extent of this zone is $4\pi p^2\,dp$. This last quantity is now multiplied by V, the volume of the enclosure. Thus $4\pi p^2\,dp\,V/h^3$ gives the number of states corresponding to momenta between the limits specified.

With photons the number of states comprehended in a given momentum range determines the number in a given frequency range, since $p = h\nu/c$ and $dp = h\,d\nu/c$. Thus, as far as this goes, in the frequency range $d\nu$ there would be

$$4\pi\left(\frac{h\nu}{c}\right)^2\frac{h}{c}\,d\nu\,V/h^3$$

states. This number has, however, to be doubled. Light possesses the property of polarization, two planes of polarization at right angles to one another being possible. Whatever this ultimately means in relation to photons, it certainly involves a doubling of the number of states, which now amount to

$$8\pi V \nu^2 \, d\nu / c^3.$$

Now photons may reasonably be taken to be indistinguishable one from another, so that the statistical considerations which apply in the light of quantum mechanics to molecules should apply at least equally well here. We may take all photons corresponding to frequencies between ν and $\nu + d\nu$ to possess energy ϵ_j and, as we have seen, there will be g_j states of this energy, where g_j has the value which has just been calculated.

Let there be N_j photons in the energy range under consideration. The problem, then, is that of allocating N_j objects to g_j compartments just as in the case of molecules already discussed (p. 136). The number of allocations is

$$\frac{(N_j + g_j - 1)!}{N_j! \, (g_j - 1)!}.$$

The combined probability for all frequency ranges is

$$P = \frac{(N_1 + g_1 - 1)!}{N_1! \, (g_1 - 1)!} \times \frac{(N_2 + g_2 - 1)!}{N_2! \, (g_2 - 1)!} \times \ldots$$

By use of Stirling's formula we obtain, neglecting unity,

$$\ln P = \sum_j \left[(N_j + g_j)\ln(N_j + g_j) - N_j \ln N_j - g_j \ln g_j \right].$$

This must be a maximum subject to the condition of a constant total energy.

In sharp contrast with the problem of energy distribution among molecules, there is here no condition that the total number of photons should remain constant like the total number of molecules.

We have simply
$$\delta \ln P = 0,$$
$$\delta \sum \epsilon_j N_j = 0.$$

Solution by the standard method (p. 29) gives the result

$$N_j = \frac{g_j}{e^{\beta \epsilon_j} - 1}.$$

If we formulate a problem about the sharing of energy between molecules and photons, there will be a condition of constant total energy once more, and the multiplier β will be common to molecules and photons. The value of β is thus as usual $1/kT$.

Thus
$$N_j = \frac{g_j}{e^{\epsilon_j/kT} - 1},$$

but
$$g_j = 8\pi V \nu^2 \, d\nu/c^3$$

and
$$\epsilon_j = h\nu,$$

so that
$$N_j = \frac{8\pi V \nu^2 \, d\nu}{c^3} \frac{1}{e^{h\nu/kT} - 1}.$$

Now $N_j h\nu/V$ is the energy in unit volume in the frequency range ν to $\nu + d\nu$, which is usually written $u_\nu \, d\nu$. Thus

$$u_\nu \, d\nu = \frac{8\pi h\nu^3}{c^3} \frac{1}{e^{h\nu/kT} - 1} \, d\nu.$$

This formula enshrines many important and remarkable results. In the first place it gives a maximum value of u_ν at a given frequency, as required by experiment, and as was inexplicable without the application of the quantum theory. This explanation is the historic triumph of Planck by which the quantum theory was founded. The account which has just been given of the matter differs, however, considerably from the original one and rests largely upon later considerations, which in their turn depended historically upon the initial discovery.

In the second place, the formula leads to *Wien's law* according to which $\nu_{\max}/T = \text{constant}$. The condition for the maximum is

$$\frac{du_\nu}{d\nu} = \frac{24\pi h\nu^2}{c^3} (e^{h\nu/kT} - 1)^{-1} - \frac{8\pi h\nu^3}{c^3} (e^{h\nu/kT} - 1)^{-2} e^{h\nu/kT} \frac{h}{kT} = 0,$$

i.e.
$$e^{h\nu/kT} \frac{h\nu}{kT} \Big/ (e^{h\nu/kT} - 1) = 3.$$

The expression on the left is a universal function of ν/T so that $\nu_{\max}/T$ is constant.

This result is also fully established experimentally and is of fundamental importance. Unless ϵ were of the form $h\nu$, the universal function of ν/T could not appear in the condition for $\nu_{\max}$ and Wien's law would not be followed. It was in fact the necessity for conforming to this law which guided Planck originally to the postulate regarding the proportionality of the quantum and the frequency.

Wien's law is often derived by a formal application of thermodynamics, but in the course of this the law of radiation pressure is assumed—and this law must depend upon some property of photons: moreover, the entropy principle is employed, which is equivalent to the proper statistical rules. There is thus no lack of coherence between the two modes of derivation.

The next matter of moment is the total radiation density expressed as a function of temperature. This density is given by $\int u_\nu \, d\nu$ over all frequencies. Let $h\nu/kT = \chi$. Then the integral becomes

$$\int_0^\infty u_\nu \, d\nu = \int_0^\infty \frac{8\pi h\nu^3}{c^3} \frac{1}{e^{h\nu/kT}-1} \, d\nu = \frac{8\pi h}{c^3} \int_0^\infty \left(\frac{kT}{h}\right)^4 \chi^3 (e^\chi - 1)^{-1} d\chi$$

$$= \text{constant} \times T^4 \int_0^\infty \chi^3 (e^\chi - 1)^{-1} d\chi.$$

The definite integral can be evaluated to give a purely numerical quantity, so that the total radiation density is seen to be proportional to the fourth power of the absolute temperature. This is *Stefan's law*, also a well-known result of experiment and the basis of high-temperature pyrometry.

Powerful as the theory of photons has proved itself, and deeply as the statistical method permits us to penetrate into the nature of radiation, there are aspects of the subject which can only be understood in terms of the electrical theory of matter and of the electromagnetic theory of light. The introduction of the electrical theme cannot be much longer deferred.

Conclusion: need for further principles

The conceptions of the kinetic theory and of chaotic molecular motion, even by themselves, provide interpretations of a surprising range of phenomena. They fail to give any account of absolute entropies, or to define the exact position of any equilibrium. They lack, as it were, an origin of reference. This failure is largely redeemed by the introduction of the quantum theory and of the statistical principles whereby the occupation of molecular states is defined.

The greater precision thus achieved is, of course, at the cost of several particular assumptions. The quantum rules are admirably summarized in the wave equation, but the formulation of this expression and the rules for its application do remain postulates of a specialized kind.

One rather radical assumption has had to be made: that, namely, of the indistinguishability of molecules, which converted the Boltzmann definition of the entropy into the quantum mechanical definition, and proved essential for the calculation of the absolute entropy. This represents the most drastic departure which we have so far met from the naïve conception of molecules as small-scale reproductions of the recognizable macroscopic objects around us. But still more drastic departures will prove necessary.

The equations of quantum mechanics and rules for their application are needed for deeper purposes than the mere prescription of energy levels. The wave equation itself is much more than a vehicle for the values of E which permit solutions: the properties of the function ψ itself assume great importance. One example has already appeared in connexion with rotational states: for the nth state there are $2n+1$ solutions and this number determines the weight of the state.

But it is not only the number of the solutions which matters: their character assumes predominant importance in some problems, and this in various peculiar ways which, however, it is only expedient to introduce as the interpretation of experimental facts demands. One concrete example arises from certain of the facts already considered. The necessity for the quantum theory itself emerges clearly from the failure of the kinetic theory to provide without it an adequate description of the energy content of matter. The need for further postulates is shown by the failure of the ideas so far introduced to account adequately for the detailed behaviour of the specific heat of hydrogen.

The molecular heat at constant volume falls from 5 to 3, owing to the decay of the rotational degrees of freedom as the temperature falls. According to the rules for rotational quanta, the partition function for a molecule composed of two similar atoms should be

$$f_{\text{rot}} = \sum_{n=0}^{n=\infty} (2n+1)e^{-\frac{n(n+1)h^2}{8\pi^2 I k T}} .$$

Since $E = RT^2 d\ln f/dT$, E_{rot} is computable, and its differential coefficient with respect to T gives the rotational contribution to the specific heat.

The formula derived, although expressing qualitatively the decay of the rotational specific heat as the temperature drops, is quantitatively quite inadequate to reproduce the course of the curve which represents this decay. If, however, the energy states are assumed to constitute two quite *independent series*, with odd and even values of n respectively, *transitions from odd to even states* and vice versa *being impossible*, and if, further, the states corresponding to odd values of n are assumed to have three times the weight of the corresponding even values, then the specific heat formula assumes the form

$$C_{rot} = dE_{rot}/dT, \quad \text{where} \quad E_{rot} = RT^2 \, d\ln f/dT = RT^2(1/f) \, df/dT.$$

Thus

$$E_{rot} = \frac{N\left\{ \displaystyle\sum_{n=\text{even}} (2n+1)n(n+1)\frac{h^2}{8\pi^2 I} e^{-\frac{n(n+1)h^2}{8\pi^2 I k T}} + 3\displaystyle\sum_{n=\text{odd}} (2n+1)n(n+1)\frac{h^2}{8\pi^2 I} e^{-\frac{n(n+1)h^2}{8\pi^2 I k T}} \right\}}{\displaystyle\sum_{n=\text{even}} (2n+1)e^{-\frac{n(n+1)h^2}{8\pi^2 I k T}} + 3\displaystyle\sum_{n=\text{odd}} (2n+1)e^{-\frac{n(n+1)h^2}{8\pi^2 I k T}}}.$$

This formula reproduces the experimental values in a satisfactory manner.

This curious result is by no means a mathematical fiction. By fractional adsorption on active charcoal at the temperature of liquid hydrogen and subsequent desorption, hydrogen can in fact be separated into two gases, *ortho-* and *para-hydrogen*. The former has a specific heat (and thermal conductivity) corresponding exactly to the possession of odd numbers of rotational quanta. The properties of the latter correspond to even numbers only. The two forms are stable and interconvertible only by atomization at high temperatures, or by special catalytic methods in which molecules are taken out of the gaseous state.

There are two important matters here. First, odd and even rotational states have different statistical weights and, secondly, transitions between the two kinds of state do not normally occur.

These extraordinary facts can be expressed in terms of the properties of the wave function ψ, but before the discussion is carried farther it is necessary to assemble a whole series of results. It is only in the light of developments proceeding from the electrical theory of matter that the necessary ideas become intelligible (see p. 193).

PART III

THE ELECTRICAL BASIS OF MATTER

SYNOPSIS

THERE are good reasons for believing matter to be built up from units which individually act upon one another with the electrostatic inverse square law of attraction or repulsion.

Atoms are discovered to consist of positive nuclei surrounded by systems of negative electrons, the various dispositions of which determine different series of atomic energy states. The rules governing the possible sequences of energy levels are ascertainable by the study of spectra and other means, and are derivable in general from the differential equation which summarizes all the other quantum laws.

The condition of any electron in an atom is characterized by four quantum numbers. It turns out that no two electrons in the atom can have all four quantum numbers the same, a rule of fundamental importance known as the Pauli principle.

The structure of the entire system of the chemical elements is explicable on the following basis: the interactions between nucleus and electrons are according to the Coulomb inverse square law: the electrons of an atom are assigned one after another to various energy levels with the succession of quantum numbers required by the wave equation and by the Pauli principle.

The electron, however, has not the properties of a macroscopic particle, and indeed the Pauli principle would probably not apply to entities possessing individual spatial identities. Electrons show properties of interference more characteristic of waves than of small discrete masses. Accordingly the distribution of electron density in an atom is discovered to be regulated by a certain amplitude function (the wave function) which already plays a key role in the differential equation defining the quantum states.

The function for an atomic system must, in order that the Pauli principle shall hold good, possess a character of antisymmetry, changing its sign when the coordinates of two electrons are interchanged. This principle, though abstract, is unambiguously related to very definite experimental facts, such as the character of the helium spectrum, and the specific heat relations of hydrogen.

The electrical distribution within atoms can now be inferred. Evidence about the distribution in molecules is also available from experimental observations on spectra, dielectric properties, and so on.

Electrical displacements within atoms and molecules are closely related to the electric and magnetic fields of light waves. The electromagnetic theory of light and the quantum theory both play their part in the interpretation of optical and other properties of various kinds of matter.

VIII

THE NATURE OF ATOMS

Introductory

MANY of the phenomena of nature, it is clear, can be described, analysed, and in a sense understood in terms of the kinetic, statistical, and thermodynamic principles so far outlined, without deeper inquiry into the character of the forces which cause particles to congregate together. This is true whether the attractions are those between atoms to give chemical compounds or those between molecules to give condensed matter. But we cannot rest content to forgo more detailed knowledge about these forces or to accept energy changes as fundamental data without further investigation of what they mean.

The study of forces proves to be intimately bound up with the electrical constitution of the atoms themselves. The whole question of their structure has so far entered into the discussion in the most indirect way only. It now emerges as a dominant theme. Once again, however, the road to deeper knowledge is full of unexpected turns.

When two pieces of the appropriate materials are rubbed together they acquire attractive and repulsive properties called electrical. A great many of the manifestations observed in the following up of this observation can be interpreted by the hypothesis that there is a something called electricity with properties roughly analogous to those of a fluid, and normally contained in matter, its distribution being disturbed by processes such as friction. Sometimes in the development of physics it proved useful to postulate two kinds of electricity, positive and negative, sometimes it was enough to assume either an excess or defect in relation to a normal content of one single kind. Currents through conductors are ascribed to movements of electricity.

Salts in aqueous solution conduct electricity and are decomposed in the process, not infrequently into their elements. Since the latter are liberated at the electrodes only, some at the positive and some at the negative one, the natural hypothesis to make is that electricity is carried through the solution by ions, such as Ag^+ or Cl^-, which give up their charges at the electrodes and become normal atoms. Among the keystones of chemistry is *Faraday's law of electrolysis* which states that the quantity of an element discharged by a given current in a given time is directly proportional to the chemical equivalent. In fact one gram equivalent of any element is dealt with by the passage of 96,500 Coulombs (one Faraday, F) of electricity.

The far-reaching consequences of this law were first clearly explained by von Helmholtz in 1881. Since one gram equivalent of an n-valent element is discharged by F, one gram atom corresponds to nF, the atomic weight being n times the equivalent. The amount of electricity by which a gram atom of an element is released is nothing other than the charge which that gram atom bears in the ionic state. Thus a gram atom must carry a charge of nF.

n is necessarily a whole number, so that the ionic charges of all elements are integral multiples, positive or negative, of a standard unit. This means no less than that electricity is atomic in character.

A fundamental unit of electricity may be postulated and all ionic phenomena explained by the supposition that atoms can possess an excess or defect of one, two, three, or more of these units. The assumption of a possible deficiency of charge units implies what is already suggested by the ready generation of electricity from all bodies by friction, namely that the electrical 'atoms' are normal constitutents of all ordinary matter.

The absolute magnitude of the unit charge, e, is obtained when F is divided by Avogadro's number,

$$e = F/N.$$

Electrons

The discovery of free electrons was made in the course of the study of *cathode rays* which are generated when an electric discharge passes through a gas at very low pressures. The path of these rays can be made visible by the use of fluorescent screens and recorded by photographic means. They are deflected by electric and by magnetic fields in a manner consistent with the assumption that they consist of negatively charged particles.

Their properties are found in the following way. Deflexion experiments give the ratio of charge to mass e/m. First, a magnetic field, H, is applied. The rays bend into an arc of a circle about the lines of force, after the manner of a flexible wire bearing a current. In a stream of particles of charge e and velocity v the magnetic force acting on each is Hev and is directed to the centre of the circle. This force provides the acceleration v^2/r required to maintain motion in the circular arc. Thus

$$Hev = \frac{mv^2}{r}. \tag{1}$$

In another kind of experiment the rays are deflected by the magnetic field H and the deflexion is then exactly annulled by the application of an electrostatic field X at right angles to H. When the electric and magnetic forces balance

$$Hev = Xe. \tag{2}$$

From (1) and (2) both v and e/m may be calculated.

The first method of finding e itself was that of Townsend, who measured with an electrometer the total charge on a cloud of water droplets condensed on the negative particles which constitute the rays. The principle is applied in a much more accurate way in Millikan's oil-drop method. Droplets of oil are sprayed into a chamber in which they can be individually observed by a microscope, and in which they can be subjected to an electric field acting in opposition to gravity. They prove to have negative charges. Normally they fall slowly under gravity, but by the application of an opposing field, X, their motion can be arrested and, if necessary, reversed. When a given droplet is held in exact balance

$$XE = Mg,$$

where E is the total charge and M is the mass of the oil drop. M may be determined by observation of the rate of fall under gravity alone, Stokes's law giving the radius of the drop in terms of the viscosity of air, the density of the oil, and g. (In practice measurements are made in air at various pressures so that deviations from the simple hydrodynamic formula can be corrected for.) E is now known, and proves to vary from droplet to droplet, and for a given one at different periods of its existence, but is always an integral multiple of a basic unit e.

This is the charge of the *electron*: it is identical with that carried by the cathode ray particles and with that borne by univalent ions in solution (F/N).

e/m and e being known, m is calculable and proves to be $1/1,850$ of the mass of the hydrogen atom.

The β-rays emitted by radio-active substances are also found to consist of negatively charged particles with properties closely similar

to those of cathode rays, except in one respect. While some of them
have values of e/m equal to that for the cathode-ray electrons, others,
and specifically those with high speeds, show values of e/m which
are a function of the velocity.

It has been found expedient to regard the charge as the fundamental and invariable quantity and to attribute changes in the ratio
to variations in m, which, in any case, would be predicted by the
theory of relativity (p. 230). On this basis the mass is found to vary
with the speed according to the formula

$$m = m_0/(1-v^2/c^2)^{\frac{1}{2}},$$

where m_0 is the mass of the particle at rest, v is the speed, and c is
the velocity of light. The increase of m above m_0 is only of importance
in comparatively rare circumstances, but some of the particles emitted
by radio-active elements do in fact possess speeds approaching that
of light and show considerably enhanced masses.

Electron waves

The picture of the electron, the fundamental negative electric unit,
as a minute mass, obeying the laws of particle dynamics seems so far
to be very satisfactory, but matters are really much more complex.
If a beam of electrons at a suitable angle of incidence is reflected
from a crystal surface, the distribution of intensities is not at all
what would be expected for a shower of projectiles, but is represented by a pattern with maxima and minima just like those occurring in the diffraction of light.

Measurements on photographs of the intensity patterns allow the
calculation of a wave-length, which is found to be a function of the
speed of the electrons. Experiments with beams accelerated by
known voltage differences established the following relation:

$$\lambda = \frac{h}{mv},$$

which is one of the fundamental results on which quantum mechanics
rests.

It is of interest to note that the formulae $\epsilon = hv$, $\lambda = h/mv$, and
the relativity relation $\epsilon = mc^2$ (p. 230) are interconnected. If, for
example, the general equation $\lambda = h/mv$ is applied to a photon,
$\lambda = h/mc$ and since $\lambda v = c$, $c/v = h/mc$; that is, $mc^2 = hv$ or $\epsilon = hv$.

The diffraction of electrons is more than an interesting special phenomenon. It shows that happenings on the scale of electronic magnitudes cannot be envisaged in the same way as ordinary macroscopic events, where it would be nonsensical to find wave properties and particulate properties mixed up in this way.

On analysis, there is no particular justification for the belief that the substratum of the visible world should merely consist of small-scale models of those very things which it underlies. But in the attempt to understand nature this naïve idea does represent the first step in relating the unknown to the known, and may properly be allowed to render what service it can.

For many purposes it remains expedient to regard electrons as particles, like those of Newtonian dynamics, but to add special rules regarding the distribution of electrons in space when problems of intensity have to be considered. From this point of view the undulatory character is a statistical property and relates to the probability of finding electrons in a given element of volume. But this mode of interpretation may also prove to be of provisional utility only.

The nuclear atom

The evolution of our ideas about matter now becomes influenced by discoveries and by theories from many quarters. Certain elements are found to show radio-activity, that is, the property of emitting rays and changing into other elements. The naturally occurring radio-elements emit three kinds of rays, α-rays or helium atoms with a double positive charge, β-rays or negative electrons, and γ-rays or radiation of wave-length shorter than ultra-violet light. The particles which make up α-rays possess immense energies and constitute projectiles with which experiments on the bombardment of matter can be carried out. The key result is that the α-particles usually pass straight through thin sheets of any element, most of them suffering inappreciable deflexions, an observation suggesting that matter consists largely of emptiness. Once in a very large number of times, however, an α-particle suffers a violent deviation, as though it had passed close to something which repelled it powerfully. On the basis of this, Rutherford founded the nuclear theory according to which the atom consists of a minute positively charged nucleus, surrounded by electrons.

The nuclear charge and the relative dimensions of nucleus and atom can be inferred from a detailed statistical investigation of the numbers of α-particles scattered through various angles on their passage through sheets of different elements. The conclusion reached is that the *nuclear charge* is equal to the *atomic number*, that is, the serial number of the element in the periodic system, and that the dimensions of the nucleus itself are so minute that it cannot be regarded as ordinary matter at all. Indeed, matter as something distinct from electricity fades out of the picture. The atom consists of the nucleus, which is somehow compounded of positive units of charge, and of electrons, which are themselves negative units. There is, however, a dissymmetry in that the positive units must bear most of the mass of the atom. If the hydrogen atom is assumed to consist of one positive unit, or proton, and one electron, then the mass of the former is 1,850 times as great as that of the latter.

The fundamentals of electrical theory are not satisfactorily describable at this stage. At the present time it is known that there exist: the *proton*, or positive unit; the *negative electron*; the *positive electron*, which appears in experiments on cosmic rays, and which in properties, though not apparently in the role it plays in nature, is symmetrical with the negative electron; the *neutron*, an uncharged particle of mass nearly equal to that of the proton. These are well-established stable particles. There are in addition *mesons*, unstable particles which decay with short periods, occurring in cosmic rays and possessing various masses intermediate between that of the electron and that of the proton, and possibly the *neutrino*, a particle of very small mass and no charge, postulated to account for certain phenomena in β-ray radio-activity.

The situation is mysterious, and a complete theory of these so-called ultimate particles is awaited.

What is interesting and important, however, is that so far as the chemistry of atoms is concerned nothing has yet been found inconsistent with the idea that negative electrons constitute the sole components outside the nucleus. Nuclear chemistry is a separate branch of study, so that much progress can be made by accepting the nucleus as a minute central positive charge equal to the atomic number, deferring inquiry into its structure, and seeking in the first instance to find what can be explained in terms of the external electrons.

Atomic structure: Bohr's theory

The existence of the periodic system of the elements shows that atoms are not unrelated individuals. The gradation in properties suggests, perhaps, varying patterns of the extra-nuclear electrons; and the periodicity suggests that these patterns from time to time complete themselves in some sense and start again. Many detailed studies confirm these ideas.

The shortest route into the heart of the matter is perhaps by the study of atomic spectra.

The frequencies of the lines in the spectrum of an element obey a rule known as the Ritz *combination principle*. All the observed values may be derived by additive or subtractive combinations of a much smaller number of quantities called *spectral terms*. Thus, if the terms are T_1, T_2, T_3,...., then the observed frequencies are related as in the following examples:

$$\nu_{31} = T_3 - T_1,$$

$$\nu_{21} = T_2 - T_1,$$

$$\nu_{32} = T_3 - T_2,$$

so that $\nu_{31} = \nu_{32} + \nu_{21}$, and so on.

One famous example is the hydrogen spectrum, where Balmer's formula

$$\nu = R(1/n_1^2 - 1/n_2^2)$$

expresses three complete series of lines according as $n_1 = 1$, 2, or 3 with n_2 as a variable integer in each case, R being constant.

The interpretation of these remarkable relations was for a long time completely baffling. In the light of the quantum theory it becomes transparently clear. If an atom can exist in a series of quantum states or energy levels, and if the energy released as it passes from one to another becomes in some way a photon of energy $h\nu$, then

$$U_{n_2} - U_{n_1} = h\nu_{21},$$

and thus

$$\nu_{21} = U_{n_2}/h - U_{n_1}/h,$$

and the general value U/h is immediately identifiable with the spectral term T.

The combination principle follows simply from the conservation of energy. Since $U_3 - U_1 = (U_3 - U_2) + (U_2 - U_1)$, $\nu_{31} = \nu_{32} + \nu_{21}$. The energy levels in question seem likely to depend upon the dynamics

M

of the negative electrons, which, as has been seen, appear to play the major role in atomic structure. The Balmer formula shows in what way this happens.

As a first approximation it suffices to consider Bohr's simple model of the hydrogen atom. This consists of a nucleus of charge E around which a single electron describes a circular orbit of radius r, and does this with a linear speed v. ($E = e$, but the two separate symbols will be used for the purpose of a subsequent extension of the calculation to certain atoms other than that of hydrogen.) The angular momentum of the electron is by ordinary dynamical rules mvr. According to the simple form of the quantum theory, mvr might be expected to possess only the discrete values $nh/2\pi$, where n is an integer. According to normal dynamics and electrostatics, the Coulomb attraction by the nucleus provides the acceleration towards the centre necessary to maintain the motion of the electron in the circular orbit.

The two conditions are expressed in the equations

$$mvr = nh/2\pi, \tag{1}$$

$$Ee/r^2 = mv^2/r. \tag{2}$$

The potential energy of the electron at a distance r from the nucleus is

$$\int \frac{Ee}{r^2}\,dr = C - \frac{Ee}{r},$$

where C is a constant. The kinetic energy is $\frac{1}{2}mv^2$, which from (2) is $\frac{1}{2}Ee/r$.

The total energy of the electron, potential and kinetic, is therefore given by

$$U = C - \frac{Ee}{2r}.$$

Elimination of r and v from (1) and (2) and substitution in the above gives

$$U = C - \frac{2\pi^2 m E^2 e^2}{h^2 n^2}.$$

As n increases, U increases also. If a transition occurs from a state where $n = n_2$ to one where $n = n_1$, then

$$U_2 - U_1 = \frac{2\pi^2 m E^2 e^2}{h^2}\left(\frac{1}{n_1^2} - \frac{1}{n_2^2}\right).$$

If $U_2 - U_1$ provides the energy of a photon of frequency ν_{21}, then this latter is $(U_2 - U_1)/h$, so that

$$\nu_{21} = \frac{2\pi^2 m E^2 e^2}{h^3}\left(\frac{1}{n_1^2} - \frac{1}{n_2^2}\right).$$

This is the Balmer formula.

Two observations are to be made here. In the first place, the value of R, the Rydberg constant, appears as $2\pi^2 m E^2 e^2/h^3$ and this agrees very closely indeed with that obtained by measurements on the spectral frequencies. Secondly, the characteristic form of the relation involving the factor $1/n^2$ in the energy would not follow from any assumption other than one equivalent to the quantization of the angular momentum.

The outstanding success of this simple model of the hydrogen atom encourages the attempt to extend and refine the ideas on which it is based. This process occurs in several stages.

X-ray spectra

A first very simple stage is the extension of the frequency formula to an atom in which the nucleus has a charge of Ze units (as may be assumed for an element of atomic number Z) but which contains a single electron only—that is to say, an atom which has lost all its electrons save this one. The frequencies are obviously given by

$$\nu = \frac{2\pi^2 m e^4 Z^2}{h^3}\left(\frac{1}{n_1^2} - \frac{1}{n_2^2}\right)$$

$$= RZ^2\left(\frac{1}{n_1^2} - \frac{1}{n_2^2}\right),$$

where R is the Rydberg constant.

Let $n_1 = 1$ and $n_2 = 2$, then

$$\nu = 3RZ^2/4,$$

or
$$\nu^{\frac{1}{2}} = Z\sqrt{(3R/4)}.$$

The square root of the frequency for corresponding lines of successive elements should vary directly as the atomic number.

Almost precisely this relation was found by Moseley for the X-ray spectra of the elements. All save the lightest emit X-ray spectra on bombardment with cathode rays. The lines of these spectra form various series. The lines of highest frequency for a given element are the K_α lines, and for these Moseley found the relation

$$\nu^{\frac{1}{2}} = (Z - a)\sqrt{(3R/4)}.$$

a is a small constant with a numerical value of about unity, apart from which the formula is exactly that derived from the hypothetical model.

Now if the elements contain numbers of electrons arranged in groups and patterns, some, the innermost, must be under the direct influence of the nucleus. The dynamics of one of these will correspond approximately, though not exactly, to that of a single electron associated with a nucleus of charge Ze. The difference will be due to the perturbing action of the other electrons. The perturbation may be represented empirically by a screening constant deducted from the real nuclear charge to give the effective nuclear charge. This is the constant a of Moseley's formula. The latter, in spite of this small empirical correction, is so strikingly in agreement with the theory that it leaves little doubt about the identity of the nuclear charge and the atomic number, or about the idea that some of the electrons in a heavier atom move under the direct influence of the multiple central charge.

There are other series of X-ray lines. For some of them a is much larger, which indicates a much more powerful screening, or in other words the presence of substantial numbers of electrons between the nucleus and that one actually responsible for the emission. There is thus direct evidence in the various X-ray series, K, L, M, and so on, of different groups of electrons at various removes from the nucleus.

Sets of energy levels

Having firm ground for the hypothesis that atoms can exist in energy states which differ from one another in the angular momentum of the electrons, and having, moreover, good evidence that in an atom of atomic number Z, Z electrons group themselves round the nucleus in patterns which must possess a certain repetitive character, the next step is to seek the rules governing these arrangements.

The study of line spectra yields a good deal of additional information which helps to this end. For atoms other than hydrogen the spectra show series relationships, but the effective atomic numbers which have to be inserted in the formula to give the correct order of magnitude of the frequencies are much lower than the real values. This shows that the emission of light is due to outer electrons, screened from the nucleus by an inner negative core. Moreover, the successive lines are no longer given by differences between terms of the form const./n^2, but of the form const./$(n+\delta)^2$, where δ is an empirical constant expressing the perturbing action of the electrons upon one another. This much is already understandable. The vital matter, however, is that, with most atoms, one series of spectral terms is no longer sufficient by its combinations to express the observed frequencies. There exist, in fact, a whole set of series of energy levels. With the alkali metals, for example, sets of spectral terms, designated, for historical reasons which no longer possess validity, S, P, D, F,..., exist, which have the property of combining with one another only according to special rules.

The most important rule is that if the sets are arranged in a certain order—that in which they have just been cited—then members of a given set will combine with members of an adjacent set but with no others. Thus, if we write

$$
\begin{array}{cccc}
1S & 1P & 1D & 1F \\
2S & 2P & 2D & 2F \\
\cdot & \cdot & \cdot & \cdot \\
\cdot & \cdot & \cdot & \cdot \\
\cdot & \cdot & \cdot & \cdot
\end{array}
$$

we may select any P term and take the difference between it and any S or D term to obtain a possible frequency. But S and D terms may not be subtracted. D may be combined with F or P, but F may not combine with P.

The obvious formal interpretation of this rule is that there exist two series of integers to define the quantum states of the atom: that successive values of one of them correspond to the successive S terms, $1S$, $2S$,..., or P terms, $1P$, $2P$,..., respectively, while successive values of the other correspond to transfers from the S set to the P, from the P to the D, and so on.

The first set of integers may be denoted by n, the second by l. To account for the peculiar sequence of S, P, D, F,... terms in the combination rule, we assume that l always changes by one unit at a time, and that the given order of the term symbols corresponds to successive increments of unity in the number l.

These conclusions are quite independent of any special hypothesis about the dynamical nature of n and l. This question will arise almost immediately, but before discussing it we had better have the complete picture of the multiplicity of possible spectral terms and therefore of atomic levels.

When a strong magnetic field is applied to emitting atoms, the spectral lines are split (*Zeeman effect*). This shows that the atom can exist in a series of states which in a magnetic field have different energies, having had the same energies in its absence, though they must have been distinct states all the time. For the numbering of these a third quantum number, which will be designated m, will be required.

The list is not yet complete. Spectrum lines may exhibit what is termed fine structure. They consist not always of 'singlets', but of 'doublets', 'triplets', and higher 'multiplets'. The fairly close pair represented by the yellow D lines of sodium is the most familiar example. Evidently, then, there exists some further factor, variation in which causes the rather delicate shifts in the atomic energy levels. Different values of this unknown factor will be denoted by different values of a quantum number r.

A still more refined kind of multiplicity can indeed be observed and is reflected in what is called the hyperfine structure of the lines. This is only revealed by special optical methods, and, to anticipate, is dependent upon nuclear effects, which at the present stage we shall not deem relevant to ordinary chemistry (though it would be wrong to suppose that they also have not their importance even in connexion with chemical behaviour).

As to the interpretation of the four quantum numbers, n, l, m, and r, there was an evolution of ideas away from the more naïve towards the less naïve—and in one respect back again, which it will be best, for once, to consider in a more or less historical order, since in this particular example the matter is most clearly seen in this way.

Interpretation of quantum numbers

The first step was made by an extension of Bohr's rule for the angular momentum of the electron. This rule, as has been seen, is a special case of the relation $\int p \, dq = nh$ (p. 119). Bohr had assumed a circular orbit, as in the calculation which was outlined above, and the natural extension to a plane elliptical orbit was soon made, largely by Sommerfeld, motion in such an orbit being as consistent with the Coulomb inverse square law as the motion of planets in their elliptical paths is with Newton's law of gravitation. Two co-ordinates, an angle, θ, and a radius vector, ρ, are needed to describe the position of a given electron with respect to the nucleus at any instant, and thus the quantum conditions become

$$\int p_\rho \, d\rho = n_\rho h \quad \text{and} \quad \int p_\theta \, d\theta = n_\theta h,$$

referring respectively to the radial and angular components of the momentum. These equations in conjunction with the dynamical conditions of the motion lead to an expression for the spectral terms of the form: constant/$(n_\rho + n_\theta)^2$. The sum $n_\rho + n_\theta$ may be written simply as n, so that the terms assume the same form as for the circular orbit, namely: constant/n^2. The value n_θ is called the azimuthal quantum number and measures the angular momentum of the electron, which would be zero of course if the motion were purely a radial oscillation. n measures the major axis of the ellipse and the ratio n_θ/n determines the eccentricity. A given value of n may be made up in various ways, for example, 5 might be made up of $4+1$, $3+2$, and so on, so that the various levels of the same total energy are really multiple.

With atoms more complex than hydrogen the perturbations due to other electrons are not the same for the different combinations of n_θ and n_ρ, so that various systems of terms exist. These would correspond to S, P, D, and F terms, which according to this interpretation correspond to different types of elliptical orbits.

n_θ might be supposed to assume any value from 1 to n. In fact it proves expedient to number the values from 0 to $n-1$. In antici-pation of the wave-mechanical developments it is also expedient to denote this adjusted quantum number by l.

Plane elliptical orbits have various possible orientations in space. Ordinarily these all correspond to the same energy, but revolving electrons possess magnetic properties, so that there will be, according to the orientation of the plane of the orbit, varying degrees of interaction with an external field. Hence the magnetic splitting of the frequencies which reveals the existence of the multiple atomic states. To define the orientation, a simple vector theory was intro-duced. The quantum number l measures units of angular momentum and can thus be regarded as a vector. It can be assumed that the resolved part of this in the direction of the magnetic field is also quantized, and that this quantization determines the possible angles of orientation. The various integral projections of l on a given line are $l, l-1, l-2, ..., 1, 0, -1, ..., -l$, that is to say, they amount to $2l+1$ values. There are, therefore, $2l+1$ possible assignments of the quantum number which was termed m.

The hypothesis introduced to account for the multiplet structure is that the electron itself is endowed with a proper spin about its own axis and that the magnetic moment of this is compounded with the moment due to the orbital motion. Two values only of r, the spin quantum number, are postulated. They are denoted $+\frac{1}{2}$ and $-\frac{1}{2}$ respectively, so as to give a difference of one unit, and they apply according as the proper spin is direct or retrograde with respect to the orbital motion.

The rules regarding n, l, and m can be derived in a more general way by the direct application of the Schrödinger wave equation to atoms of the same type as hydrogen. And by this method much additional information may be obtained about the actual distribution of electrons in atoms.

Before this matter is dealt with, however, the verification of the rules themselves by application to some characteristic spectroscopic phenomena may be profitably considered. These phenomena are, of course, important in themselves, but even more so in so far as they confirm the quantum rules, which will presently provide the key to the whole structure of the periodic system of the elements.

Spectra and atomic structure in the light of the quantum rules

First, the status of the principal quantum number, n, is assured not only by the various series in the hydrogen spectrum, but also by the succession of terms in the spectra of other elements. The general form is $C/(n+\delta)^2$, and although δ is an empirical constant, which is of considerable magnitude, non-integral and negative, within a given series n increases by one unit at a time.

The value of C, as has been explained, depends upon the nuclear charge less the screening effect of other electrons. For the K_α series of X-ray frequencies it varies nearly as Z^2. As the degree of ionization of the atom increases with more intense methods of spectral excitation, for example, passage from flame spectra to spark spectra, C increases. For the spectrum of ionized helium (nuclear charge 2, one electron) it is four times the value for hydrogen (nuclear charge l, one electron), apart from a small correction due to the fact that the nucleus, instead of remaining fixed, really moves about the common centre of gravity of itself and the electron.

Secondly, the existence of the second quantum number, l, is attested by the existence of the various types of series in the spectra of elements such as the alkali metals. The order of the terms with respect to the l values can be inferred from the combining possibilities and in other ways. As will appear presently, the true value of n for the lowest state of an atom can be inferred from other considerations. The value $(n+\delta)$, the effective quantum number, of the lowest term of a given series can be found from spectral data. The difference decreases steadily for terms of the types S, P, D, and F in this order, which correspond to values of $l = 0$, 1, 2, and 3 respectively. The higher values of l belong, according to the theory of elliptical orbits, to more nearly circular paths and the lower values to eccentric orbits in which the electron must pass close to the nucleus. In this latter circumstance the perturbation may be supposed to be much more serious and the value of δ, therefore, to be correspondingly larger. In this way the assignment of the l values to the terms can be checked.

Thirdly, the facts of magnetic splitting are accounted for by the rules regarding the quantum number m.

Fourthly, the multiplicities are accounted for by the existence of r, having for each electron values of $+\frac{1}{2}$ or $-\frac{1}{2}$. With the aid of one additional hypothesis, of a reasonable character, a great variety of facts, at first sight complex, can be explained. The required hypothesis relates to the so-called *coupling* of the orbital and the spin angular momenta of electrons. The value of l measures the angular momentum of the electron. If the atom contains several electrons in the outermost group, the respective values of l are supposed to compound to a resultant L. The spin moments are supposed to compound independently to their own resultant S. L and S are then assumed to compound to a resultant $L+S$, and the number of possible values for this determines the multiplicity of the state and of the corresponding spectral term.

As a first example the alkali metals may be considered. Since they are univalent and readily form positive ions with a single charge, it is natural to suppose that they possess a single electron in the outermost and least tightly bound system, and that this electron is responsible for the optical spectrum. It has two possible spin numbers, $+\frac{1}{2}$ and $-\frac{1}{2}$. Suppose $l = 0$, then there is only one absolute value of $l+s$, namely $\frac{1}{2}$, the sign being irrelevant when $l = 0$ since there is no other rotation to which to relate the sense of the spin. Hence the terms appear single. If, however, $l = 1$, $l+s$ may have the values $1+\frac{1}{2}$ and $1-\frac{1}{2}$, that is $\frac{3}{2}$ and $\frac{1}{2}$. Thus there are two energy levels and the terms are doublets.

Now in a given spectral series the frequency is always the difference between a constant and a variable term, the latter diminishing to zero as n, the principal quantum number, increases. If the constant term is a doublet and the variable term single-valued, the separation of the frequencies will remain constant throughout all the series. If, on the other hand, the constant term is single-valued and the variable term a doublet, the separation will gradually diminish to zero as n increases, and it will vanish when n tends to infinity, that is as the series converges to its limit. This explains the interesting fact that in some of the series shown by the alkali metals the doublets converge to a common series limit, while in others they have two separate limits, the frequency difference being in fact constant throughout.

On passage from the alkali metals to the alkaline earths the number of electrons in the optical system may reasonably be supposed to increase from one to two. With two electrons, S may have the values $\frac{1}{2}-\frac{1}{2} = 0$, or $\frac{1}{2}+\frac{1}{2} = 1$. With $S = 0$ there is only one value of $L+S$ for a given value of L. This means singlet terms (whatever value L itself may actually have). With $S = 1$, the values of the resultant of L and S can be $L+1$, L, or $L-1$, that is to say there is a triplet state.

With three electrons in the optical system of the atom, S may be $1\frac{1}{2}$ or $\frac{1}{2}$, since two electrons give 0 or 1 and the extra one either adds $\frac{1}{2}$ to the 1 or subtracts $\frac{1}{2}$ from it. With $S = \frac{1}{2}$, the resultant of the vector $L+S$ can have the values $L+\frac{1}{2}$ or $L-\frac{1}{2}$, giving doublets, and with $S = 1\frac{1}{2}$ it can be $L+1\frac{1}{2}$, $L+\frac{1}{2}$, $L-\frac{1}{2}$, $L-1\frac{1}{2}$, giving quadruplets.

We have in general

alkali metals	one electron	doublets
alkaline earths	two electrons	singlets and triplets
trivalent metals	three electrons	doublets and quadruplets.

The *law of alternation* here revealed is fully confirmed by observation.

Atom building

The foregoing and other facts place the rules about quantum numbers upon a sure empirical foundation. As has been seen, Moseley's X-ray spectrum rules and the variation of spectral type from element to element clearly show that the periodic system possesses an underlying unity. The principle upon which the whole is constructed becomes apparent in the light of certain conceptions introduced by Bohr.

Given that atoms are built up of positive nuclei and negative electrons, the study of Mendeleev's classification already makes very obvious the existence of closed stable groups of electrons. The inert gases display no chemical reactivity, that is, no tendency to enter into other states of combination. Their atoms may, therefore, be regarded as possessing maxima of stability. Each inert gas is preceded in the system by an element whose atoms are very ready to appear in the form of univalent negative ions, that is, as structures with an extra electron. Correspondingly the inert gas is succeeded by an element whose atoms are ready to lose an electron with formation of a univalent positive ion. Thus it seems clear that the first electron added to the inert gas configuration is the sole representative of a new group and readily lost, while if the configuration in question lacks a single electron, it will have considerable avidity for one, the capture of which from somewhere will complete a stable group.

Elements forming divalent positive ions follow those forming univalent positive ions, and those forming divalent negative ions precede those forming univalent negative ions. Thus there appears a progressive character in the process of atom building, involving the addition of fresh electrons to configurations which tend to repeat themselves.

But the process is not one of simple repetition, or the periodicity of the system would be uniform, which in fact it is not. The number of electrons which must be added to form the successive inert gases does not show equal increments. They form the series 2, 8, 18, 32, which is representable by the formula $2n^2$ where $n = 1, 2, 3,$ or 4. Helium occurs at the atomic number 2, neon at $2+8 = 10$, and so on. The subsequent expansions of the intervals make room for the transition elements and then for the series of the rare earths and later for the series of closely related transuranic elements.

The interpretation of this remarkable fact depends upon two principles: the Pauli principle and the atom-building principle of Bohr.

The Pauli principle may be discovered by a careful survey of all the types of spectral term encountered among the different elements. No atom ever exists in a state where two of its electrons have all the quantum numbers the same, or where in other words there are two electrons which are indistinguishable from one another. Since the quantum numbers are to some extent interrelated, this provision evidently limits the number of electrons which can constitute a group with a given value of n.

If $n = 1$, then by the rules, l must be zero, m may vary from $-l$ to $+l$ and thus is zero also. This leaves two possibilities only, namely for two values of r, $+\frac{1}{2}$ and $-\frac{1}{2}$. According to this there could be only two electrons in any atom with $n = 1$. Hydrogen can have $n = 1$ and one electron, helium $n = 1$ and two electrons. The group with $n = 1$ is then closed.

If the nuclear charge is raised to three and three electrons must be accommodated, two of them can form a closed group of the helium type and the third must be added in a different way.

Bohr's building principle now comes into play. The very nearly self-evident hypothesis is this: the normal state of the third electron (in lithium) will correspond in the value of the principal quantum number to what would have been the first excited level in hydrogen. In other words, even in the unexcited state, the third electron of lithium, its optical or valency electron, has $n = 2$.

If $n = 2$, l may be 0 or 1. With $l = 0$, $m = 0$ and $r = \pm\frac{1}{2}$: two possibilities. If $l = 1$, $m = 1, 0,$ or -1, and for each of these $r = \pm\frac{1}{2}$: six possibilities. Thus altogether there are eight possibilities. When these are exhausted, we arrive at neon, an inert gas, and a new electron, in sodium, must go into a state corresponding to $n = 3$, even for the normal unexcited atom.

From the relation of the element in question to the inert gases, the value of n can thus normally be inferred. Comparison with the apparent value, in spectral terms, gives δ and hence information about the penetration of electron paths into regions near the nucleus, as referred to earlier.

The triumph of the Pauli principle and of the quantum number rules is that the complete structure of the periodic system follows immediately from them.

The number of electrons in successive complete quantum groups may be calculated as follows. Let the principal quantum number be n. Then l may vary from 0 to $n-1$. For each value of l there are $2l+1$ values of m (from $+l$ through 0 to $-l$), and for each of these there are two values of r. Thus for each value of n and l there are $4l+2$ values of m and r.

Summing over all the range from $l = 0$ to $l = n-1$, we have for a given n the possibilities

$$\sum_{l=0}^{l=n-1} (4l+2) = 4\left(\frac{n-1+0}{2}\right)n + 2n$$
$$= 2n^2 - 2n + 2n$$
$$= 2n^2.$$

This is precisely the number of electrons which complete successive groups in atoms, as judged from the position of the inert gases in the periodic classification. There can be no doubt, therefore, that the system of the elements owes the main lines of its structure to the Pauli principle. A great many details about the interrelationships of the elements and about the variations in properties with atomic number are also interpretable in the light of the different rules which have been outlined.

Before the discussion of atomic properties is developed farther, however, a more formal codification of these rules will be considered.

Quantum mechanical rules

The quantum laws themselves represent a considerable departure from the naïve hypothesis that happenings on the atomic scale are reduced models of those in which macroscopic objects are observed to participate in everyday life. The Pauli principle proceeds still farther in this direction. Although in a sense one can easily enough think of various types of state as so many boxes into a given one of which an electron may or may not go according as there is or is not a vacancy, nevertheless we know perfectly well that these boxes are nothing but fictions. Two other major examples of analogous intangible constraints have been encountered already. Rotating hydrogen molecules form two separate groups, those possessing respectively odd and even numbers of rotational quanta, and no conversions from the one set to the other normally occur. Nothing suggested by the dynamics of large-scale events even remotely provides an explanation of this.

Again, as we have seen, the correct calculation of absolute entropies and properties depending upon them requires that the identity of individual molecules should be disregarded. The number of molecules in a given state is important, but the different assignments of individuals to make up that number do not count as variations which are in any way detectable. Objects such as coins, even if they appear identical, are in fact individual entities and are in principle capable of having labels attached to them. The discovery that, for purposes of statistical mechanics, molecules are in effect incapable of bearing labels marks once again the fact that they are not so many microscopic versions of ordinary objects.

It is interesting to note that St. Thomas Aquinas had already applied the Pauli principle to angels, and for reasons which give what in some ways is an illuminating hint about its meaning in physics. He says that since angels are not composed of matter and form, it follows that there cannot be two of the same species: each must be unique.†

The wave function

The construction of a special code of dynamical rules for systems on the molecular scale being called for, we need not, from what has been said, expect it to be other than *sui generis*. Some of the rules must now be developed and illustrated. They are not always immediately illuminating, since they have been established partly by trial and error and partly by mathematical analogies of a somewhat abstract kind.

The first step is taken in the recognition of the wave-like element in the nature of the electron. The insertion of the wave-length, $\lambda = h/mv$, in the general equation of wave propagation leads, as has been shown (p. 126), to the Schrödinger equation

$$\frac{\partial^2 \psi}{\partial x^2} + \frac{\partial^2 \psi}{\partial y^2} + \frac{\partial^2 \psi}{\partial z^2} + \frac{8\pi^2 m (E-U)}{h^2} \psi = 0,$$

or

$$\nabla^2 \psi + \frac{8\pi^2 m (E-U)\psi}{h^2} = 0.$$

† The actual text runs: 'Si ergo angeli non sunt compositi ex materia et forma, ut dictum est supra, sequitur quod impossibile sit esse duos angelos unius speciei.' He also says of their motions, in a passage for knowledge of which I am indebted to my colleague Mr. Kneale: 'Motus angeli potest esse continuus et discontinuus sicut vult. . . . Et sic angelus in uno instante potest esse in uno loco, et in alio instante in alio loco, nullo tempore intermedio existente.' Orbital motions and quantum transitions were thus provided for.

To this is added a series of rules of operation and interpretation which constitute what is called wave mechanics or quantum mechanics. The evolution of the rules is briefly as follows.

The Schrödinger equation is assumed to be valid not only for electrons but for any dynamical system. When a single particle is concerned the problem is wholly defined by the value of the potential energy; for example, if the particle is freely moving, $U = 0$; if it is an electron at a distance r from the nucleus of a hydrogen atom, $U = -e^2/r$ and so on.

For the case of several particles the equation is tentatively generalized in a way which proves satisfactory in practice, and assumes the form

$$\frac{1}{m_1} \nabla_1^2 \psi + \frac{1}{m_2} \nabla_2^2 \psi + \ldots + \frac{8\pi^2(E-U)}{h^2} \psi = 0,$$

where

$$\nabla_1^2 = \frac{\partial^2}{\partial x_1^2} + \frac{\partial^2}{\partial y_1^2} + \frac{\partial^2}{\partial z_1^2},$$

x_1, y_1, and z_1 being the coordinates of the first particle, and ∇_2^2 refers similarly to the second particle.

As has been stated and illustrated, the Schrödinger equation possesses physically acceptable solutions (continuous, finite, and single-valued) only for certain definite values of the energy—the characteristic or proper values (*Eigenwerte*). These define the quantum states of the system. The way in which vibrational, rotational, and translational quantization follow has already been considered (p. 126).

Application to the problem of a single electron under the influence of a nucleus, as in a hydrogen atom, leads to the result that there are various arrays of quantum states, specified by values of three numbers, n, l, and m. The relations between them are precisely those which have been discussed and which, in conjunction with the Pauli principle, define the structure of the periodic system. The details of the calculations will be given in a separate section.

There is no doubt, therefore, that as a mode of specification of energy levels the wave equation is empirically justified.

As will appear, the calculation of the states available when pairs of atoms coexist in molecules provides also a solution of the problem of interatomic forces.

The immediate development of the ideas with which the present section began depends upon a closer consideration of the function ψ itself, which has so far only served as an auxiliary quantity. The conditions for acceptable solutions of the wave equation define the values of E, and to each value of E there corresponds a value of ψ, which is a function of the spatial coordinates x, y, and z (or the corresponding polar coordinates r, θ, and ϕ). ψ is taken, *as a special assumption suggested by the wave-like aspect of particles*, to be a function of time such that

$$\psi = \psi_0 e^{2\pi i \nu t}.$$

As a *further special assumption* ν is expressed in the form

$$\nu = E/h,$$

so that

$$\psi = \psi_0 e^{2\pi i (E/h)t}.$$

The wave equation as already written down deals only with the space variation of ψ, and is therefore referred to as the amplitude equation. An equation in which the time enters explicitly is obtained by combining

$$\nabla^2 \psi + \frac{8\pi^2 m (E - U)\psi}{h^2} = 0$$

and

$$\psi = \psi_0 e^{2\pi i (E/h)t}.$$

Differentiation of the latter and substitution in the former with elimination of E leads to

$$\nabla^2 \psi - \frac{4\pi m i}{h} \frac{\partial \psi}{\partial t} - \frac{8\pi^2 m U}{h^2} \psi = 0.$$

ψ is now given an interpretation: or rather, a *series of conventions are established* for the expression of molecular events in terms of ψ. We have $\psi = \psi_0 e^{2\pi i \nu t}$. The so-called conjugate of ψ, written $\bar{\psi}$, is $\psi_0 e^{-2\pi i \nu t}$.

$$\psi \bar{\psi} = \psi_0^2.$$

This product is independent of time. It depends upon the space coordinates and is assumed to be *proportional to the probability of finding the particle at the point* x, y, z corresponding to a given value of ψ, or in a small volume element in the vicinity of this point.

If the particle is an electron, then $\psi \bar{\psi}$ is proportional to the average *electric density* at x, y, z. $\psi \bar{\psi}$, being independent of time, can be represented in space as a continuous cloud of electrification varying from point to point in a manner shown by the solution of the wave equation which has yielded ψ. Although this cloud is fictitious and corresponds to a probability or to a time-average, it is very convenient to visualize its spatial symmetry, and even to look upon the electrical distribution as a real one. This in one sense illustrates the reluctance with which naïve realism is forsaken.

In general, in its application to an electron and a nucleus the ψ function passes through maxima and minima as the radial distance of the former from the latter increases, and finally it dies away asymptotically to zero at great distances. The electric density rises and falls and finally drops to zero. The places where the density is zero are called nodes. According to the various relations of n, l, and m, there are varying numbers of nodes and the cloud possesses either spherical symmetry or various kinds of axial symmetry. The symmetry and the values of the wave function in various directions prove to be very significant in problems of valency and determine the spatial orientation of valency bonds. These matters will be illustrated more fully in a later section.

These various rules about the interpretation of ψ will prove to be justified by their results. An extension of them states that the *probable value of any quantity* X, characteristic of a particle at a given point is *proportional to* $X\psi\bar{\psi}$ at that point.

Transitions

Further special rules are found to be appropriate for the treatment of problems about the transitions of systems from one energy state to another. Suppose the wave equation has solutions corresponding to two permitted energy levels, E_1 and E_2. If there are two possible solutions of a differential equation, it is easily seen that the sum of the two, or indeed any linear combination of them, is also a solution. Thus if $\psi_1 e^{2\pi i E_1 t/h}$ and $\psi_2 e^{2\pi i E_2 t/h}$ are solutions, then

$$\psi = c_1 \psi_1 e^{2\pi i E_1 t/h} + c_2 \psi_2 e^{2\pi i E_2 t/h}$$

is also one, c_1 and c_2 being constants. (This is easily verified by trial.)

The combination written above is not intended to mean that the system is in two energy levels at the same time, but to express the fact that for a large assembly of systems *both states are possible*. The squares of the coefficients c_1 and c_2 are taken to give the probabilities of the levels E_1 and E_2 respectively.

If these coefficients themselves become functions of time, it means that transitions are occurring between the two states.

The orthogonal property of wave functions

A very considerable part in the description of nature is being assigned to a particular differential equation, so that clearly its detailed properties are of no little moment. One property which is of special technical significance is the *orthogonal* character of its solutions. This means that $\int \psi_k \psi_l \, dxdydz$ taken over the whole range of coordinates is zero unless $k = l$. (An example of orthogonality is $\sin mx$, the integral $\int_0^{2\pi} \sin mx \sin nx \, dx$ being zero unless $m = n$.) Products such as $dxdydz$ will be written $d\omega$ for brevity.

The reason why the orthogonal property is of importance is best shown at once. When there are solutions of the wave equation ψ_1, $\psi_2,..., \psi_k, \psi_l,...,$ the combination

$$c_1\psi_1 + c_2\psi_2 + ... + c_k\psi_k + ... = \sum c_k \psi_k$$

is also a solution which needs frequently to be used for the purpose mentioned above. A device is required for determining the coefficients. To find c_k one may multiply the whole by ψ_k and integrate. Every integral except $c_k \int \psi_k \psi_k \, d\omega$ will be zero, so that the value of the coefficient c_k can be isolated, just as in the determination of the coefficients of a Fourier sine or cosine series.

The proof of the orthogonal property for a one-dimensional problem is given below. The extension to three dimensions involves no new principles.

$$\frac{\partial^2 \psi_k}{\partial x^2} + \frac{8\pi^2 m}{h^2}(E_k - U)\psi_k = 0,$$

$$\frac{\partial^2 \psi_l}{\partial x^2} + \frac{8\pi^2 m}{h^2}(E_l - U)\psi_l = 0.$$

Multiply the former by ψ_l and the latter by ψ_k and subtract:

$$\psi_l \frac{\partial^2 \psi_k}{\partial x^2} - \psi_k \frac{\partial^2 \psi_l}{\partial x^2} + \frac{8\pi^2 m}{h^2}(E_k - E_l)\psi_k \psi_l = 0.$$

Integration gives

$$\int_{-\infty}^{+\infty} \left(\psi_k \frac{\partial^2 \psi_l}{\partial x^2} - \psi_l \frac{\partial^2 \psi_k}{\partial x^2} \right) dx = \frac{8\pi^2 m}{h^2}(E_k - E_l) \int_{-\infty}^{+\infty} \psi_k \psi_l \, dx.$$

$$\psi_k \frac{\partial^2 \psi_l}{\partial x^2} - \psi_l \frac{\partial^2 \psi_k}{\partial x^2}$$

may be seen by trial to be the result of the operation

$$\frac{\partial}{\partial x}\left(\psi_k \frac{\partial \psi_l}{\partial x} - \psi_l \frac{\partial \psi_k}{\partial x} \right).$$

Therefore

$$\left[\psi_k \frac{\partial \psi_l}{\partial x} - \psi_l \frac{\partial \psi_k}{\partial x}\right]_{-\infty}^{+\infty} = \frac{8\pi^2 m}{h^2}(E_k - E_l) \int_{-\infty}^{+\infty} \psi_k \psi_l \, dx.$$

For physically significant cases ψ_k and ψ_l vanish at infinity, so that the left-hand side of the last equation is zero. If $k = l$, $E_k = E_l$ and the right-hand side vanishes automatically. If, however, k is not equal to l, then it only vanishes on condition that $\int \psi_k \psi_l \, dx = 0$, which is thereby proved.

Applications of the orthogonal property will appear in due course.

IX

DESCRIPTION OF STATES BY WAVE FUNCTIONS

General

A SOMEWHAT formidable array of rules has been laid down for the description of microscopic phenomena. Some further consideration of their status in relation to directly ascertainable experimental facts is now called for.

We remember that one of the principal objects of scientific interpretation is the relating of the unknown to the known. The description of atoms and molecules in terms of everyday macroscopic objects having proved inadequate, they are to be described in terms of a mathematical formalism constituting the new 'known' to which the unknown is to be referred. The success of the process can be gauged only by reasonably wide experience.

Given that atomic systems are to be represented by wave functions obeying a special kind of differential equation, it is perhaps best to go to the heart of the matter and start by considering some general rules about the types of wave function which are in fact required for the purpose.

Suppose a system to consist of two dissimilar particles, which may be designated 1 and 2. In the first instance they may be considered as quite independent, neither exerting any influence on the energy of the other. The states of particle 1 are defined by the equation

$$\frac{1}{m_1} \nabla_1^2 \psi(1) + \frac{8\pi^2}{h^2} (E_1 - U_1)\psi(1) = 0. \tag{1}$$

One of the solutions permits an energy E_a with a value of

$$\psi(1) = \psi_a(1).$$

Similarly one of the solutions of the analogous equation

$$\frac{1}{m_2} \nabla_2^2 \psi(2) + \frac{8\pi^2}{h^2} (E_2 - U_2)\psi(2) = 0 \tag{2}$$

for particle (2) permits an energy E_b with a value $\psi(2) = \psi_b(2)$.

When the two particles are considered together, the wave equation assumes the form

$$\frac{1}{m_1} \nabla_1^2 \psi + \frac{1}{m_2} \nabla_2^2 \psi + \frac{8\pi^2}{h^2} (E - U)\psi = 0,$$

according to the basic convention, where ψ is the wave function of the joint system.

$$E = E_1 + E_2, \qquad U = U_1 + U_2.$$

If $\psi_a(1)$ and $\psi_b(2)$ are solutions of the separate equations, then

$$\psi = \psi_a(1)\psi_b(2)$$

is a solution of the composite equation. For

$$\frac{1}{m_1}\nabla_1^2\psi_a(1) + \frac{8\pi^2}{h^2}(E_a - U_1)\psi_a(1) = 0,$$

so that $\qquad \psi_b(2)\dfrac{1}{m_1}\nabla_1^2\psi_a(1) + \dfrac{8\pi^2}{h^2}(E_a - U_1)\psi_a(1)\psi_b(2) = 0.$

Also $\qquad \dfrac{1}{m_2}\nabla_2^2\psi_b(2) + \dfrac{8\pi^2}{h^2}(E_b - U_2)\psi_b(2) = 0,$

so that $\qquad \psi_a(1)\dfrac{1}{m_2}\nabla_2^2\psi_b(2) + \dfrac{8\pi^2}{h^2}(E_b - U_2)\psi_b(2)\psi_a(1) = 0.$

Addition of the last line and the last but two gives

$$\psi_b(2)\frac{1}{m_1}\nabla_1^2\psi_a(1) + \psi_a(1)\frac{1}{m_2}\nabla_2^2\psi_b(2) +$$

$$+ \frac{8\pi^2}{h^2}(E_a + E_b - U_1 - U_2)\psi_a(1)\psi_b(2) = 0.$$

Since ∇_1^2 represents partial differentiation with respect to the coordinates of particle 1, which do not apply to particle 2, and conversely for ∇_2^2, the first two terms are the same as

$$\frac{1}{m_1}\nabla_1^2\psi_a(1)\psi_b(2) + \frac{1}{m_2}\nabla_2^2\psi_a(1)\psi_b(2).$$

The equation thus becomes

$$\frac{1}{m_1}\nabla_1^2\psi_a(1)\psi_b(2) + \frac{1}{m_2}\nabla_1^2\psi_a(1)\psi_b(2) +$$

$$+ \frac{8\pi^2}{h^2}(E_a + E_b - U_1 - U_2)\psi_a(1)\psi_b(2) = 0.$$

Therefore $\psi = \psi_a(1)\psi_b(2)$ is a solution of the composite equation.

Since $\qquad \psi\bar\psi = \psi_a(1)\bar\psi_a(1)\psi_b(2)\bar\psi_b(2),$

the result simply states that the probability of finding particle 1 in state a and particle 2 in state b is the product of the independent probabilities of finding the one in the one state and the other in the other. Since we postulated lack of interaction, this result is in accordance with reason. It follows from the differential equation and it is consistent with the interpretation of $\psi\bar{\psi}$ as a probability.

Now let us consider the two particles to be not dissimilar but identical. First let them be thought of as two separate systems. Suppose that one of them is in the state a with energy E_a and wave function $\psi_a(1)$, and the second in state b with energy E_b and wave function $\psi_b(2)$. By analogy with the dissimilar particles, the wave function $\psi_a(1)\psi_b(2)$ might be constructed to describe the joint system constituted by the two particles together, and this expression would indeed be a solution of the Schrödinger equation. A second system is conceivable in which the first particle is in state b and the second in state a. The energy would be the same as before, but the wave function would now be $\psi_b(1)\psi_a(2)$.

The discussion of absolute entropies has shown that there is no statistical significance in the distinction represented by $\psi_a(1)\psi_b(2)$ and $\psi_b(1)\psi_a(2)$. As we have seen, there is sense in saying that we have two particles, one in state a and the other in state b, but no significance in the further specification as to which individual is in which state. Thus the two wave functions under consideration, although mathematically correct, do not correspond to the needs of the situation.

Since, however, $\psi_a(1)\psi_b(2)$ and $\psi_b(1)\psi_a(2)$ are solutions of the wave equation, any linear combination of them is also a solution, and certain linear combinations do in fact express just what is required. They are

$$\psi_S = \psi_a(1)\psi_b(2)+\psi_b(1)\psi_a(2)$$

and

$$\psi_A = \psi_a(1)\psi_b(2)-\psi_b(1)\psi_a(2).$$

These obey the wave equation and they give for the probability of the joint system $\psi_S\bar{\psi}_S$ or $\psi_A\bar{\psi}_A$, which in turn are represented by

$$\psi_a(1)\psi_b(2)\bar{\psi}_a(1)\bar{\psi}_b(2)+\psi_b(1)\psi_a(2)\bar{\psi}_b(1)\bar{\psi}_a(2)\pm$$

$$\pm\{\psi_a(1)\psi_b(2)\bar{\psi}_b(1)\bar{\psi}_a(2)+\psi_b(1)\psi_a(2)\bar{\psi}_a(1)\bar{\psi}_b(2)\}.$$

Whether the positive or the negative sign is taken, the expression for the probability involves no decision whatever about the allocation of particles 1 and 2 to states a and b respectively, since *all combinations* of 1 and 2 with a and b appear in *each* form.

ψ_S and ψ_A may therefore be accepted as satisfying requirements.

The actual values of these wave functions differ, however, in one respect. If particles 1 and 2 are interchanged, ψ_S retains its identical value, and is therefore called the *symmetrical combination*, while if the corresponding exchange is made ψ_A changes sign, since

$$\psi_a(1)\psi_b(2)-\psi_b(1)\psi_a(2) = -\{\psi_a(2)\psi_b(1)-\psi_b(2)\psi_a(1)\}.$$

ψ_A is called the *antisymmetrical combination*, as is any combination which changes sign on interchange of the two particles.

We now arrive at a principle of enormous importance. ψ_A and ψ_S are both satisfactory functions in so far as they express the rule about the product of independent probabilities, without attributing statistical significance to interchanges of identical particles. But they cannot *both* be valid functions for a real system *at the same time*. If they were, a linear combination of both of them would also be valid, and a linear combination of ψ_A and ψ_S leads straight back to $\psi_a(1)\psi_b(2)$ or to $\psi_b(1)\psi_a(2)$ which reassert the distinguishability of particles. Hence for real systems—if the lessons learnt from the insufficiency of Boltzmann's statistical scheme are correct—the wave function must be either symmetrical or antisymmetrical, but it cannot be both.

As will appear, for certain kinds of particle, notably electrons, the wave functions describing natural systems are in fact necessarily antisymmetrical, while for others they are symmetrical.

Let us now attempt to bring these curious doctrines about the nature of things as immediately as possible into relation with observation.

Perhaps the most striking connexion is that between the *antisymmetrical character of electron wave functions* and the *Pauli principle*.

Pauli principle in terms of wave functions

Consider two electrons, 1 and 2, in an atom. If one is in state a and one in state b, we have

$$\psi_S = \psi_a(1)\psi_b(2)+\psi_b(1)\psi_a(2),$$
$$\psi_A = \psi_a(1)\psi_b(2)-\psi_b(1)\psi_a(2).$$

Suppose ψ_S is possible, and consider what happens to it if state a is now assumed to become identical with state b.

$\psi_S = 2\psi_a(1)\psi_a(2)$ and $\psi_S\bar{\psi}_S$ can have a perfectly definite value. This contradicts the Pauli principle which denies the existence in an atom of two electrons in the same state.

On the other hand, if a becomes identical with b,

$$\psi_A = \psi_a(1)\psi_a(2) - \psi_a(1)\psi_a(2) = 0,$$

and the probability $\psi_A \bar{\psi}_A$ is also zero. Thus the assertion that the electronic wave function is antisymmetrical is very similar to the Pauli principle itself, and lies indeed at the basis of the whole structure of the periodic system.

Evidence from the helium spectrum

A less grandiose but more specific verification of the principle comes from the study of the helium spectrum. This contains two sets of terms which do not combine. So completely independent are they that at one time they were ascribed to two modifications, known respectively as ortho-helium and para-helium. The para terms are singlet and the ortho terms triplet. The normal or ground state of the atom belongs to the para system. This state of affairs first becomes explicable in terms of the symmetry of the wave functions.

The fine structure is ascribed to differences depending upon the modes of electron spin. The helium atom has two electrons. Each electron has two spin possibilities represented by the quantum numbers $+\frac{1}{2}$ and $-\frac{1}{2}$. The spin allocations can, in principle, be described by wave functions, the state where each electron has, for example, $+\frac{1}{2}$ being represented by $\psi(\frac{1}{2})\psi(\frac{1}{2})$. Provided that the other quantum numbers differ, so that the two electrons can have the same spin without violating the Pauli principle, the possibilities are

(1) $\psi(\frac{1}{2})\psi(\frac{1}{2})$,

(2) $\psi(-\frac{1}{2})\psi(-\frac{1}{2})$,

(3) $\psi(\frac{1}{2})\psi(-\frac{1}{2}) + \psi(-\frac{1}{2})\psi(\frac{1}{2})$,

(4) $\psi(\frac{1}{2})\psi(-\frac{1}{2}) - \psi(-\frac{1}{2})\psi(\frac{1}{2})$,

the last two replacing $\psi(\frac{1}{2})\psi(-\frac{1}{2})$ for the reasons already explained. Of these combinations, (1), (2), and (3) are symmetrical and (4) antisymmetrical.

The *weight* of the *symmetrical* spin combinations is thus *triple*.

Now the total wave function of the electronic system can be represented as the product of two parts, one describing the orbital motion of the electrons and one describing the spin relations. We have

$$\psi_{\text{total}} = \psi_{\text{orbital}}\psi_{\text{spin}}.$$

This form follows from the principle outlined earlier (p. 191). If ψ_{total} is to be symmetrical, ψ_{orbital} and ψ_{spin} must be both symmetrical or both antisymmetrical. (If both are symmetrical, the product is obviously so: if both change sign together when the electrons are interchanged, the product is unaltered.) If, on the other hand, ψ_{total} is to be antisymmetrical, either ψ_{orbital} or ψ_{spin} must change sign when the electrons are interchanged, but both must not do so together. Thus one must be symmetrical and the other antisymmetrical.

The symmetrical spin functions have been seen to be triplet and the antisymmetrical to be singlet. Furthermore, the singlet states include the lowest or ground state, where presumably the two electrons have their orbital quantum numbers equal. Thus the antisymmetrical spin combination is associated with the symmetrical orbital wave function to give a total wave function which is antisymmetrical. This result verifies the principle of the antisymmetrical character of electron wave functions.

Conversely, since ψ_{total} has this character when ψ_{orbital} is antisymmetrical (different electronic orbital quantum numbers), the spin combinations must be symmetrical. There are three of them and the triplet ortho states result.

Quantum statistics

When particles are describable only by antisymmetrical wave functions, no two may occupy identical states. The statistical distribution among energy states may be thereby profoundly affected. The particles are said to follow *Fermi–Dirac statistics*. When the wave functions are symmetrical, the particles are said to obey *Bose–Einstein statistics*. If their states were describable by symmetrical as well as by antisymmetrical wave functions, then, as shown, individual allocations to states would acquire significance and they would be obeying the *Boltzmann statistics*.

Evidence from rotational specific heats

The problem which had to be left unsolved at an earlier stage can now be dealt with. The mode of variation with temperature of the rotational component of the specific heat of hydrogen indicated clearly that hydrogen molecules are divisible into two well-defined groups, those with even numbers of rotational quanta and those with odd numbers. In the light of what has just been discussed there seems a likelihood that this state of affairs is connected with the symmetry requirements of the relevant wave function. In the definition of the rotational quanta the important magnitudes are the masses and positions of the two hydrogen nuclei in each molecule. The behaviour of these nuclei can be described by means of a wave function χ which, as already shown, might be symmetrical or antisymmetrical with respect to an interchange of them. If we assume that the nuclei are capable of a proper spin with two possible values as for electrons, then for a pair of them the possible combinations may be expressed by a wave function Σ which has three symmetrical forms and one antisymmetrical form. This result follows from considerations exactly analogous to those discussed for the two electrons of the helium atom.

If now we imagine the condition that the product $\chi\Sigma$ must be antisymmetrical, then the three possibilities with Σ_{symm} must be associated with χ_{antisymm} and the one possibility with Σ_{antisymm} must be associated with χ_{symm}.

The next question is the relation between the symmetry of χ and the number of rotational quanta.

In polar coordinates the Schrödinger equation assumes the shape

$$\frac{1}{r^2}\frac{\partial}{\partial r}\left(r^2\frac{\partial\psi}{\partial r}\right)+\frac{1}{r^2\sin\theta}\frac{\partial}{\partial\theta}\left(\sin\theta\frac{\partial\psi}{\partial\theta}\right)+\frac{1}{r^2\sin^2\theta}\frac{\partial^2\psi}{\partial\phi^2}+\frac{8\pi^2m}{h^2}(E-U)\psi=0,$$

as found by the usual methods of changing coordinates in a differential expression. For a rigid rotator, $r=$ constant, $U=0$, and for m the reduced mass μ may be written. Since $\mu r^2 = I$, the moment of inertia, the equation becomes

$$\frac{1}{\sin\theta}\frac{\partial}{\partial\theta}\left(\sin\theta\frac{\partial\psi}{\partial\theta}\right)+\frac{1}{\sin^2\theta}\frac{\partial^2\psi}{\partial\phi^2}+\frac{8\pi^2I}{h^2}E\psi=0.$$

ψ may be expressed in the form $\psi=\boldsymbol{\theta}(\theta)\boldsymbol{\varphi}(\phi)$, where $\boldsymbol{\theta}$ and $\boldsymbol{\varphi}$ are functions of θ and ϕ respectively.

A solution for $\boldsymbol{\varphi}$ is given by

$$\boldsymbol{\varphi}=e^{im\phi},$$

where m is an integer.

For $\boldsymbol{\theta}$ is found by substitution

$$\frac{1}{\sin\theta}\frac{\partial}{\partial\theta}\left(\sin\theta\frac{\partial\boldsymbol{\theta}}{\partial\theta}\right)-\frac{m^2\boldsymbol{\theta}}{\sin^2\theta}+\frac{8\pi^2I}{h^2}E\boldsymbol{\theta}=0.$$

Solutions of this standard differential equation are possible for values of E given by

$$E = \frac{h^2}{8\pi^2 I} J(J+1),$$

where J is an integer. The corresponding values of ψ are the set of functions written $P_J^m(\cos\theta)e^{im\phi}$.

χ for the rigid rotator is thus represented by a set of functions of this form, θ and ϕ being the two angular coordinates of the motion, and m and J being integers. The functions P are exemplified by the following members of the set:

$$P_0^0 = 1, \qquad P_1^0 = \cos\theta, \qquad P_2^0 = \tfrac{3}{2}\cos^2\theta - 1,$$

$$P_1^1 = \sin\theta, \quad P_2^1 = 3\cos\theta\sin\theta, \quad P_3^1 = \tfrac{1}{2}(15\cos^2\theta - 3)\sin\theta.$$

If the two nuclei of the rotating molecule are interchanged, it is equivalent to making θ into $\pi - \theta$ and ϕ into $\pi + \phi$. Inspection of the P functions shows that this substitution *leaves the sign unchanged if J is even, but changes it if J is odd.*

Thus χ is a symmetrical function for even values of J and an anti-symmetrical function for odd values of J.

Now since the χ_{symm} must be associated with Σ_{antisymm} and vice versa, it follows that the even values of J correspond to the single antisymmetrical spin funetions and the odd values of J to the triple symmetrical spin functions.

The states with the higher statistical weight are called ortho (as with the triplet states of ortho-helium). Thus *ortho-hydrogen* has the *odd* numbers of rotational quanta and *para-hydrogen* the *even* numbers.

If equilibrium were established between the two forms, then at high temperatures the proportion would be governed by the statistical weights, and there would be three times as much ortho as para. At low temperatures, on the other hand, the proportion would be governed mainly by the occupation of the energy levels. Thus there would be a predominant tendency to occupy the zero level, and since zero, being next below one, is an even number, para-hydrogen would tend to exist in an almost pure state.

These expectations are fulfilled with the reservation that the equilibrium is established with almost infinite slowness except in special circumstances. This matter will receive consideration in the next section.

First, however, the behaviour in respect of rotational energies of molecules other than hydrogen must be dealt with.

Deuterium proves to have its ortho states (higher statistical weight, antisymmetrical spin function) associated with even numbers of rotational quanta. Thus its total wave function is symmetrical, and it is said to follow the Bose–Einstein statistics. Moreover, the nuclear spin appears to have the value 1 instead of the value $\frac{1}{2}$ as with hydrogen.

The basis of this conclusion is as follows. Suppose the spin of a nucleus has the value r, then, allowing for the *quantized projection of r on a defined axis*, there are $2r+1$ states for each (from $-r$ to r). For the two nuclei there are $(2r+1)^2$ states. There are, of course, $2r+1$ of these in which the two are in identical conditions, and which thus correspond to symmetrical spin wave functions. Therefore there are $(2r+1)^2-(2r+1)$, that is $2r(2r+1)$, in which the particles are not in identical conditions. The corresponding wave functions, in the way already explained, divide themselves into $r(2r+1)$ symmetrical and $r(2r+1)$ antisymmetrical ones. The total number of symmetrical wave functions is thus $(2r+1)+r(2r+1)$ or $(r+1)(2r+1)$ and the total number of antisymmetrical functions is $r(2r+1)$.

Thus
$$\frac{\text{symmetrical}}{\text{antisymmetrical}} = \frac{(r+1)(2r+1)}{r(2r+1)} = \frac{r+1}{r}.$$

If $r = \frac{1}{2}$, this ratio is $1\frac{1}{2}/\frac{1}{2} = 3$, as for ortho- and para-hydrogen. With $r = 1$, it becomes 2. This latter value is in fact required to do justice to the observations on the specific heat of deuterium, with which, moreover, the ortho form predominates when equilibrium is established at low temperatures.

The rotational states of other molecules consisting of two identical atoms can be studied in the structure of their band spectra, and further information about the nuclear spins may be inferred. Most nuclei of even atomic weight, such as deuterium, seem to follow the Bose–Einstein statistics. Protons and electrons follow the Fermi statistics.

With full allowance for *internal* conditions of the nuclei themselves, which after all are composite particles, they would all no doubt conform to a single pattern of behaviour.

Transitions and the symmetry of states

The establishment of equilibrium between ortho- and para-hydrogen is very difficult. The reason is that, were it not for perturbing factors which relax the ban, transitions between symmetrical and antisymmetrical states would be impossible.

This conclusion follows from the nature of the fundamental postulates of quantum dynamics. In the wave equation written in the form which contains the time explicitly

$$\frac{1}{m}\nabla^2\psi - \frac{4\pi i}{h}\frac{\partial\psi}{\partial t} - \frac{8\pi^2 U}{h^2}\psi = 0$$

$\nabla^2\psi$ is a symmetrical function of the coordinates. (If there are two particles, the operator has the form $\frac{1}{m_1}\nabla_1^2\psi + \frac{1}{m_2}\nabla_2^2\psi$.) U is symmetrical with respect to all the particles. Thus the symmetry of $\partial\psi/\partial t$ is the same as that of ψ. Hence if ψ is symmetrical, changes in it are also symmetrical and therefore it retains its original character.

A rather more detailed picture of transition probabilities is obtained as follows. Suppose there are a number of molecular systems which exert slight forces upon one another. These perturbing influences can be expressed by the addition of a small extra term r to the potential energy U. Thus

$$\nabla^2\psi - \frac{4\pi m i}{h}\frac{\partial\psi}{\partial t} - \frac{8\pi^2 m(U+r)}{h^2}\psi = 0. \tag{1}$$

If r were zero, possible solutions of the equation would be $\psi_1 e^{2\pi i E_1 t/h}$ and $\psi_2 e^{2\pi i E_2 t/h}$, and also the linear combination

$$\psi = c_1\psi_1 e^{2\pi i E_1 t/h} + c_2\psi_2 e^{2\pi i E_2 t/h}, \tag{2}$$

where c_1 and c_2 are constants.

The last equation expresses the fact that constant fractions of the molecules can exist in the one or in the other state together. When, however, r is not zero, the linear combination with constant values of c_1 and c_2 will *not* satisfy the equation.

Substitution of (2) in (1) gives values for dc_1/dt and dc_2/dt, thus

$$\psi_1 e^{2\pi i E_1 t/h}\frac{dc_1}{dt} + \psi_2 e^{2\pi i E_2 t/h}\frac{dc_2}{dt} = \frac{2\pi i}{h}r(c_1\psi_1 e^{2\pi i E_1 t/h} + c_2\psi_2 e^{2\pi i E_2 t/h}). \tag{3}$$

In forming (3) it is borne in mind that (2) satisfies (1) when $r = 0$.

We now multiply (3) by ψ_2 and integrate, choosing the units so that $\int \psi_2 \psi_2 \, d\omega = 1$. The orthogonal property makes $\int \psi_2 \psi_1 \, d\omega = 0$.

$$\frac{dc_2}{dt} e^{2\pi i E_2 t/h} = \frac{2\pi i}{h} \left(\int c_1 \psi_1 r \psi_2 \, e^{2\pi i E_1 t/h} \, d\omega + \int c_2 \psi_2 r \psi_2 \, e^{2\pi i E_2 t/h} \, d\omega \right).$$

Suppose we start with all the molecules in the state corresponding to E_1, when $c_2 = 0$, so that the initial rate of transfer to the second state dc_2/dt is seen to be proportional to the integral $\int \psi_1 r \psi_2 \, d\omega$ (which, of course, is not the same as $r \int \psi_1 \psi_2 \, d\omega$ since r is a function of the coordinates).

Integrals of this form, according to the theory, determine all transition probabilities. For a transition from a symmetrical to an anti-symmetrical state the probability would depend upon $\int \psi_S r \psi_A \, d\omega$. r is a symmetrical function of the coordinates. ψ_S would not change if two particles were interchanged. ψ_A, on the other hand, would change, so that all the contributions to the integral would change sign when the coordinates of the particles were exchanged. The integral must therefore consist of two parts, positive and negative in balance, and its total value is zero.

The arguments about the signs of functions are the only intelligible account which can be given of the reluctance of hydrogen molecules to pass from odd to even rotational states, as of helium atoms to change from singlet to triplet levels.

For the further development of the theory of atoms and molecules a more detailed knowledge of wave functions and associated electronic distributions proves to be of great importance. We now proceed to this question.

Electron distributions from wave functions

For the application of the wave equation to an atom similar to that of hydrogen, consisting of a charged nucleus and a single electron, transformation to polar coordinates is necessary.

$$\nabla^2 \psi + \frac{8\pi^2 m}{h^2} (E - U)\psi = 0$$

by a standard method then yields

$$\frac{1}{r^2} \frac{\partial}{\partial r}\left(r^2 \frac{\partial \psi}{\partial r}\right) + \frac{1}{r^2 \sin\theta} \frac{\partial}{\partial \theta}\left(\sin\theta \frac{\partial \psi}{\partial \theta}\right) + \frac{1}{r^2 \sin^2\theta} \frac{\partial^2 \psi}{\partial \phi^2} + \frac{8\pi^2 m (E - U)}{h^2} \psi = 0.$$

$$(1)$$

This may be satisfied by a product of separate functions, namely

$$\psi = \mathbf{R}(r)\boldsymbol{\theta}(\theta)\boldsymbol{\varphi}(\phi),\tag{2}$$

provided that
$$\frac{d^2\varphi}{d\phi^2} + m^2\varphi = 0, \tag{3}$$

$$\frac{1}{\sin\theta}\frac{d}{d\theta}\left(\sin\theta\frac{d\theta}{d\theta}\right) + \left(L - \frac{m^2}{\sin^2\theta}\right)\theta = 0, \tag{4}$$

and
$$\frac{1}{r^2}\frac{d}{dr}\left(r^2\frac{dR}{dr}\right) + \left\{\frac{8\pi^2 m}{h^2}(E-U) - \frac{L}{r^2}\right\}R = 0, \tag{5}$$

as may be verified by substitution. m and L are constants. From (3) is taken the solution

$$\varphi = Ae^{im\phi},$$

where A is a further arbitrary constant. For single-valued solutions m must be integral (since $e^{im\phi} = \cos m\phi + i\sin m\phi$ and whenever ϕ increases by 2π the value must repeat itself). (4) is a standard differential equation which has been thoroughly studied. L is best written in the form $l(l+1)$, where l is another constant, in which case it proves that there are acceptable solutions for all integral values of l greater than m. In general there are $2l+1$ values of m which permit a solution for each value of l. Thus the relation of l and m corresponds precisely to that of the two quantum numbers to which these letters have already been assigned.

The solutions of (5) depend upon the form of U. For a hydrogen-like atom it can be written in the form $-Ze^2/r$. States in which the atom is not completely ionized correspond to values of E which are negative (with respect to the separate nucleus and electron). For these the theory of differential equations gives the values

$$E_n = -2\pi^2 m_e Z^2 e^4/h^2 n^2,$$

where m_e is the mass of the electron, e the electronic charge, Z the nuclear charge. $n = n'+l+1$ where n is an integer (not negative).

n corresponds to the principal quantum number. l, as is obvious from this relation, cannot be greater than $n-1$. The Bohr energy levels are thus predicted, as also are the correct relations of n and l.

If the potential energy loses the simple form Ze^2/r, as it does when there are mutual perturbations of more than one electron, then E no longer depends upon the total value of n alone, but upon the separate values of n' and l. The energy levels corresponding to the same principal quantum number are then split according to the values of l, and S, P, D,... states result.

The wave functions themselves assume various forms according to the values of n, l, and m. The following are a few examples:

$$n = 1, l = 0, m = 0, \quad \psi = \frac{1}{\sqrt{\pi}}\left(\frac{Z}{a}\right) e^{-r/a},$$

$$n = 2, l = 0, m = 0, \quad \psi = \frac{1}{4\sqrt{(2\pi)}}\left(\frac{Z}{a}\right)^{\frac{3}{2}}\left(2 - \frac{r}{a}\right) e^{-r/2a},$$

$$n = 2, l = 1, m = 0, \quad \psi = \frac{1}{4\sqrt{(2\pi)}}\left(\frac{Z}{a}\right)^{\frac{3}{2}}\frac{r}{a} e^{-r/2a}\cos\theta,$$

$$n = 2, l = 1, m = 1, \quad \psi = \frac{1}{4\sqrt{(2\pi)}}\left(\frac{Z}{a}\right)^{\frac{3}{2}}\frac{r}{a} e^{-r/2a}\sin\theta\cos\phi,$$

$$n = 2, l = 1, m = -1, \quad \psi = \frac{1}{\sqrt{4(2\pi)}}\left(\frac{Z}{a}\right)^{\frac{3}{2}}\frac{r}{a} e^{-r/2a}\sin\theta\sin\phi.$$

It is obvious that the description of atomic systems has led far away from any sort of crudely pictorial representation, and yet this form continually tends to creep back, and where it is not definitely incorrect, it is convenient and helpful.

Since $\psi\bar{\psi}$ represents the probability of finding an electron in a given volume element, the value of this function, expressed in suitable units, can be taken to represent the density of a sort of electric cloud surrounding the nucleus. Such an electronic cloud can be visualized in simple examples.

For a hydrogen-like atom, when $l = 0$, ψ is a function of r only. For the so-called S states, therefore, one may visualize a spherically symmetrical distribution of electricity. ψ and $\psi\bar{\psi}$ have their maxima when $r = 0$, as may be seen from the list given above. Thus the S states correspond to a frequent penetration of the electron to the immediate vicinity of the nucleus. According to the older orbital theory, $l = 0$ would correspond to an oscillation along a line passing through the nucleus. The two pictures thus agree in respect of the deep penetration of the atom. The spherical symmetry of the later theory is at first sight in sharp contrast with the linear oscillation of the earlier one, but appears less so if every possible orientation in space of the line is imagined.

For $n = 1$, $l = 0$ the dependence of ψ upon r is shown in Fig. 15. $\psi\bar{\psi}$ follows a similar but steeper curve. The probability of finding an electron at a given distance r depends not upon $\psi\bar{\psi}$ itself but upon this quantity multiplied by $4\pi r^2\,dr$, the volume of a spherical shell

at this distance. The latter quantity follows a curve of the form
shown in Fig. 16. There is a maximum probability at a given
distance r_0.

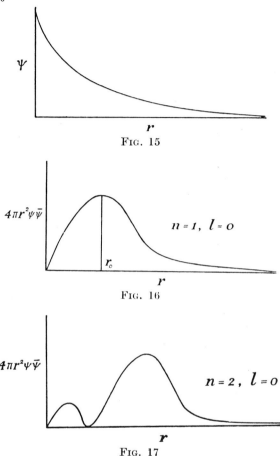

Fig. 15

$n = 1$, $l = 0$

Fig. 16

$n = 2$, $l = 0$

Fig. 17

For $n = 2$, $l = 0$ the corresponding quantity is as shown in Fig.
17.

When $l = 1$, the spherical symmetry is replaced by symmetry
about either the x-, the y-, or the z-axis, with an electrical distribution
approximately as shown in perspective in Fig. 18.

The wave functions are called P wave functions and the corresponding states P states.

D states correspond to $l = 2$ and F states to $l = 3$. These have
more complicated distributions of density.

o

The electron density assumes great importance in the problem of chemical valency. Before this important subject is approached, something must be said about the nature of forces in general.

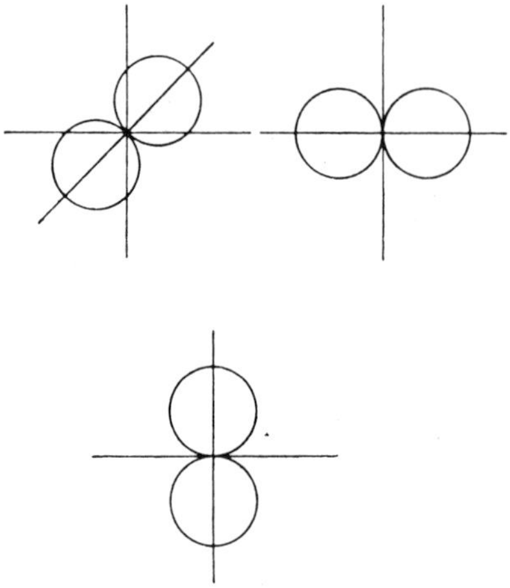

FIG. 18

Some considerable knowledge about the electrical make-up of molecules is, however, derivable from the study, on the one hand, of the dielectric properties of substances, and, on the other hand, of band spectra. The former study yields information about the charge distribution between the atoms, and incidentally many interesting facts relating to molecular structure generally. The latter reveals the kinds of electronic transition which occur in molecules and also provides a method for the determination of various important molecular constants.

A related matter which will claim attention is the interaction of atoms and molecules with electromagnetic radiation.

X

ELECTRICAL PHENOMENA IN
MOLECULES AND IN SPACE

Introduction

THE electrical theory of matter has proceeded through various stages, from the conception of an electric fluid to the recognition of the primary particles, and from the discovery that atoms bear charges to the realization that they consist of nothing else. The principle on which atoms are built emerges from obscurity in the light of the quantum theory, and unexpected developments of a highly abstract kind are expressed in the character of wave functions.

Electrical phenomena occur in space as well as in atoms. Radiation consists of electromagnetic waves in which there is a propagation of alternating fields. A close connexion exists between these fields and the movement of charges in atoms and molecules. The laws of such interactions must now be explored, partly because they are of the greatest importance in their own right and partly because they reveal many intimate details about the economy of the molecules themselves.

First comes the question of the crude charge distribution within the molecule, which largely determines the nature of its interaction with radiation. Then there comes the quantum theory of molecular emission and absorption, and finally the electromagnetic theory of radiation itself.

Molecular dipoles

In atoms the centres of gravity of the positive and negative charges coincide. In molecules they may not, since even in a diatomic structure A—B the hold of the atom A on the electrons may be tighter than that of atom B, and there will result a distribution representable by $\overset{-}{\text{A}}$—$\overset{+}{\text{B}}$. If $\pm e$ is the effective charge on A and B and l is the distance between the centres of gravity of the two atoms, $el = \mu$, and is called the *dipole moment*. Knowledge of it may be obtained without detailed information about e or l individually.

The dipole moment of its constituent molecules is closely related to the dielectric constant of a substance in bulk.

Coulomb's law states that the force between two charges e_1 and

e_2 in a vacuum is given by $e_1 e_2/r^2$, r being the distance between them. In a medium of dielectric constant K this force is weakened to $e_1 e_2/K r^2$. The weakening can come about in two ways. First, the field induces a separation of positive and negative charges in the molecules in such a way as partially to neutralize itself. Secondly, the field causes orientation of molecules possessing natural dipoles, which set themselves in opposition to it and counteract its influence.

The first effect is independent of temperature, the second not. Thermal agitation continuously destroys orientation, so that the higher the temperature the smaller is the contribution which the permanent dipoles can make to the neutralization of the field.

Detailed calculation leads to the formula

$$\frac{K-1}{K+2}\frac{M}{\rho} = \frac{4\pi N}{3}\left(\alpha + \frac{\mu^2}{3kT}\right),$$

where K is the dielectric constant, M the molecular weight, ρ the density, N Avogadro's number, and α is the polarizability, defined by the relation:

$$\text{induced dipole} = \alpha \times \text{field strength.}$$

The principles of the derivation are as follows. If a dipole makes a given angle with the field, it has a calculable potential energy, and it makes a calculable contribution to the neutralization of the field. Boltzmann's equation for the relative numbers of configurations in regions of stated potential energy gives an expression for the distribution of angles and the temperature, and hence predicts the effect on K as a function of T.

The equation written down above contains two terms: one, involving α, independent of temperature, the other, involving μ, strongly temperature-dependent. Hence, in principle, measurements of the temperature coefficient of the dielectric constants of gases yield the values of the dipole moments.

The general ideas upon which the theory is based are very fully confirmed by the fact that vapours containing symmetrical molecules such as CCl_4, or CH_4, in which any internal dipoles would neutralize one another in respect of their external action, have dielectric constants which are independent of temperature, and that the temperature-dependence increases in a regular manner as the molecules are made less symmetrical by substitution, as for example in CH_3Cl or $CHCl_3$.

In practice, the elaborate measurements of dielectric constants of gases at different temperatures are usually circumvented, on the one hand by the use of dilute solutions and the application of additive relations for solvent and solute, and, on the other hand, by the theoretical calculation of α from the refractive index, so that μ can be found from measurements at one temperature only.

Knowledge of the dipole moment finds valuable application in many problems of molecular structure. This field constitutes a large special study and only one or two examples will be quoted to illustrate its place in the scheme of things. We are primarily concerned with the dipolar character of the molecule as an expression of its power to interact with radiation, and, as will appear, with other molecules.

The moments of benzene derivatives such as (benzene ring with X at top) and (benzene ring with Y at top) can be measured. In a first approximation, the moments of (benzene ring with X at top and Y at upper-right), (benzene ring with X at top and Y at lower-right)

and (benzene ring with X at top and Y at bottom) are calculable by vector addition from those of the mono-derivatives. The compound (benzene ring with X at top and X at bottom) has moment zero, and that of (benzene ring with X at top and Y at bottom) is the sum or difference of the values for the mono-derivatives according as the directions of the dipoles are the same or opposite. In this way from one reference compound the absolute signs of dipoles can be found.

If we know the moment of (benzene ring with X at top), then from that of the molecule (two benzene rings joined at top through O with angle θ, each ring bearing X at bottom) and the vector addition principle the valency angle, θ, can be calculated in a first approximation. Actually the mutual influences of dipoles are by no means negligible, and in more than approximate treatments must be allowed for. This also constitutes an interesting field of study.

Evidence from band spectra. Absorption and emission by molecules

Band spectra yield information about the electronic levels in molecules and about the types of symmetry shown by wave functions. They also provide values for molecular vibration frequencies, energies of dissociation, and moments of inertia.

In order to understand how this is possible, it is first necessary to know something about the general nature and structure of band spectra. At one time they appeared to be of a quite unintelligible complexity, which, however, the applications of the quantum theory and of wave mechanics have shown to depend upon combinations of relatively simple elements.

Line spectra are emitted by atoms, band spectra by molecules, as is clear both from the conditions under which they are observable and from the theoretical interpretation of their characteristics.

Emission or absorption occurs, of course, in quanta when the molecule makes a permitted transition from one to another of the possible energy levels. The transitions in question generally involve concurrent changes in electronic energy, ΔE_e, vibrational energy, ΔE_v, and rotational energy, ΔE_r, so that the total energy change ΔE is given by

$$\Delta E = \Delta E_e + \Delta E_v + \Delta E_r.$$

The three terms in this expression are in a first approximation independent, and need not be of the same sign, so that very varied combinations occur, and the emitted or absorbed frequency $\nu = \Delta E/h$ has many values.

If E_r alone changes, a series of frequencies in the remote infra-red or short radio region occur. They are defined by the transitions between the energy levels of the series

$$E_r = J(J+1)h^2/8\pi^2 I,$$

where J is an integer and I is the moment of inertia of the molecule. J changes by one unit at a time, in virtue of what is called a *selection rule* (p. 225).

The spacing of the vibrational levels is much greater, E_v being given by $(n+\tfrac{1}{2})h\omega$, where ω is a normal vibration frequency of the molecule itself. If E_v alone changed, there would be a series of lines characteristic of the various molecular frequencies. But since E_v is very much greater than E_r, there is no reason to expect changes in the former without the likelihood of concomitant changes in the latter. Thus

$$\nu = \frac{1}{h}[\Delta E_v + \Delta E_r],$$

where ΔE_v defines the general position of absorption or emission, and the various positive or negative values of ΔE_r impart to it the fine structure which gives the band its characteristic appearance.

Absorption may be considered for definiteness. ΔE_v is then positive. J may remain the same, or it may increase or decrease by one unit. Correspondingly there are three parts to the band, usually called the P, Q, and R branches (Q for $\Delta J = 0$). If J increases from J to $J+1$, ΔE_r is given by

$$\frac{h^2}{8\pi^2 I}\{(J+1)(J+2)-J(J+1)\} \quad \text{or} \quad \frac{h^2}{4\pi^2 I}(J+1).$$

This increases by equal steps as the original value of J increases. Thus on the high-frequency side of the line corresponding to $\Delta E_v/h$ there is a series of equally spaced lines, corresponding to the rotational transitions 0 to 1, 1 to 2, 2 to 3, and so on (*not*, it is to be noted, 0 to 1, 0 to 2, 0 to 3). If J decreases, the total energy absorbed is less than ΔE_v,

$$\frac{h^2}{8\pi^2 I}\{(J-1)J-J(J+1)\},$$

being $-h^2 J/(4\pi^2 I)$. In a rough approximation this result means a series of lines equally spaced on the other side of the central line.

From what has been said the rotational band would appear to have the symmetrical structure shown in Fig. 19. In fact it is somewhat unsymmetrical in virtue of changes in I accompanying the changes in the rotational state. The intensity variations of the different lines are determined by the Maxwell–Boltzmann distribution of the initial values of J.

Vibrational bands with rotational fine structure occur in the short infra-red region of the spectrum. The variations in I itself become still more important in band spectra of the visible region. Here ΔE_e determines a *band system*, ΔE_v governs a progression of bands within the system, and ΔE_r imparts a fine structure to each band. For a given system, corresponding to one single electronic transition in the molecule, ΔE_v may have values $\Delta(n+\tfrac{1}{2})h\omega$. For low values of n this leads to a number of equally spaced bands. But as n increases the binding in the molecule weakens and ω itself drops towards zero, so that the bands come closer and closer together.

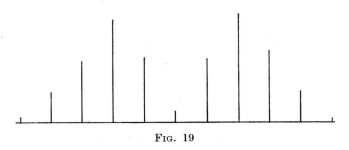

FIG. 19

Theoretically, the spacing becomes zero when the vibrational energy corresponds to the energy of dissociation of the molecule. The convergence point is seldom observable. But empirical formulae expressing the gradual diminution of the frequency differences can be applied to the existing bands and used to calculate by extrapolation what the dissociation energy would be. This procedure is of importance in principle, but of some uncertainty in practice, since the extrapolation is usually over a rather wide range.

In discussing the fine structure of a rotation-vibration band it was permissible as an approximation to assume a constant moment of inertia. Bands of the visible region involve electronic transitions which so modify the molecular structure that I is not even approximately constant. When the molecule passes from the initial to the final state I changes to I'. This is responsible for one of the most characteristic features in the appearance of the bands. For given values of ΔE_e and ΔE_v those of ΔE_r are

$$\frac{(J+1)(J+2)}{8\pi^2 I'} - \frac{J(J+1)}{8\pi^2 I},$$

or

$$\frac{(J-1)J}{8\pi^2 I'} - \frac{J(J+1)}{8\pi^2 I}.$$

The terms in J^2 no longer vanish as they do when $I = I'$. The two expressions are quadratics in J of the forms

$$\frac{J^2}{8\pi^2}\left(\frac{1}{I'}-\frac{1}{I}\right)+\frac{J}{8\pi^2}\left(\frac{3}{I'}-\frac{1}{I}\right)+\frac{1}{8\pi^2}\left(\frac{2}{I'}\right)$$

and

$$\frac{J^2}{8\pi^2}\left(\frac{1}{I'}-\frac{1}{I}\right)-\frac{J}{8\pi^2}\left(\frac{1}{I'}+\frac{1}{I}\right).$$

If I' is less than I, then the coefficient of J^2 is positive in both these expressions, but that of J is positive in one and negative in the

FIG. 20

other. If I' is greater than I, the coefficient of J^2 is negative in both. $3/I'$ will still be greater than $1/I$, so that the coefficient of J will be positive in the first expression and negative in the second. Thus the frequencies of the lines making up the band will form progressions of the types

$$\nu_0 \pm aJ \pm bJ^2,$$

where a and b are positive. When the progression is of the form $\nu_0 + aJ - bJ^2$, the frequencies of successive lines at first increase, while the J term dominates the expression: then, when the J^2 term grows, the lines crowd closer together until finally ν no longer increases. Further increase in J leads to a more and more rapidly diminishing frequency, so that the band has the appearance shown in Fig. 20, where the dotted lines belong to the frequencies in the region where the bJ^2 term outweighs aJ.

The limit beyond which the frequency shows no further increase is called the band head. It might, from its appearance in the spectrum, have been supposed to have special significance. Actually it has not, representing simply the frequency at which the terms in a quadratic happen to balance. According to the relative values of the different constants, the band head may lie on the side of longer or of shorter wave-lengths. The crowding of the lines in the one direction and the spreading out in the other give the spectrum the peculiar appearance sometimes described as fluted.

As to the determination of molecular constants, the spacings of rotational lines in the infra-red, visible, or ultra violet give information about the moments of inertia. This is frequently precise enough to serve for the unequivocal identification of the species responsible for the absorption or emission. The progression of bands in the visible yields, when enough terms are determinable to allow a satisfactory extrapolation, a value for the dissociation energy. The vibration-rotation bands of the short infra-red yield direct information about the frequencies of molecular vibration. Long infra-red and short radio waves provide values for rotations and yield moments of inertia.

Evidence from the Raman effect

Not all molecular frequencies lead to absorption in the infra-red. Many which do not, however, may be discovered by an examination of what is called the *Raman effect*.

When light of the visible range of frequency is scattered, there may appear not only the original frequency ν_0 of the incident beam but the frequencies $\nu_0+\nu_1$ and $\nu_0-\nu_1$, where ν_1 is one of the molecular vibration frequencies of the scattering substance. The quantum $h\nu_0$ is absorbed and returned plus or minus a levy of $h\nu_1$ according as the molecule has passed to a lower or a higher vibrational level in the process. ν_1 will, of course, be small compared with ν_0.

In general, molecular vibration frequencies do not appear both in the infra-red and in the Raman spectra. To couple with infra-red radiation directly the molecule must undergo a vibration attended with a displacement of its electrical centre of gravity: that is, its dipole moment must change during the course of its vibration. This condition will become clearer after the discussion of the electromagnetic theory later in the present chapter. To give rise to a Raman line the molecule must suffer a change, as it vibrates, not in *moment*, but in *polarizability*.

The reasons for these conditions may be seen in a general way as follows. Light waves involve periodic fluctuations of electro-magnetic fields, and for the generation of such waves there must be an oscillation of electric charges. Hence the need for a change in the dipole moment for infra-red activity.

The symmetrical vibration of the molecule illustrated in (a) would not be attended with a variation of moment nor, therefore, by

(a) ←○   ○   ○→

(b) ○→   ←○   ○→

infra-red emission or absorption. On the other hand, the antisymmetrical vibration (b) gives a fluctuating moment and corresponds to an observable infra-red frequency.

Where the Raman effect is concerned the important thing is not the moment but the mutual interaction of the vibrations caused by the visible light and the vibrations of the molecule itself. The light induces in the molecule a fluctuating moment with a period equal to its own. This is given by

$$\mu = \alpha F = \alpha F_0 \sin 2\pi\nu_0 t,$$

where α is the polarizability of the molecule, F is the field due to the wave, and ν_0 its frequency. Now α may or may not be a function of the displacements which the molecule suffers in virtue of its own vibrations. If it is, then there will be a Raman frequency to correspond. Suppose α varies with x, the displacement in a given molecular vibration of frequency ν_1. α may now be written

$$\alpha = \alpha_0 + kx = \alpha_0 + kx_0 \sin 2\pi\nu_1 t,$$

where α_0 and k are constants. Substitution gives

$$\mu = (\alpha_0 + kx_0 \sin 2\pi\nu_1 t)F_0 \sin 2\pi\nu_0 t.$$

The moment, μ, which determines the subsequent emission by the molecule of the scattered light, contains one term in $\sin 2\pi\nu_0 t$ corresponding to an unchanged frequency ν_0 and another term with the product

$$\sin 2\pi\nu_1 t \sin 2\pi\nu_0 t.$$

This expression is equivalent to

$$\left(\frac{e^{2\pi i\nu_1 t} - e^{-2\pi i\nu_1 t}}{2i}\right)\left(\frac{e^{2\pi i\nu_0 t} - e^{-2\pi i\nu_0 t}}{2i}\right),$$

and when multiplied out contains terms in $e^{2\pi i(\nu_0 \pm \nu_1)t}$, representing frequencies $\nu_0 \pm \nu_1$ (as can also be seen by transformation of the sine product by the usual trigonometrical formula).

The vibration (a) shown above, although not attended by a change of moment, will clearly be accompanied by variations in α since the interatomic distances alter during the movement. It will appear, therefore, as a Raman frequency.

Electronic transitions in molecules

So far nothing has been said about the nature of the electronic transitions in molecules. These, of course, determine the fabric on which the vibrational and rotational fine structure of the visible spectra is embroidered.

The energy of the electronic transition itself corresponds, as with atomic spectra, to the difference of two terms characteristic respectively of an upper and a lower state. The molecular states present close analogies with the S, P, D,... states of atoms, and the values of ΔE_e are generally of the same order of magnitude as those which determine atomic spectra. Higher terms sometimes fall into sequences of the Rydberg type, so that they evidently do not differ fundamentally from atomic terms.

In the application of the quantum theory to the simplest example of a diatomic molecule, the important new factor is the existence in the molecule of an axis defining a specific direction. An atom possesses no such axis. There exists therefore for the molecule a quantum number Λ which measures the number of units of angular momentum in the component of the electronic orbital motion *projected along the axis joining the nuclei*. According as $\Lambda = 0, 1, 2,...$, the state is called Σ, Π, Δ,..., by analogy with the atomic states S, P, D,..., which are determined by the values of l (p. 199).

The molecular terms may show multiplicity and, once again, this is interpretable in relation to the electron spins. The resultant spin, S, has a component of Σ' units about the molecular axis, and the sum, $\Omega = \Lambda + \Sigma'$, gives a new quantum number which has multiple values according to the magnitude of S and its possible projections.

In general the different values of Ω for a given Λ correspond to different states of energy, but if $\Lambda = 0$, as it is in a Σ state, the magnetic field in the line of the axis is zero and no actual splitting of the spectral lines occurs in a non-rotating molecule.

The interaction of molecular rotation and electronic motion is, however, of great importance, and forms the basis of the most usual method for the diagnosis of the nature of the electron terms—whether

Σ, Π, and so on. In the simplest kind of coupling Λ and Σ' first combine to give Ω, the total units of electronic angular momentum about the axis: and then Ω forms a resultant, J, with the angular momentum of the molecular rotation about the axis. It is J which now determines the sequence of the rotational states. According to the wave equation, in this case the energies are a function not simply of J but of J and of Ω. Although, for a given set of lines, Ω is constant, it affects the possible values of J. When Ω is greater than zero, some of the lower rotational levels are missing.

Thus the detailed analysis of the rotational structure of bands will reveal the type of electronic transition with which they are associated. If the resultant spin is zero and $\Lambda = 0$, then the state is a singlet Σ state, and the simple theory of rotational fine structure given previously is uncomplicated by further considerations of multiplicity. In general, however, the rotational fine structure is a function of the electronic transition itself.

The fact that the molecular terms are determined by principles fundamentally similar to those defining atomic terms suggests a procedure, which leads to useful results, whereby the former are qualitatively derivable, or at least guessable, from the latter. The terms being known for two atoms A and B, the problem is to ascertain in what respects they will change when the isolated atoms are brought together to form a molecule.

The two atoms are in states with angular momenta defined by l_A and l_B respectively As they approach, an axial field develops and the components L_A and L_B emerge, quantized in the direction of the axis. When the molecule has been formed, it possesses a value of Λ given by $L_A + L_B$. All possible integral values of L_A and L_B combine to give the various possibilities for Λ itself. Two atomic S states with $l = 0$ must give rise to a Σ state with $\Lambda = 0$. If L_A can be as great as 2, as in a D state, and if L_B is zero, as with the second atom in an S state, Λ can be either 0, 1, 2, -1, or -2, so that Σ, Π, and Δ states become possible.

The more detailed discussion of these matters leads to a classification of molecular states according to the symmetry characteristics of the wave functions defining them. States are negative ($-$) or positive ($+$) according as the wave function changes sign or not on reflection in a plane passing through the nuclei, and odd (u) or even (g) according as it changes sign on passage through the centre of the line joining the nuclei and from one side of the axis to the other.

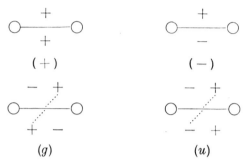

The decision as to whether the atomic terms become positive or negative, odd or even, when combined to give molecular terms depends upon detailed prescriptions derivable from the wave equation.

Analogous qualitative argument about the origin and nature of molecular terms can be based upon an imaginary genesis of a molecule by the splitting of a given atom of known configuration into two fragments which are then drawn apart. For example, there should be a discernible relation between the atomic terms of calcium and the molecular terms of magnesium oxide: the calcium nucleus is thought of as dividing into Mg and O while still surrounded by all its electrons. The two nuclei then part company with a continuous adjustment of the electron configurations until the whole system turns into MgO. In general, this line of investigation leads to intelligible, though, of course, not quantitative, results. But it seems clear that no fundamentally new laws govern the behaviour of electrons when they happen to be assigned to two nuclei rather than to a single nucleus.

Stable and unstable levels

The application of these principles is limited in practice by the fact that many of the formally possible molecular levels are unstable. If the molecule is excited to one of these, it decomposes before it has a chance to return to the initial state. The fragments formed by the dissociation can carry away varying amounts of kinetic energy, and the result is a continuum in the absorption spectrum.

For the emission of the normal band spectrum a molecule must be capable of vibrations in the upper and in the lower electronic states, and the condition for this is that the relation between potential energy (U) and interatomic distance (r) should be of the general form shown in Fig. 21 (a) and (b), where the energy is a minimum at the equilibrium interatomic distance (r_0). The energy relations for an unstable level are represented by the curve (c) where the continuous increase with diminishing distance corresponds to a steadily increasing repulsion between the atoms and the absence of an equilibrium state.

The excitation of one of the electrons to a higher level frequently weakens the binding between the atoms and a large number of the higher molecular states are represented by potential energy curves of the type (c). Were the stable states more numerous, the complexity of band spectra would be even greater than it is and might never have been disentangled.

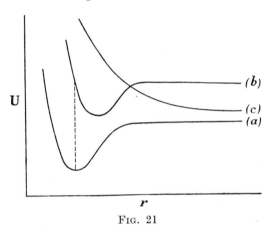

FIG. 21

Morse curves

The curves (a) and (b) of Fig. 21 are conveniently represented by the equation of Morse

$$E(r) = De^{-2a(r-r_0)} - 2De^{-a(r-r_0)},$$

where $E(r)$ is the energy, measured in relation to such a standard level that it becomes zero for infinite separation of the atoms. When $r = r_0$, the equilibrium distance, $E(r)$, according to the equation, has a minimum value of $-D$, which thus represents the energy of formation of the molecule from its atoms (in the states in which they would be produced by dissociation). When $r = 0$, $E(r)$ assumes, not an infinite value as it should really do, but a high one which is a good enough approximation. The great advantage of the Morse equation is that on insertion into the wave equation it yields for the permitted vibrational levels of the molecule a series of the same form as one of the most useful empirical formulae derived from experimental spectroscopy. The nth level is defined by the relation

$$W(n) = h\nu_0(n+\tfrac{1}{2}) - \frac{h^2\nu_0^2}{4D}(n+\tfrac{1}{2})^2,$$

where n is an integer and ν_0 is the frequency of oscillations still small enough to be simple harmonic. The vibrational levels of actual bands can often be well enough expressed by

$$W(n) = h\nu_0(n+\tfrac{1}{2}) - x(n+\tfrac{1}{2})^2,$$

where x is the so-called anharmonicity constant. This formula gives levels which at first are equally spaced and then converge to a limit.

The Franck–Condon principle

Transitions between the molecular levels are governed by a principle, formulated by Franck and Condon, according to which the passage of the electron from one to another occurs in too short a time for the much more massive atoms to have suffered appreciable displacement. The transfers, therefore, occur along a vertical line of the diagram in Fig. 21, and since the maxima of the upper and lower states seldom correspond, a change in the vibrational levels nearly always accompanies the electronic excitation. This principle, as can be seen, has a good deal to say regarding the intensities of the vibrational bands observed in spectra.

Sometimes the potential energy curves of stable and unstable excited states cut one another, as with (b) and (c) in the diagram, and in such circumstances excitation may be followed by dissociation after a varying delay. If this time lies between the periods of rotation and of vibration, the rotational fine structure may disappear from the vibration bands: there is still enough time for vibrations, but not enough for the slower rotations.

Interaction of matter and radiation: electromagnetic theory of light

The interaction of matter and light manifests itself in absorption and emission, in reflection, refraction, and dispersion, in diffraction and polarization, as well as in the chemical changes which radiation may bring about in a molecule which absorbs it.

The quantum theory describes many of the phenomena with little more concern about the apparatus of radiation than that involved in the knowledge of the mode in which the transfers are parcelled up. This suffices for the theory of spectra—in most respects—and certainly for photochemistry, which depends only upon the stability or otherwise of the excited states into which the absorbed quanta lift the molecules.

In other ways, however, the attempt to understand the nature of things is powerfully helped by an appreciation of the profound connexion between the electrical theory of matter and the electromagnetic theory of light. The ideas underlying this theory have still a great deal of importance, although their place in the general structure of physics has greatly changed since the days of their introduction.

The theory of electricity and magnetism developed from the study of macroscopic phenomena such as the mutual attraction of magnets or of electrically charged bodies, and of the forces exerted by magnets on wires carrying electric currents. Faraday was convinced that the various effects were transmitted from one body to another through a field which involved happenings of some kind in the intervening space, and Maxwell proposed the laws of this field in one of the most wonderful of all physical theories.

He began with the bold and brilliant hypothesis that certain rules discovered for macroscopic systems such as electric circuits would be applicable, when suitably formulated, to elementary regions of space. For example, the law of electromagnetic induction discovered by Faraday states that the electromotive force induced in a circuit is proportional to the total rate of change in the number of lines of magnetic force passing through the area. Electromotive force is the work involved in the transport of unit charge, and can therefore be expressed as the integral of a force with respect to a distance. Maxwell accordingly assumes that for any small closed curve in space

$$\int E \, ds = -\frac{\mu}{v} \int\int \frac{\partial H}{\partial t} \, dS, \qquad (1)$$

where E is the electric field, ds an element of the curve, H the magnetic field, μ the magnetic permeability, and dS the area of the elementary region of space (corresponding to Faraday's circuit although it contains no conductor). The factor v is to convert the field E, normally measured in terms of Coulomb's law in electrostatic units, into the electromagnetic system of units which is based upon

P

current–magnet interactions. It is an experimental constant. The negative sign in the equation takes account of the fact that the induced electromotive force is always in opposition.

Maxwell needed an equation to balance (1). Now it is well known from the elementary laws of galvanometers that the work done in carrying unit magnetic pole round a wire bearing a current i is $4\pi i$. This work is independent of the distance, provided that a complete circuit is made. Thus we have

$$\int H\,ds = 4\pi i. \qquad (2)$$

The left-hand side is already symmetrical with (1). As to the right, Maxwell assumed that there is a quantity which he called the displacement, D, whose variation with time in a non-conducting medium corresponds to the current in a conductor. Thus we have

$$i = \int\int \frac{\partial D}{\partial t}\,dS, \qquad (3)$$

the current being replaced by the integral of $\partial D/\partial t$ taken over the complete area of the elementary region considered. D itself has a simple relation to the electric field, E. At a distance r from a charge e in a medium of dielectric constant K the force is given by

$$E = e/Kr^2 \quad \text{or} \quad e = Kr^2E.$$

Maxwell imagined that when a charge e establishes the field around itself, the displacement spreads outwards through space. At a distance r the area is $4\pi r^2$, and $4\pi r^2 D$ represents the total, as it were, polarization of space, $4\pi r^2 D$ balancing e, so that

$$e = 4\pi r^2 D = Kr^2E, \quad \text{whence} \quad D = KE/4\pi.$$

Combining this with (3) and inserting the result in (2) we find

$$\int H\,ds = K \int\int \frac{\partial E}{\partial t}\,dS,$$

$\partial E/\partial t$ representing what is virtually a current, but E itself being normally expressed in electrostatic units. The empirical conversion factor must thus be applied and we obtain

$$\int H\,ds = \frac{K}{v} \int\int \frac{\partial E}{\partial t}\,dS. \qquad (4)$$

(1) and (4) now constitute an almost symmetrical pair.

From this point on, Maxwell's development of (1) and (4) is purely mathematical and consists in showing that the electric and magnetic fields in space are so related that waves can be propagated, and that the velocity of these waves is $v/\sqrt{(\mu K)}$. A brief derivation of this for the simplified case of a plane polarized wave travelling along one axis will illustrate the principles.

E and H have the components E_x, E_y, E_z and H_x, H_y, H_z. It is easy to show that round a circuit in the XY-plane†

$$\int E\, ds = \int\int \left(\frac{\partial E_y}{\partial x} - \frac{\partial E_x}{\partial y}\right) dS.$$

There will thus arise six equations for the various components of H and E respectively. Of these, from (1),

$$-\frac{\mu}{v}\frac{\partial H_x}{\partial t} = \frac{\partial E_y}{\partial z} - \frac{\partial E_z}{\partial y}$$

is typical. (H_x is combined with E_y and E_z since it is round a circuit in the YZ-plane that electromotive force is induced by variation of the magnetic field along the x-axis.)

We shall now simplify the problem by considering the case where E_x and $E_y = 0$, with E_z as the only effective component of the electric field. E_z, moreover, is to be uniform over the whole XY-plane (plane and plane-polarized electromagnetic wave).

† The reader unacquainted with simple properties of vectors can satisfy himself about this by working out $E\, ds$ for the circuit shown in the diagram. The contributions from the traversing of the sides 1, 2, 3, 4 are

$$+\left(E_y + \frac{1}{2}\frac{\partial E_y}{\partial x}\delta x\right)\delta y - \left(E_x + \frac{1}{2}\frac{\partial E_x}{\partial y}\delta y\right)\delta x - \left(E_y - \frac{1}{2}\frac{\partial E_y}{\partial x}\delta x\right)\delta y + \left(E_x - \frac{1}{2}\frac{\partial E_x}{\partial y}\delta y\right)\delta x.$$

The sum of these is $\left(\dfrac{\partial E_y}{\partial x} - \dfrac{\partial E_x}{\partial y}\right)\delta x \delta y$

and integration over a larger circuit gives the result required. It can be substituted in (1) and the integral signs dropped on both sides of the resulting equation.

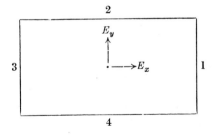

Then of the six equations we are left with

$$\frac{K}{v}\frac{\partial E_z}{\partial t} = \frac{\partial H_x}{\partial y} - \frac{\partial H_y}{\partial x}, \tag{5}$$

$$-\frac{\mu}{v}\frac{\partial H_y}{\partial t} = \frac{\partial E_z}{\partial x}. \tag{6}$$

E_z cannot vary with time without affecting H_x and H_y, nor can H_y vary with time without affecting E_z. Moreover, the variations in space and time are interconnected, so that everything is as required for the propagation of waves.

Differentiation of (5) gives

$$\frac{K}{v}\frac{\partial^2 E_z}{\partial t^2} = \frac{\partial}{\partial t}\left(\frac{\partial H_x}{\partial y}\right) - \frac{\partial}{\partial t}\left(\frac{\partial H_y}{\partial x}\right) = \frac{\partial}{\partial y}\left(\frac{\partial H_x}{\partial t}\right) - \frac{\partial}{\partial x}\left(\frac{\partial H_y}{\partial t}\right)$$

$$= -\frac{\partial}{\partial x}\left(-\frac{v}{\mu}\frac{\partial E_z}{\partial x}\right) = \frac{v}{\mu}\frac{\partial^2 E_z}{\partial x^2}$$

(the term $\partial H_x/\partial t$ being zero since it is $\partial E_y/\partial z - \partial E_z/\partial y$, and $E_y = 0$ and $\partial E_z/\partial y = 0$).

Therefore

$$\frac{\mu K}{v^2}\frac{\partial^2 E_z}{\partial t^2} = \frac{\partial^2 E_z}{\partial x^2},$$

and similarly

$$\frac{\mu K}{v^2}\frac{\partial^2 H_y}{\partial t^2} = \frac{\partial^2 H_y}{\partial x^2}.$$

These last equations represent the propagation of E_z and H_y as plane waves. It is easily verified by substitution that the equations are satisfied by expressions of the form

$$E_z = \phi(x - Vt),$$

where

$$V = v/\sqrt{(\mu K)}.$$

For a vacuum μ and K are unity and $V = v$. v, the empirical conversion factor of electromagnetic and electrostatic units, is 3×10^{10} cm./sec. which is none other than c, the velocity of light in free space.

This remarkable result left nobody in any doubt that light waves are in fact propagated electromagnetic vibrations.

The electromagnetic theory suffered a certain eclipse with the advent of the quantum theory, and yet it cannot really be said to be superseded. The quantum laws are quite distinct from anything implicit in Maxwell's equations, and, of course, in flat contradiction to any idea that frequencies of electromagnetic waves are related to the actual frequencies of movements of electrons in atoms. The relation $\Delta E = h\nu$ for the frequency of the radiation emitted in a transition between two stationary states seems at first sight to replace this idea in a quite radical manner. But the fact remains that ν refers to some character of the radiation which governs many of its most important properties, including refraction and dispersion.

Though there is a so-called quantum theory of dispersion, it includes elements directly derived from the electromagnetic theory, and still postulates alternating fields associated with light waves.

There is in fact a formal way in which the conception of the fluctuating field of the light wave and the quantum transition in the atom can be in some measure reconciled.

If an atom can exist in the two levels E_1 and E_2 then, as shown on p. 185, the wave equation takes the form

$$\psi = c_1 \psi_1 e^{2\pi i E_1 t/h} + c_2 \psi_2 e^{2\pi i E_2 t/h},$$

where $\psi_1 e^{2\pi i E_1 t/h}$ and $\psi_1 e^{2\pi i E_2 t/h}$ are individual solutions. The electric density (in so far as we visualize this in more than a statistical sense) is given by

$$\psi\bar{\psi} = c_1^2 \psi_1^2 + c_2^2 \psi_2^2 + c_1 c_2 \psi_1 \psi_2 [e^{2\pi i (E_1 - E_2)t/h} + e^{-2\pi i (E_1 - E_2)t/h}]$$

$$= c_1^2 \psi_1^2 + c_2^2 \psi_2^2 + 2c_1 c_2 \psi_1 \psi_2 \cos[2\pi(E_1 - E_2)t/h]$$

$$= c_1^2 \psi_1^2 + c_2^2 \psi_2^2 + 2c_1 c_2 \psi_1 \psi_2 \cos 2\pi \nu' t.$$

Thus when the two energy levels coexist, the density contains a term which varies periodically with time. This term has not a frequency equal to that of either of the separate values E_1/h or E_2/h but one equal to $(E_1 - E_2)/h$. Thus we obtain a link between the wave-mechanical theory of the atom and the classical theory of the field which is formally very striking, though, in the light of any statistical interpretation of the electric density, it cannot be said that the problem is entirely free from mystery.

In view of general experience of the ultimate failure of all macroscopic analogies to explain microscopic phenomena, and indeed of the essentially illogical character of the demand that they should, one can hardly regard the analogies which suggested Maxwell's equations as more than suggestive. The possibility of other formal schemes which express the properties of radiation and its interaction with matter in quantum phenomena lies open. Such field theories lie, however, beyond the present bounds of physical chemistry.

Refraction and Dispersion

Refraction and dispersion are matters of some physico-chemical interest and merit brief attention at this stage. If we ask why the presence of atoms in the path of light waves should hinder their propagation, the answer in qualitative terms is somewhat as follows. The rate of propagation of any disturbance depends upon the restoring force called into play by the displacements occurring in the medium which transmits the waves. The presence of particles which are set in forced vibration, whether as a result of mechanical or of any other kind of interaction, contributes to the system an extra element of inertia which is formally equivalent to a weakening of the elastic constants. Hence the lowering of the velocity which is observed.

The treatment of refraction and dispersion in terms of the quantum theory proceeds more or less in the following way. Suppose an atom becomes polarized in the direction z, and thereby develops a moment ze. Then, in the alternating field of a light wave, its potential energy will contain an extra term $Aez \cos 2\pi\nu t$, where A is a constant and ν is the frequency of the field. (We note that the electromagnetic theory holds its own at this stage.) The modified potential energy term is inserted into the wave equation which gives the permitted states of the atom, and hence the effective moments which it can exhibit under the influence of the light wave. These moments, which in effect determine the polarizability, affect K (the dielectric constant of the region through which the light travels) and hence modify the velocity of propagation, which, as shown, depends upon $1/\sqrt{K}$.

Increased polarizability means increased K and hence lowered speed of propagation. The ratio of the velocity in free space to that in the medium is the refractive index. The detailed calculation shows that the refractive index depends upon the relation between ν, the frequency of the light, and the $h\nu'$ corresponding to the various transitions between stationary states in the atom. Hence it is a function of the light frequency. This is the phenomenon of dispersion.

Various functions of the refractive index multiplied by the molecular weight have been found to be partly additive and partly constitutive. They are made up additively from contributions by the various atoms in the molecule, provided that corrections are applied for the modes of binding of individual atoms. At one time the study of molecular refractivities was much used as a diagnostic test for various types of structure.

Optical activity

We will now turn to the consideration of a phenomenon which has played a very special part in structural chemistry, that, namely, of the influence of molecules on polarized light. According to the theory which, even before the advent of Maxwell's ideas, described most of the phenomena of physical optics, light waves are transverse, with displacements perpendicular to the line of propagation. In plane polarized light the displacements are confined to one single plane, the plane of polarization. Two light waves polarized at right angles and of equal amplitude compound to give a wave with what is called circular polarization. Thus if the vibrations in one are represented by

$$x = a \sin \omega t$$

and in the other by

$$y = a \cos \omega t,$$

then

$$x^2 + y^2 = a^2,$$

so that the path of the point (x, y) is a circle. Conversely a circularly polarized wave may be resolved into two plane waves of equal amplitude at right angles to one another. The components of two circular motions executed in opposite directions are

$$x_1 = a \sin \omega t, \qquad x_2 = a \sin \omega t,$$
$$y_1 = a \cos \omega t, \qquad y_2 = -a \cos \omega t,$$

and the sum of these gives

$$x = x_1 + x_2 = 2a \sin \omega t,$$
$$y = y_1 + y_2 = 0,$$

a plane polarized vibration.

A plane polarized vibration is thus equivalent to two circular motions executed in opposite senses. The points imagined to execute these motions cross when $\omega t = 0, \pi, 2\pi$, and so on. Suppose one of the circular motions suffers a retardation relatively to the other so that while

$$x_1 = a \sin \omega t, \qquad y_1 = a \cos \omega t$$

the other two values change:

$$x_2 = a \sin(\omega t + \phi), \qquad y_2 = -a \cos(\omega t + \phi).$$

We now refer the motions to a new set of rectangular axes making an angle θ with the former set. According to the standard rules for transformation of axes, if x_1, x_2, y_1, y_2 become respectively x_1', x_2', y_1', y_2' then

$$x_1 = x_1' \cos\theta - y_1' \sin\theta,$$
$$y_1 = x_1' \sin\theta + y_1' \cos\theta,$$

with a corresponding pair of equations for x_2 and y_2.

Thus

$$a \sin\omega t = x_1' \cos\theta - y_1' \sin\theta,$$
$$a \cos\omega t = x_1' \sin\theta + y_1' \cos\theta,$$

whence

$$x_1' = a \sin(\omega t + \theta),$$
$$y_1' = a \cos(\omega t + \theta).$$

Similarly

$$x_2' = a \sin(\omega t + \phi - \theta),$$
$$y_2' = -a \cos(\omega t + \phi - \theta).$$

If $\phi = 2\theta$, then

$$x_1' = a \sin(\omega t + \theta), \qquad x_2' = a \sin(\omega t + \theta),$$
$$y_1' = a \cos(\omega t + \theta), \qquad y_2' = -a \cos(\omega t + \theta).$$

These combine to give a plane polarized vibration in the line making an angle θ with the original.

Now if a medium were related to one of the circular components of a plane polarized light wave as the female thread to the male thread of a helical screw, it would be expected to transmit that one more easily than the oppositely directed one, and so cause a rotation of the plane of polarization. We have therefore to examine the conditions under which the analogy of the screw might be applicable. Some crystalline media, for example certain forms of quartz, do in fact possess a space lattice with a helical configuration of atoms, and the successive actions of these on the light waves can be imagined to produce retardations depending on the direction of the circular component.

Optical activity is, however, also shown in solution. It is due to molecules which themselves lack a plane of symmetry. In virtue of this lack they cannot be brought into coincidence with their own mirror images, any more than right-handed and left-handed helices can be superposed. They have in fact the same geometrical property as the helical media in causing a selective retardation of one of the two circular vibrations, each of the mirror image forms retarding a different component of the wave.

That the collective effect of a randomly oriented assemblage of molecules does not give a zero resultant can be realized if it is borne in mind that a right-handed helix remains right-handed even when it is turned through 180°, as common observation will show. Thus the sign of the effect on the one or the other circular component of the wave does not depend upon the direction in which the molecule is traversed. Hence the randomly oriented solution behaves for this purpose like a medium of definite geometrical form.

Selection rules

Atoms and molecules change their energy levels and emit or absorb radiation. All transitions between states, even though the states themselves are possible, are not necessarily legitimate. The restrictions imposed upon transfers are known as *selection rules*. Rather closely related to them are the prescriptions which define the state of polarization of an emitted light wave, such a formulation amounting to a selection rule applicable to particular components of the wave.

Examples of selection rules have already been mentioned: in the condition that the atomic quantum number l must change by one unit at a time; in the requirement that the rotational quanta responsible for the fine structure of molecular band spectra change by one unit or zero; and, in a more general way, in the prohibition of transfers from symmetrical to antisymmetrical states.

Most selection rules emerge from long and detailed calculation of transition probabilities, and only the general principles of the matter will be outlined here.

As already explained (p. 198), transition probabilities depend upon integrals of the form $\int \psi_1 r \psi_2 \, d\omega$, where the two wave functions refer to the initial and final states and r is a small potential energy term. *Selection rules are derived from the conditions that the integral should have a value different from zero.*

Emission of light will depend upon the moment of the fluctuating part of $\psi \bar{\psi}$ (p. 221). The z component of this moment is of the form $\int z \psi \bar{\psi} \, d\omega$. If this vanishes for all three directions, then the line will not appear in the spectrum. If it vanishes for all directions except z, then there is a plane polarized emission: if the z component vanishes while there are equal x and y components (in the right phase), then we have a circularly polarized emission.

Detailed working out is necessary for each special case. The simplest possible is given as an example. Suppose we have a rotator with a fixed axis. Its motion is describable by a one-coordinate wave equation thus:

$$\frac{d^2\psi}{d\theta^2} + \frac{8\pi^2 I}{h^2} E\psi = 0,$$

since there is no potential energy, and the moment of inertia replaces the mass when the angular coordinate θ is used to describe the movement. The equation has a simple solution

$$\psi = \sin\left(\frac{8\pi^2 I E}{h^2}\right)^{\frac{1}{2}}\theta.$$

Each time θ becomes a multiple of 2π, ψ must begin to repeat itself, so we write $\psi = \sin n\theta$ with n integral. Suppose the rotator is an electron (or something bearing a charge), and that the x and y components are $a \sin \theta$ and $a \cos \theta$. Now imagine the rotator capable of existing in two of its energy states with $n = n_1$ and n_2 respectively. The probability of a transition from one to the other depends upon

$$\int x \sin n_1 \theta \sin n_2 \theta \, d\theta \quad \text{and} \quad \int y \sin n_1 \theta \sin n_2 \theta \, d\theta,$$

the emission of radiation being determined by the *electric moment*. The values of

$$\int_0^{2\pi} x \sin n_1 \theta \sin n_2 \theta \, d\theta \quad \text{and} \quad \int_0^{2\pi} y \sin n_1 \theta \sin n_2 \theta \, d\theta$$

are in turn proportional to

$$\int_0^{2\pi} a \sin n_1 \theta \sin n_2 \theta \sin \theta \, d\theta \quad \text{and to} \quad \int_0^{2\pi} a \sin n_1 \theta \sin n_2 \theta \cos \theta \, d\theta.$$

To take the first as an example, $\sin n_1 \theta \sin n_2 \theta$ can be expressed in terms of a difference of cosines of $(n_1+n_2)\theta$ and of $(n_1-n_2)\theta$; these in their turn when multiplied by $\sin \theta$ lead to integrals of the form

$$\int_0^{2\pi} \cos(n_1+n_2)\theta \sin \theta \, d\theta \quad \text{and} \quad \int_0^{2\pi} \cos(n_1-n_2)\theta \sin \theta \, d\theta,$$

which vanish unless $n_1+n_2 = 1$ or $n_1-n_2 = 1$ respectively. If $n_1+n_2 = 1$, then n_1 or $n_2 = 0$, so that in either case the difference of n_1 and n_2 is unity. Thus we see that n_1 can only differ *by one unit* from n_2. The other combinations lead to the same result. This calculation establishes, for the simple case, the well-known selection rule about rotational quantum numbers.

PART IV
FORCES

SYNOPSIS

THE nature of the forces which hold together all the various groupings and sub-groupings of particles making up matter has so far remained largely unknown. The emission or absorption of energy which accompanies a change of configuration has been a fundamental datum introduced empirically into statistical theories and their thermodynamic counterparts.

Force itself is a convenient descriptive term which relates energy changes to potential muscular sensations, and mathematically it can be replaced by a differential coefficient of energy with respect to a space coordinate. Essentially a theory of forces is a theory about energies. When particles tend to enter into a new configuration of lower energy they are said to exert an attractive force on one another.

The principal groupings which take place on appropriate occasions are: the union of protons and neutrons (and possibly of other entities) to give atomic nuclei; the gathering of electrons round these nuclei to form atoms; the combination of atoms to molecules; and the aggregation of molecules to condensed phases of solid and liquid. These associations may be said to occur under the influence respectively of nuclear forces, intra-atomic forces, valency forces, and van der Waals forces.

Nuclear forces are not fully understood, but important contributions are made by proton–neutron attractions and by the electrostatic repulsion of protons for one another. The theory of relativity, which evolved from certain observations on the propagation of light, leads to a relation between the binding energy of a nucleus and the departure of the mass from a whole number of units ($c^2 \Delta m = \Delta E$), so that an empirical method of judging nuclear stability is available.

Intra-atomic forces prove to be simply the Coulomb attractions and repulsions of the positive nuclei and negative electrons for one another. But it is the quantum theory and the Pauli principle which impose a structure on the atom and dictate the rules for the building up of the periodic system of the elements.

Valency forces are also electrostatic in nature. A consistent application of the quantum laws to two hydrogen atoms shows that the pair may exist in a lower energy level than the isolated individuals, but only on condition that their electrons have opposite spins. This condition is imposed by the requirement of antisymmetry in the wave function. Analogous conclusions apply to other atoms, and the limitations on the possible electron states which the Pauli principle demands restrict combination to the saturation of specific valencies. Valency forces fall off exponentially as distance between atoms increases.

The amplitude functions of the wave equation yield information about the general types of electrical density distribution in molecules of different kinds, and provide a foundation for stereochemistry and for the detailed study of molecular properties.

Molecular vibration frequencies, force constants, bond lengths, and dissociation energies provide experimental methods for studying interatomic forces in detail.

Van der Waals forces are also electrostatic, and, generally speaking, dipolar: they exist in virtue of (a) permanent dipoles in molecules, (b) dipoles induced by other permanent dipoles and, most characteristically, (c) the coupling of the zero-point oscillations of positive and negative charge which must occur even in molecules without an observable moment. Van der Waals forces normally fall off as the inverse seventh power of the distance.

When one atom has received electrons from another so that a pair of ions is formed, the Coulomb forces between the two obey the inverse square law. Such forces act therefore over long ranges and profoundly affect the properties of solutions of ionized substances.

XI

THE BUILDING OF ATOMS AND MOLECULES

Forces

AN ever-recurring theme in what has been said so far is the conflict between the random motions of the constituent particles of matter and the forces which tend to order them into structures. So far little or nothing has been said about the character of these forces, the operation of which has been expressed simply in the various energy terms entering into kinetic, statistical, or thermodynamic calculations. It is now necessary to examine this problem more explicitly, and to consider what can be said about the ways in which entities such as neutrons and protons are held together in atomic nuclei, electrons are grouped round nuclei in atoms, atoms form molecules, and molecules become aggregated into the varied kinds of structure constituting ordinary matter.

The notion of force itself is not quite simple. It is derived primarily from the sensation of muscular effort. This is something so familiar that to relate other things to it may be deemed to increase understanding. Muscular effort is expended in setting bodies in motion or in stopping them again, and when gravitating or electrified bodies are observed to hasten together or apart, they are said, in the first instance in a somewhat anthropomorphic sense, to exert on one another forces of attraction or repulsion.

The science of mechanics provides objective criteria by which forces may be compared. Newton's laws relate force, mass, and acceleration. In a strict sense the mere formulation of the rule force = mass × acceleration is not helpful, since by it force cannot be defined except in terms of mass, nor mass except in terms of force. But the value of mechanics lies in the coherence of the system to which it leads. If masses are compared in terms of the accelerations imparted by a constant force, such as gravity at a given place (about which nothing need be postulated save its constancy), then the order found will in fact determine their relative behaviour under the influence of quite different forces. A very vast system of observed phenomena can be correlated in terms of the auxiliary quantities force and mass, even though a logician uninterested in calculations about the actual behaviour of matter may see little point in their introduction.

Force interests the less sophisticated investigator because it suggests familiar sensations, but for most purposes the quantity known as the potential energy is more convenient to work with. For a particle of mass m, if x is a space coordinate and P_x the component of force in that direction, $\int P_x \, dx = $ work.

$$\int m\ddot{x} \, dx = \int m\frac{dv}{dt} dx = \int m\frac{dx}{dt} dv = \Delta\left(\frac{mv^2}{2}\right),$$

where Δ represents total change.

If a particle acted upon by forces which could impart *kinetic energy* to it may be said to possess *potential energy*, then the sum of these two energies is constant. Since, moreover, according to the kinetic theory, heat is the sum of the invisible molecular energies, this rule will be quite general. In certain connexions calculations of energies are made directly, and the interpretation of the results in terms of forces is introduced only as an afterthought. Two hydrogen atoms, for example, according to the rules of quantum mechanics, may exist in a state where the energy is lower than the sum of the energies which they would possess in isolation. If they come together and enter into this state, therefore, energy must be removed from them. This means that they will have appeared to move together under the influence of an attractive force. Some people say that force has become a superfluous conception. In a purely formal mathematical system it is not really needed, and is simply the differential coefficient of a potential energy. Yet for descriptive purposes forces may often be more conveniently spoken of.

Mass and energy

In the original Newtonian conception mass was a permanent and invariable quantity. This idea, however, was substantially modified by the advent of the theory of relativity, according to which mass and energy are interconvertible. If particles possessed of mass coalesce, as for example may be supposed to happen when the constituents of an atomic nucleus come together, there may be a powerful release of energy, probably as radiation, and the mass of the composite system may be less than the sum of the individual isolated masses. The transformations are related by the equation $c^2 \Delta m = \Delta E$, where ΔE is the emission of energy corresponding to a diminution of mass Δm, and c is the velocity of light. This surprising relation is of fundamental importance in connexion with the structure and stability of atomic nuclei, and with the whole problem of atomic energy.

The evolution of ideas which has led to the mass–energy equation is a quite strange one. ·It begins with the famous Michelson and Morley experiment, the original object of which was to detect if possible the absolute motion of the Earth through space. The principle of the experiment is as follows. Suppose a swimmer crosses a river one mile wide and returns to the starting-point, taking time t_1 over the double transit. Suppose then that he swims one mile upstream against the current and returns to the starting-point, taking a total time t_2. A simple arithmetical calculation shows t_1 and t_2 to be different. It was expected that in a similar way there would be a difference in the time required by a light ray to make a return journey of given length according as its path lay in or perpendicular to the direction of the Earth's motion through space. In a suitable experimental arrangement the time difference should be revealed by a displacement of interference fringes. No such effect can be detected.

The result of a long process of experimentation and discussion was the remarkable but inescapable conclusion that in the nature of things no composition of another velocity with the velocity of light can lead to a value for the latter different from the standard value c. In fact, a *new law for the combination of velocities* has to be established. A comparatively simple formula satisfies the requirements. If u and v are two parallel velocities, their resultant is not $u+v$ but $\dfrac{u+v}{1+uv/c^2}$. When u and v are small compared with c, this reduces to the usual form $u+v$. In the limit, when $v = c$, the resultant becomes

$$\frac{u+c}{1+uc/c^2} = c,$$

as required by the generalized implication of the Michelson and Morley experiment.

The new law for velocity composition is best arrived at by a more formal process of coordinate transformation. Coordinates x and t in terms of which a given observer might record his dynamical observations are normally related to the coordinates x' and t' of a second observer, in motion along the x-axis relative to the first with velocity v, by the simple and obvious transformations

$$t = t',$$

$$x = x'+vt'.$$

These lead to the law $u \pm v$ for the composition of parallel velocities, and certainly would not account for the result of the Michelson and Morley experiment. To arrive at the required relation one has to apply what is called the *Lorentz transformation*. According to this

$$x = \frac{x'+vt'}{(1-v^2/c^2)^{\frac{1}{2}}},$$

and t is no longer equal to t', but is given by

$$t = \frac{t'+(v/c^2)x'}{(1-v^2/c^2)^{\frac{1}{2}}}.$$

The velocity composition law follows from these transformations. Suppose someone on a ship measures the speed of an object moving on the deck (for simplicity in the direction of the ship's motion). He determines a distance which he records as x' and divides it by a time which he records as t'. He then sets $u = x'/t'$. Suppose now the same moving object is observed from an aeroplane flying in a parallel course with speed v relative to the ship. With his own instruments the observer records a distance x and a time t and calculates a velocity x/t. On the old basis this would be $u+v$. On the new basis it is given by

$$\frac{x}{t} = \frac{x'+vt'}{(1-v^2/c^2)^{\frac{1}{2}}} \Big/ \frac{t'+(v/c^2)x'}{(1-v^2/c^2)^{\frac{1}{2}}} = \frac{u+v}{1+uv/c^2}$$

as already stated.

There is nothing mysterious about the origin of the Lorentz transformation. It is invented to give an invariable value for the velocity of light and to reduce to the normal law for small speeds. Much discussion has in fact arisen as to possible metaphysical implications of these changed dynamical rules, and upon the nature and conditions of physical observations in general. Whatever may be said on this score, it is clear that new rules for compounding velocities must have repercussions on other parts of dynamics. In particular, the principle of the conservation of momentum encounters difficulties. Suppose an experiment is performed by observer A, who verifies the fact that in a collision of two masses momentum is conserved. Suppose now that this identical experiment is witnessed by observer B who is in motion with speed v relative to A. All the velocities measured by A will be measured by B according to the new law of composition, and a simple algebraical calculation shows that if A finds momentum to be conserved, B, according to his own measurements on the same process, will not.

For the most satisfactory and coherent system of dynamics and physics the *conservation of momentum* must be retained, and what now emerges is that even in the modified dynamical theory (special theory of relativity) the observers A and B would both verify the constancy of momentum if the mass of a body were itself assumed no longer to be invariable but to be a *function of its velocity* in the particular system where the measurement is made. Einstein concluded that there would be a variation according to the equation

$$m = \frac{m_0}{(1-u^2/c^2)^{\frac{1}{2}}},$$

where m_0 is the mass of the body at rest and m its mass when it moves with speed u.

If the observations of one observer are related to those of another, the respective measures of mass are different. The combination of the Einstein mass–velocity relation and the new rule for the composition of velocities shows, however, that the conservation of momentum will now hold for both. The following equations show the various relations. With non-relativity mechanics, observer A would make measurements represented by (1) and observer B measurements represented by (2):

$$m_1 u_1 + m_2 u_2 = \text{constant}, \tag{1}$$

$$m_1(u_1+v) + m_2(u_2+v) = m_1 u_1 + m_2 u_2 + (m_1+m_2)v$$
$$= \text{constant}. \tag{2}$$

The constancy of total momentum holds during a collison in which u_1 and u_2 change. With the Lorentz transformation and an assumed constancy of mass the corresponding observations would be given by ($1a$) and ($2a$):

$$m_1 u_1 + m_2 u_2 = \text{constant}, \tag{$1a$}$$

$$\frac{m_1(u_1+v)}{1+u_1 v/c^2} + \frac{m_2(u_2+v)}{1+u_2 v/c^2} \neq \text{constant}. \tag{$2a$}$$

With the assumption of variable mass the relations are replaced by ($1b$) and ($2b$):

$$\frac{m_1 u_1}{(1-u_1^2/c^2)^{\frac{1}{2}}} + \frac{m_2 u_2}{(1-u_2^2/c^2)^{\frac{1}{2}}} = \text{constant} = \mu, \tag{$1b$}$$

$$\frac{m_1\left(\dfrac{u_1+v}{1+u_1 v/c^2}\right)}{\left\{1-\dfrac{1}{c^2}\left(\dfrac{u_1+v}{1+u_1 v/c^2}\right)^2\right\}^{\frac{1}{2}}} + \frac{m_2\left(\dfrac{u_2+v}{1+u_2 v/c^2}\right)}{\left\{1-\dfrac{1}{c^2}\left(\dfrac{u_2+v}{1+u_2 v/c^2}\right)^2\right\}^{\frac{1}{2}}}$$
$$= \frac{1}{(1-v^2/c^2)^{\frac{1}{2}}}[\mu + Mv] = \text{constant}. \tag{$2b$}$$

($2a$) can by no means be reduced to a form independent of the separate values of u_1 and u_2: ($2b$) can, and if μ is found constant in an experiment, the expression in ($2b$) will be found constant also.

The mass–velocity relation introduced in this way, for the convenience of retaining the conservation of momentum in the relativity system of mechanics, has been directly verified by experiments on the m/e ratios of electrons with differing velocities. Some of the β-particles emitted by radioactive atoms have velocities which amount to a considerable fraction of c, and m/e (measured in deflexion experiments) is much higher than for slow electrons. The variation is well expressed by Einstein's mass equation. It is much more convenient to attribute the variability to m than to e, since an electron is a certain quantity of electricity and could scarcely be deemed to retain its identity if e itself varied.

The mass–velocity relation acquires on the strength of these experiments a status independent in a considerable measure of the arguments from the special theory of relativity upon which it is primarily based.

Given that mass is variable, some reconsideration of the energy principle is forced upon us. The kinetic energy must continue to be representable as the difference between the total energy of a body moving in a given system with speed u and that of the same body at rest in the same system. For speeds which are small compared with c the result should be $\frac{1}{2}m_0 u^2$. Thus

$$E_1 - E_0 = \tfrac{1}{2}m_0 u^2.$$

To retain this result it is found that one must make a radical new assumption and introduce the relation $E = mc^2$, where mc^2 is what is called the *proper energy*. The relation implies an equivalence of mass and energy and suggests at least the formal possibility of their interconversion, since in virtue of its existence a mass has energy as it were stored up in it.

The kinetic energy equation now becomes:

$$\text{K.E.} = E_1 - E_0 = \frac{m_0 c^2}{(1 - u^2/c^2)^{\frac{1}{2}}} - m_0 c^2$$

$$= m_0 c^2 [(1 - u^2/c^2)^{-\frac{1}{2}} - 1]$$

$$= m_0 c^2 [\tfrac{1}{2}u^2/c^2 + \text{higher powers}]$$

$$= \tfrac{1}{2}m_0 u^2 \quad \text{when} \quad u \ll c.$$

This last result shows the appropriateness of the relation $E = mc^2$, which reduces to the traditional form for low speeds.

This mass–energy relation must dominate the whole question of the genesis of elements, the dynamics of stars, the origin of cosmic radiations, and other fundamental matters. The only respect in which it affects ordinary terrestrial chemistry is in connexion with the stability of atomic nuclei. The changes which occur in chemical reactions are too small to affect practically the traditional principle of mass conservation upon which so much of chemical theory has been based.

Nuclear stability

In a survey of forces which bind material systems into their various configurations the first question to arise is that of the interactions in the atomic nucleus itself. To this question only a partial answer can be given. The real components of the nucleus are not definitively known, and the part played by mesons is uncertain, but a reasonable working hypothesis, which accounts for at least some of the facts, is that the building-blocks consist of neutrons and protons. Between these two kinds of particle an attractive force is postulated, and in opposition to the attraction there is the Coulombic repulsion of the protons for one another. If there are Z protons and N neutrons, the approximate atomic weight A will be given by $A = N+Z$, and the atomic number, or nuclear charge will be Z.

In a very rough first approximation the potential energy of a nucleus will be lowest when the numbers of the two kinds of mutually attracting particle are more or less equal. If $N \sim Z$, then $Z \sim A/2$, and indeed atomic numbers are not very far removed from half the corresponding atomic weight.

The problem can, however, be considered in a somewhat higher degree of approximation than this. Two kinds of evidence exist; on the one hand, the precise values of the atomic masses, determined by the mass spectrometer for individual isotopes of the elements and, on the other hand, the occurrence of the different types of radio-activity in various nuclei, natural and artificial.

Atomic weights of pure isotopes are nearly enough whole numbers to suggest very strongly indeed that the nuclei are built up from common units. The deviations, however, are not only large enough to be significant, but are spread throughout the roll of the elements according to a more or less regular pattern. Taken together, these two facts point to the hypothesis that the amount by which a given nuclear mass falls below that of an integral number of H nuclei is a measure of the binding energy of its components, and that the mass defect will be related to the energy of binding by the relativity relation $c^2\Delta m = \Delta E$. In other words, there are nuclei which have different mass defects because they have radiated away varying amounts of their mass as energy during their formation.

The relation of the mass defect to the atomic number is shown in the well-known curve of Aston (Fig. 22). A quite rough model of the nucleus provides some sort of explanation for the existence of the minimum in Aston's curve. The main binding force is the proton–neutron attraction. This is opposed by the proton repulsion, which becomes more serious the greater the number of protons present, and tends to reduce stability in the larger nuclei. On the other hand, these larger nuclei tend to gain stability from their compactness and from the smaller ratio of surface to volume, whereby the waste of

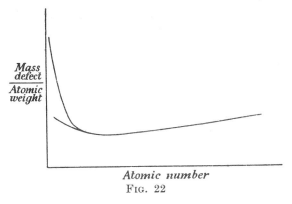

Fig. 22

unsaturated forces at their boundaries is lessened. The opposing trends of increasing proton repulsion and diminishing unsaturation are supposed to account for the minimum in the curve of stability.

Somewhat more subtle considerations indicate that in the nucleus neutrons and protons respectively may form closed groups consisting of pairs, perhaps with opposing spins, and that successive pairs must occupy progressively higher energy levels. The general analogy between this and what is known of electrons in atoms is obvious. The experimental evidence is less conclusive. It consists in the statistical study of what isotopes are possible, and of the relations between A and Z. As very rough generalizations the following may be said:

(a) For a given even value of A, several values of Z occur, themselves usually *even*.

(b) For a given *odd* value of A, there is usually one value only for Z, with about an equal probability of its being odd or even.

These are tendencies rather than rules and may be interpreted as follows. Suppose one starts with A, the approximate integral mass number, at an *even* value A_0, and that Z has also the even value Z_0. Then N, the number of neutrons, is even and all the particles will occupy closed groups. Now let another particle be added so that A

becomes odd. Whether the addendum is a proton or a neutron, it will be unpaired, and there is no predictable advantage in favour of either, so that A_0+1 (odd) may be associated with (Z_0+1, N_0) or (Z_0, N_0+1). Thus Z may be odd or even. This corresponds to the regularity (b).

Now let a further particle be added. There is an advantage in pairing off whichever existing particle is unpaired, so that the building of the stabler structures will proceed as follows:

$$A_0, Z_0, N_0 \nearrow A_0+1, Z_0+1, N_0 \to A_0+2, Z_0+2, N_0$$
$$\text{even} \searrow A_0+1, Z_0, N_0+1 \to A_0+2, Z_0, N_0+2.$$

In this scheme we have arrived from a given A_0 at A_0+2 which is even and associated with two values of Z both even, a result which corresponds to (a).

The same pairing process can be invoked to explain the stability of the α-particle, which consists of 2 protons and 2 neutrons, and which seems, if not to exist ready-made in nuclei, at least to be formed and emitted with some facility in various transformations of radioactive elements.

The tendency of nuclei to achieve an approximate balance of neutrons and protons explains the emission of β-particles or of positrons according as there is under- or over-representation of the positive constituents of the system.

Knowledge of nuclear forces is thus in one way very definite. The mass defects, which can be determined with considerable precision, yield quite reliable information about the relative energies of formation from possible constitutents. The quantitative application of the equation $c^2\Delta m = \Delta E$ is well illustrated by the example of the reaction occurring when a fast proton causes the disintegration of lithium:

$$H^1 + Li^7 = 2He^4.$$

In this transformation the changes in mass defect and the energy balance have been verified with precision.

The nature of the nuclear forces themselves is less clear. Proton–proton repulsions relate one term in the energy to familiar ideas. Proton–neutron attractions are also intelligible in so far as they can be roughly envisaged as an interaction between two structures, one $(+)$ and the other $(+-)$. A quantum-mechanical calculation depending upon the so-called exchange principle can also be invoked.

The two systems neutron–proton and proton–neutron being indistinguishable and the one being derivable from the other by a change in the assignment of an embodied electron, the energy relation can be treated in a way somewhat similar in form to that which will be employed in dealing with the interaction of hydrogen atoms (p. 240). In this way semi-quantitative theories can be developed.

The pairing principle seems to be supported by good evidence and is of great importance. It means that interaction energies are determined in some measure, not by laws of force, but by numerical rules about the energy levels which can be occupied, a state of affairs very familiar in the theory of the electronic constitution of the atoms themselves.

But a considerable element of mystery still shrouds the nucleus, as is perhaps understandable for an entity so remote from ordinary things. It is smaller in size than the electrons which on occasion it can generate. It is possessed of a spin, and obeys sometimes Fermi–Dirac and sometimes Bose–Einstein statistics, in accordance, presumably, with the symmetry of its internal make-up. It emits α-particles with a discrete energy spectrum and β-particles as a continuum, to reconcile which with momentum conservation laws a new particle, the neutrino, devoid of charge and nearly devoid of mass, is sometimes postulated. The occurrence in cosmic rays of a range of labile particles with masses believed to lie between that of the electron and that of the proton, the mesons, raises the question of the part which these too may play in the strange world of the atomic depths.

Yet most of chemistry needs to know little of the nucleus beyond the fact of its smallness, the charge it bears, and the form of statistics it obeys.

Atom building

Atoms by comparison are familiar objects, and the forces which govern atomic structures are simply the electrostatic Coulomb interactions of nuclei and electrons. These forces follow the law of inverse squares and provide the central accelerations required to maintain the electrons in orbital motion about the nuclei. The numbers and modes of disposition of electrons are governed not by laws of force but by quantum rules, a matter which has already been discussed in some detail.

The mass of the electron determines the de Broglie wave-length $\lambda = h/mv$ and so fixes the scale of the quantum phenomena in which it participates. It is because the electron is of small mass that the atom has a radius very many times greater than the nucleus. The electrons being remote, the nucleus may be treated as a point charge with a high degree of approximation, and most of chemistry thus becomes an affair of the electron patterns alone.

Molecules

The next stage in the hierarchy of structural patterns is the molecule.

The simplest kind of chemical interaction is that due to what is called *electrovalency*. The quantum laws prescribe maxima of elec-

(1) $+$ $-$ $-$ $+$

(2) $+$ $-$ $+$ $-$

FIG. 23

tronic stability for the configurations corresponding to the inert gases. Atoms with arrangements possessing one, two, or three electrons short of the stability maximum will tend to capture the appropriate amount of negative electricity and give rise to ions, with one, two, or three charges respectively. Atoms with numbers in excess of the stability maximum will tend to lose electrons giving positive ions with corresponding charges.

Positive and negative ions will normally exist together, in the gas phase, in solution, or in the regular geometrical arrangement of a crystal lattice, in numbers such that electrical neutrality is preserved. We then speak of electrovalent chemical compounds. Such compounds possess the well-known property of electrical conductivity. They are in fact only compounds to the extent that the positive and negative ions are present in fixed proportions: they are not bound together in any more profound sense than this.

In covalent compounds the atoms are united into a single structure. The problem of the mode of formation long eluded theoretical treatment. The difficulty may be seen by reference to Fig. 23, which crudely represents two hydrogen atoms. In (1) there will clearly be repulsion, in (2) attraction. Until the advent of quantum mechanics there was no means of specifying what might be called the relative phases of the two atoms and so predicting whether in fact they should attract or repel.

The equations of wave mechanics, however, allow the composite system of the two atoms to be treated, and the behaviour of two electrons under the influence of two nuclei to be prescribed.

Quantum-mechanical theory of covalency

The theory of chemical combination by covalencies still assumes that the interactions between atoms are electrostatic in nature. The principle can be illustrated by reference to the example of two hydrogen atoms.

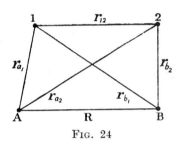

FIG. 24

In Fig. 24 A and B are two nuclei, and 1 and 2 are two electrons, the various intervening distances being as indicated.

Suppose, first, that the combination (A, 1) is very remote from (B, 2). The potential energies of the isolated atoms are respectively $-\epsilon^2/r_{a_1}$ and $-\epsilon^2/r_{b_2}$ (ϵ being the charge), and the atomic energy levels are defined by the two equations

$$\nabla_1^2 \psi_1 + \frac{8\pi^2 m}{h^2}\left(E_0 + \frac{\epsilon^2}{r_{a_1}}\right)\psi_1 = 0 \tag{1}$$

and

$$\nabla_2^2 \phi_2 + \frac{8\pi^2 m}{h^2}\left(E_0 + \frac{\epsilon^2}{r_{b_2}}\right)\phi_2 = 0. \tag{2}$$

The total energy of the two atoms in their ground states is $2E_0$.

Now suppose the atoms are brought together into a configuration similar to that in the figure. Two considerations arise. In the first place, neither of the two electrons can be regarded as belonging to a single nucleus. In thought, the atoms can be constituted as (A, 1), (B, 2) and also as (A, 2), (B, 1). Neglecting for the moment all interactions except that of a given nucleus and what we may choose to call its own electron, we have (A, 1) and (B, 2) described by equations

(1) and (2), and (A, 2) and (B, 1) described by equations (3) and (4), namely

$$\nabla_2^2 \psi_2 + \frac{8\pi^2 m}{h^2}\left(E_0 + \frac{\epsilon^2}{r_{a_2}}\right)\psi_2 = 0, \tag{3}$$

$$\nabla_1^2 \phi_1 + \frac{8\pi^2 m}{h^2}\left(E_0 + \frac{\epsilon^2}{r_{b_1}}\right)\phi_1 = 0. \tag{4}$$

If there were no more to it than the ambiguity of ownership, then these four equations would suffice. Mathematically possible solutions for the combined systems would be $\psi_1\phi_2$ and $\psi_2\phi_1$. Since, however, either of these implies that there is a sense in the conception of private ownership of electrons by nuclei, by arguments precisely analogous to those developed on p. 190 we conclude that either the symmetrical combination or the antisymmetrical combination,

$$\chi_S = \psi_1\phi_2 + \psi_2\phi_1 \tag{5}$$

or

$$\chi_A = \psi_1\phi_2 - \psi_2\phi_1, \tag{6}$$

is the correct one to describe the system.

Furthermore, the electrons possess spin, and, as already shown, symmetrical and antisymmetrical spin functions, σ_S and σ_A, are possible. By the principle that the total wave function must be antisymmetrical (p. 191) we see that the combinations must be $\chi_S \sigma_A$ or $\chi_A \sigma_S$.

So much for considerations depending upon particle identities and symmetry of wave functions. An entirely different set of considerations arise from the fact that as the two atoms approach, the potential energy assumes a more complicated form, since in addition to nucleus–electron interactions there are repulsions between the two nuclei and the two electrons respectively and attractions between each nucleus and the electron of what was originally the other atom.

The complete expression assumes the shape

$$U = \frac{\epsilon^2}{R} + \frac{\epsilon^2}{r_{12}} - \frac{\epsilon^2}{r_{a_1}} - \frac{\epsilon^2}{r_{a_2}} - \frac{\epsilon^2}{r_{b_1}} - \frac{\epsilon^2}{r_{b_2}}. \tag{7}$$

An attempt on the lines of classical physics to find the stable configuration of the atom by making the potential energy a minimum collapses, of course, since it would predict the falling of the electrons into the nuclei. A further attempt on the basis of the older forms of the quantum theory also fails because they do not specify anything about the relative phases of the electronic motions, and, as these vary, the atoms could either attract or repel.

In principle, quantum mechanics yields the solution. The value of U given by (7) is introduced into the Schrödinger equation, and energy levels are (in theory) defined in the usual way. These are functions of R, and a graph of the energy of the ground level as a function of R shows whether there is a minimum value for any particular separation, R_0. If there is, then stable molecule formation is possible and R_0 is the equilibrium distance.

In practice, however, it is not such plain sailing, since the equation

$$(\nabla_1^2 + \nabla_2^2)\chi + \frac{8\pi^2 m}{h^2}(E-U)\chi = 0 \qquad (8)$$

cannot be solved directly with U in the form given by (7).

Various approximate methods are employed. The general nature of the procedure is illustrated quite well by the original method of Heitler and London, which is based upon a so-called 'perturbation' computation.

If the two atoms did not exert special forces on one another as they approached, (8) would assume the form

$$(\nabla_1^2 + \nabla_2^2)\chi_0 + \frac{8\pi^2 m}{h^2}(E-V)\chi_0 = 0. \qquad (9)$$

E would be simply $2E_0$ and solutions would include products, $\psi_1\phi_2$ and $\psi_2\phi_1$, of solutions of (1), (2), (3), and (4).

With the extra terms, U becomes $V+u$. χ now becomes χ_0+f and E becomes $E+e$.

$$(\nabla_1^2 + \nabla_2^2)\chi + \frac{8\pi^2 m}{h^2}(E+e-V-u)\chi = 0. \qquad (10)$$

Replacement of χ by χ_0+f gives

$$(\nabla_1^2 + \nabla_2^2)\chi_0 + (\nabla_1^2 + \nabla_2^2)f + \frac{8\pi^2 m}{h^2}(E-V)\chi_0 +$$

$$+ \frac{8\pi^2 m(E-V)}{h^2}f + \frac{8\pi^2 m(e-u)}{h^2}\chi_0 = 0, \qquad (11)$$

if products of f with e and u are neglected. This latter condition introduces a considerable restriction, and reduces the whole procedure to one of approximation.

Subtraction of (9) from (11) gives

$$(\nabla_1^2 + \nabla_2^2)f + \frac{8\pi^2 m(E-V)}{h^2}f + \frac{8\pi^2 m(e-u)}{h^2}\chi_0 = 0. \qquad (12)$$

For χ_0 the combination $a\psi_1\phi_2 + b\psi_2\phi_1$ is taken. f is expanded in a series of terms
$$f = \sum c\psi_1^m \phi_2^n,$$
where ψ_1^m means the mth proper value of ψ_1.

Since $(\nabla_1^2 + \nabla_2^2)\psi_1^m \phi_2^n + \dfrac{8\pi^2 m}{h^2}(E_{mn} - V)\psi_1^m \phi_2^n = 0$

by the nature of ψ_1 and ϕ_2, E_{mn} being the appropriate energy, it follows that
$$(\nabla_1^2 + \nabla_2^2)f + \sum c\,\frac{8\pi^2 m}{h^2}(E_{mn} - V)\psi_1^m \phi_2^n = 0. \tag{13}$$

Subtraction of (13) from (12) gives
$$\sum_{} c\,\frac{8\pi^2 m}{h^2}(E - E_{mn})\psi_1^m \phi_2^n + \frac{8\pi^2 m}{h^2}(e - u)(a\psi_1\phi_2 + b\psi_2\phi_1) = 0$$

or $\sum c(E - E_{mn})\psi_1^m \phi_2^n = -(e - u)(a\psi_1\phi_2 + b\psi_2\phi_1).$ (14)

We now multiply by $\psi_1\phi_2$ and integrate over the whole range of the spatial coordinates, remembering that u, a function of these coordinates, must not be taken outside the integral sign.

$$\sum c(E - E_{mn}) \int \psi_1^m \phi_2^n \psi_1 \phi_2\, d\omega = -ea \int (\psi_1\phi_2)^2\, d\omega + a \int u(\psi_1\phi_2)^2\, d\omega -$$
$$-eb \int \psi_1\phi_2\psi_2\phi_1\, d\omega + b \int u\psi_1\phi_2\psi_2\phi_1\, d\omega.$$

By the orthogonal property the integral on the left-hand side of the equation is zero unless $\psi_1^m = \psi_1$ and $\phi_2^n = \phi_2$, in which case $E = E_{mn}$. The whole of the left-hand side is thus zero, in either event. On the right, the integral multiplying the term $-eb$ is also zero in virtue of the orthogonal property. The units, moreover, are deemed to be so chosen that $\int (\psi_1\phi_2)^2\, d\omega = 1$, a process called normalization.

We then have
$$-ea + a \int u(\psi_1\phi_2)^2\, d\omega + b \int u\psi_1\phi_2\psi_2\phi_1\, d\omega = 0.$$

Equation (14) is next multiplied by $\psi_2\phi_1$ and an analogous process of argument leads to
$$a \int u\psi_1\psi_2\phi_1\phi_2\, d\omega - be + b \int u(\psi_2\phi_1)^2\, d\omega = 0.$$

The numerical values of $\int u(\psi_1\phi_2)^2\, d\omega$ and $\int u(\psi_2\phi_1)^2\, d\omega$ being equal, the last two equations may be written
$$(e - K)a - bS = 0,$$
$$-Sa + (e - K)b = 0,$$

where $\qquad K = \int u(\psi_1 \phi_2)^2 \, d\omega$

and $\qquad S = \int u\psi_1 \psi_2 \phi_1 \phi_2 \, d\omega.$

Solution gives $\qquad e = K \pm S$

and correspondingly $\qquad a = \pm b.$

e is the displacement of the energy level due to the interaction of the two atoms, and its magnitude is seen to depend upon whether a is $+b$ or $-b$, that is, whether the symmetrical or the antisymmetrical combination of $\psi_1 \phi_2$ and $\psi_2 \phi_1$ is taken as the starting-point.

u is of the form obvious from (7). ψ_1, ψ_2, ϕ_1, ϕ_2 are ground state wave functions of single hydrogen atoms, as given on p. 200, each with the appropriate spatial coordinates. The integrals are calculable in principle, though, here again, there are certain difficulties in practice.

What emerges is that the symmetrical function χ_S corresponds to a *lower* energy, and indeed an energy with a minimum at a definite value of R. Such a state of affairs represents the possibility of a stable molecule formed from the two atoms.

As already pointed out, χ_S must be associated with σ_A. In other words, the stable molecule is formed from two atoms in which the electrons have opposite spins. χ_A, which is associated with σ_S, and thus with parallel spins, corresponds to repulsion of the two atoms at all distances.

When approximate values of the wave functions are known, the electron distribution in the molecule can be calculated. For the symmetrical wave function corresponding to molecule formation there is a concentration of electric charge in the region between the two nuclei. This, in one sense, is what constitutes the chemical bond, the negative electron cloud acting, as it were, as a cement between the two mutually repelling nuclei.

If, then, the question is asked: why do two hydrogen atoms combine? the answer is that the two electrons of opposite spins move in such a way that on the average the electrostatic attractions of electrons and nuclei outweigh the mutual repulsions of electrons for electrons and of nuclei for nuclei. To the further question: why do the electrons move in this particular way? the answer is that this way corresponds to the electric density distribution prescribed by the wave equation and to the requirement that the total wave function must be antisymmetrical.

That an accumulation of negative charge between them should bind two positive nuclei can be made the basis of a naïve picture of the chemical bond. That its occurrence is determined by the symmetry of the wave function, however, can not.

From this point the theory of valency develops in various directions. First, qualitative extensions of the Heitler–London result to atoms heavier than hydrogen are attempted. Secondly, efforts are made to improve the kind of approximation upon which the treatment of the hydrogen atom itself has been based. Thirdly, a number of more or less empirical rules, supported by but not strictly derivable from the principles of quantum mechanics, are introduced for the handling of special types of problem.

Extension to systems more complex than the hydrogen molecule

The first steps in extending the theory may be illustrated by the example of three hydrogen atoms, which may be labelled A, B, and C. Each of them possesses one electron, the spin function of which must be S or A, and may be referred to shortly as plus or minus. The approximate wave function which serves as a basis for the perturbation calculation will consist of combinations of positive and negative spins with assignments to A, B, and C. The complete function must be antisymmetrical. The detailed treatment of the general case is very complicated, but the most important result can be arrived at by the consideration of two atoms in close proximity and the third at a considerable distance. Such a system represents the interaction of a molecule and an approaching atom. The sign and magnitude of the various integrals involved is such as to indicate that the atom will be repelled by the molecule.

In a rough-and-ready way the result can be seen to be of this kind by the following argument. In the molecule two electrons are paired, that is to say they have opposite spins. The electron of the third atom, which is approaching, must have a spin parallel to that of one of those already paired in the molecule. The Pauli principle disallows the inclusion of this extra electron in the group of valency electrons, and therefore the triatomic combination is not permissible.

For two normal helium atoms a wave function must be constructed to describe a system of two nuclei and four electrons, and antisymmetrical in all the latter. Estimation of the energy of such a combination leads to the conclusion that repulsion will occur. In an elementary way, the inclusion of more electrons in the closed group of the two $1s$ electrons already present in the normal helium atom may be regarded as forbidden by the Pauli principle.

If helium atoms are excited to higher levels by any means, they no longer have their electrons paired, since the principal quantum numbers themselves now differ, and in these circumstances fresh electrons may be admitted to the valency system. In consequence, excited helium does form chemical compounds, as exemplified by the diatomic molecules He_2 which may be detected spectroscopically when electric discharges are passed through the gas.

Detailed calculations about the more complex atoms are virtually impossible to perform, but the Pauli principle provides the general rules of valency, and, furthermore, certain empirical extensions of wave mechanics prove of great utility in the treatment of such matters as the spatial direction of valency bonds.

The principles of this subject will be sufficiently well illustrated by reference to carbon, nitrogen, and oxygen. According to Bohr's atom-building principle, the electronic system of carbon is made up of six electrons to balance the nuclear charge, two $1s$ electrons with paired spins completing an inner group, and four more belonging to a group with principal quantum number 2. With $n = 2$, one may have $l = 0$, $m = 0$, $r = \pm\frac{1}{2}$; or $l = 1$, $m = 1, 0, -1$, and $r = \pm\frac{1}{2}$. The first two, with $l = 0$, are s electrons and the next six possibilities relate to p electrons. Since p wave functions are axially symmetrical, the six may be divided into pairs of p_x, p_y, and p_z electrons. Carbon being quadrivalent, its four electrons with $n = 2$ are presumably unpaired—since one may suppose that orbits are filled as far as possible without pairing—so that the probable assignment would appear to be $(2s)^1$, $(2p_x)^1$, $(2p_y)^1$, and $(2p_z)^1$, the index showing the number of electrons in each state.

Things are not, however, quite so simple as this, as will appear in a moment. But first let us consider nitrogen and oxygen. For the former, one more electron must be added to the carbon group. No new type of orbit is possible and therefore pairing with the $2s$ electron seems likely. Thus we have the assignment $(2s)^2$, $(2p_x)^1$, $(2p_y)^1$, $(2p_z)^1$.

For oxygen, by a similar argument we arrive at $(2s)^2$, $(2p_x)^2$, $(2p_y)^1$, $(2p_z)^1$.

If the valency is equated to the number of unpaired electrons, then nitrogen is tervalent and oxygen bivalent as required by their normal chemical behaviour. These prescriptions are not rigid and this circumstance corresponds to the fact of variable valency. In carbon there might well be paired s electrons, and the group $(2s)^2$ would leave unpaired $(2p_x)^1$ and $(2p_y)^1$ only. This would signify a bivalent atom. Carbon does indeed exist in a bivalent form, and, what is still more significant, energy is required to raise the atom from the bivalent to the quadrivalent state.

The so-called quinquivalent state of nitrogen and the quadrivalent state of oxygen arise of course in a quite different manner. Compounds in which these forms of the elements seem to appear are really ionic: for example $(NH_4)^+Cl^-$. The chlorine having removed an electron from the nitrogen atom, the latter is left with four unpaired electrons which can pair with the four electrons of the hydrogens to give the ammonium ion.

The interaction of the unpaired electrons of atoms such as carbon, nitrogen, and oxygen with the electrons of other atoms cannot be directed calculated. The formation of valency bonds, however, may be treated in terms of a rule called the *principle of maximum overlap*. This asserts that the valency bond is formed in such a direction that there occurs a maximum overlap of the wave function concerned, that is in the directions of maximum electron density of the original atoms.

s electrons being described by wave functions which represent a spherically symmetrical distribution of electricity, all directions are equally likely for bond formation. p wave functions have axial symmetry. Thus if a p_x electron participates in a bond, that bond will tend to be formed in the direction of the x-axis.

This principle, which is not in fact proved rigidly from the equations of quantum mechanics, provides the theoretical basis of stereochemistry.

The three valencies of nitrogen are at right angles and in consequence the molecule NH_3 should be pyramidal in shape with angles of 90° between the three valencies. This corresponds roughly, though by no means accurately, to the truth.

The two valencies of oxygen should be at right angles to one another (p_x and p_y). The shape of the water molecule is indeed much more nearly rectangular than linear, though the actual angle between the valencies appreciably exceeds 90°.

Carbon presents a rather special problem. Its four valencies are equal and disposed symmetrically in space, as we know from the evidence of stereochemistry itself. The scheme $(2s)^1$, $(2p_x)^1$, $(2p_y)^1$, $(2p_z)^1$, which implies four valencies not all equal, has evidently been modified.

It is customary to speak of what has happened in terms of a process called *hybridization* of the wave functions.

In this method of description the separate functions

$$\psi(2s), \quad \psi(2p_x), \quad \psi(2p_y), \quad \psi(2p_z)$$

are replaced by linear combinations of the following forms:

$$\psi(2s)+\psi(2p_x)+\psi(2p_y)+\psi(2p_z),$$
$$\psi(2s)+\psi(2p_x)-\psi(2p_y)-\psi(2p_z),$$
$$\psi(2s)-\psi(2p_x)+\psi(2p_y)-\psi(2p_z),$$
$$\psi(2s)-\psi(2p_x)-\psi(2p_y)+\psi(2p_z).$$

These represent equal concentrations of density along four symmetrically directed spatial axes. Accordingly, if the principle of maximum overlapping is valid, methane, for example, will possess a tetrahedral structure—as of course it has to do.

Hybridization can also be employed in the description of molecules in which the valency angles do not correspond to the expectations based upon the simple application of the theory of maximum overlapping.

Once again it must be emphasized that we are here dealing not with a phenomenon predicted by quantum mechanics, but with a convenient mode of description, in terms of approximations, of matters to which those approximations ought really never to have been applied. That they have been so applied in an imperfect world is a necessity imposed by the absence of methods which are at the same time precise and manageable. A correct solution of the wave equation for a combined carbon atom (in methane) would presumably predict four symmetrically disposed axes of maximum electric density for the configuration of minimum energy, and not the existence of $2s$ and $2p$ wave functions. The latter apply to isolated atoms in any case. Interaction with other atoms modifies the density distribution, as is seen from the fact that two hydrogen atoms, each with a spherically symmetrical distribution, give a molecule with an axial concentration between the two. Thus the principle of maximum overlapping as applied to unmodified wave functions is not likely to be exact. Hybridization in one sense is a mathematical fiction expressing the extent to which the approximate principle may be adjusted to the equally inexact conception of unmodified atomic wave functions.

The foregoing observation does not, of course, constitute a criticism of the computational methods that have to be used. It does, however, bear upon the question of what we are to think about the theory of chemical forces as a whole. In the last resort these depend simply upon the Coulomb electrostatic law, the condition of minimum energy consistent with acceptable solutions of the wave equation, and the Pauli principle in its generalized form. All the other principles, such as maximum overlapping and hybridization, are really auxiliaries introduced for the purposes of practical calculation. Used with discretion they are also helpful in permitting us to construct certain naïve pictures of molecules and atoms, which, however, must not be taken too literally.

Description of molecules by wave functions

In the treatment of the interaction of hydrogen atoms by the method of Heitler and London it is, as has been explained, impossible to solve the appropriate wave equation by frontal attack, and thereby to derive the correct wave functions for the description of the hydrogen molecule. What has to be done, not from choice but from necessity, is to postulate an inherently reasonable form of wave function and to insert it tentatively into Schrödinger's equation. In the calculation already outlined the combination chosen was $a\psi_1\phi_2+b\psi_2\phi_1$, where the individual functions apply to isolated and unperturbed atoms. It is as well, however, not to forget that there is no quite rigid justification for this procedure, which is sensible but essentially empirical, and we only create difficulties for ourselves if we seek deeper reasons where they do not exist. With the above combination, however, it was possible to obtain an approximate solution of the problem: Given that the interaction of the atoms introduces an extra term into the potential energy, by what amount is the total energy altered? The answer gave a measure of the valency force.

R

In all such problems it is necessary to have a ready-made wave function to replace that which would emerge from the fundamental equation could it be solved. With the aid of this tentative solution the energy can be calculated. In principle, certainty that the procedure has been the correct one can only be reached by the trial of innumerable empirical functions and the demonstration that none leads to a lower value of the energy than that chosen. The correct solution must always be that which gives the lowest energy.

This last principle provides a method by which many problems can be treated. Quite frequently it appears obvious that the true wave function must be somewhere between χ_1 and χ_2, which are functions corresponding to the solutions applicable under simpler or more nearly ideal conditions. A tentative function is then constructed by a linear combination of the two, $\chi = a\chi_1 + b\chi_2$. This is inserted in the wave equation, and the values of a and b are determined for which the energy is a minimum. These express the best possible combination of the type specified. The corresponding value of the energy is more nearly the true one, the more skilfully χ_1 and χ_2 have been chosen. Here again the method is really empirical, and the determination of a and b does not in any way establish the appropriateness of the two functions themselves.

A simple analogy describes the situation fairly well. Suppose we assume that three points A, X, and B lie on a straight line, then, if we determine the ratio AX/BX, we shall define the position of X accurately in relation to the other two. Suppose now we assume that we can define the position of Rugby by a linear interpolation between Manchester and London, we shall not do badly. If, on the other hand, we make the best computation of the position of Plymouth on such a basis, it will be a very poor best at that. Everything thus depends upon the initial choice of the reference functions.

The combination of wave functions, $\psi_1\phi_2 \pm \psi_2\phi_1$, used in the Heitler–London calculation fixes attention on the electron–nucleus assignments A1, B2, and A2, B1, where A and B represent nuclei and 1 and 2 represent electrons. The individual members of the combination are simple $1s$ wave functions of the hydrogen atom. The first elaboration which can be introduced in seeking a more accurate solution is no longer to use $1s$ wave functions for electrons moving in the field of a nucleus with unit charge, but to give the nuclear charge the effective value Ze. The value of Z at a given nuclear distance, R, can be adjusted so as to yield the minimum value for the energy.

The next possibility in elaborating the calculation is to take into account assignments of the type (A1, 2) (B) and (A) (B1, 2), where both electrons belong to the one or to the other nucleus. These represent the polar molecules H^-H^+ and H^+H^-. The form of wave function in such a case is then

$$a(\psi_1 \phi_2 + \psi_2 \phi_1) + b(\psi_1 \psi_2 + \phi_1 \phi_2),$$

ψ_1, ψ_2, ϕ_1, and ϕ_2 themselves being ordinary wave functions of unperturbed atoms, or, if desired, wave functions of unperturbed atoms with effective nuclear charges empirically modified as in the first method. The ratio a/b and, if necessary, the value of Z, can be so chosen as to give a minimum energy.

There is, in principle, no limit to the complexity of the combinations which may be set up. The ratios of constants such as a and b can be determined by the minimum energy condition, and, in this sense, it is possible to speak of the relative contributions of various forms of structure to the make-up of the hydrogen molecule. For example, one can speak of the molecule as receiving contributions in such-and-such proportions from polar and non-polar forms respectively.

But there is a good deal of convention about this mode of description. The ideal forms in terms of which the state is described have no real existence, and they are only important in so far as they are simple limiting cases about which it is convenient to think. Neither the Heitler–London hydrogen molecule nor the polar H^+H^- molecule exists in nature. As is well known, the superposition of two photographs of human faces gives a composite portrait not very like either. Certain individuals might be imitated fairly well by superposition, in varying proportions of intensity, of pictures say of Napoleon and of Dante, and it might be a convenient mnemonic to remember that X was 30 per cent. of the former and 70 per cent. of the latter, yet in fact he is neither, but just himself. It must be admitted, however, that the reference systems in the case of the polar and non-polar hydrogen molecules are not quite so far removed from their mean as those of the analogy.

In building up convenient wave functions for the exploration of the minimum energy state one special distinction assumes a great deal of importance, that, namely, between what are called *atomic orbitals* and *molecular orbitals* respectively. In the Heitler–London hydrogen molecule the contributions to the wave function for each electron are always of the form which they assume when that electron belongs to one single nucleus. Thus A1, B2 and A2, B1 lead to $\psi_1\phi_2\pm\psi_2\phi_1$. The electrons are here said to be assigned to atomic orbitals. Alternatively, one could try to construct a wave function by taking the first electron to belong to both nuclei and writing its function in a form such as $\psi_1+\phi_1$, and similarly for the second. A possible form for the complete function is then $(\psi_1+\phi_1)(\psi_2+\phi_2)$. The two electrons are said in such circumstances to be assigned to molecular orbitals.

Calculations on molecules by the variation method

At this stage it will be expedient to illustrate certain methods of calculation, not because we propose to develop the technique of such matters, but in order that the principles of the processes may be clearer and the significance of the results seen in better perspective.

The considerations which follow are based upon the theorem that if an incorrect value of ψ is inserted in the wave equation, the calculated energy will be greater than the true energy.

To prove this theorem formally it is first convenient to express the wave equation in an abbreviated conventional form. If it is written, not in the manner used hitherto,

$$\nabla^2\psi+\frac{8\pi^2m}{h^2}E\psi-\frac{8\pi^2m}{h^2}U\psi = 0,$$

but

$$\left(-\frac{h^2}{8\pi^2m}\nabla^2+U\right)\psi = E\psi,$$

the term in the bracket on the left is an *operator* which is commonly written H, the main equation then assuming the shape

$$H\psi = E\psi.$$

Multiplication by $\bar{\psi}$ and integration over the whole range of coordinates then gives

$$\int \bar{\psi}H\psi\, d\omega = \int \bar{\psi}E\psi\, d\omega = E\int \psi\bar{\psi}\, d\omega,$$

since E is a simple quantity, not an operator. Therefore

$$E = \frac{\int \bar{\psi}H\psi\, d\omega}{\int \psi\bar{\psi}\, d\omega}.$$

If the units are so chosen that $\int \psi\bar{\psi}\, d\omega = 1$, then

$$E = \int \bar{\psi} H \psi\, d\omega.$$

In the equation $H\psi = E\psi$, if ψ is not correct, then by the theorem just enunciated E will be too great.

Consider a function ϕ expressed as a series

$$\phi = \sum a_n \psi_n \quad \text{with} \quad \bar{\phi} = \sum a_n \bar{\psi}_n,$$

where

$$\sum a_n^2 = 1.$$

Now let

$$E' = \int \bar{\phi} E \phi\, d\omega = \int \sum a_n \bar{\psi}_n H(\sum a_n \psi_n)\, d\omega.$$

But

$$H(\sum a_n \psi_n) = \sum a_n H\psi_n = \sum a_n E_n \psi_n.$$

Substitution in the energy integral gives

$$E' = \sum a_n^2 E_n,$$

since $\int \bar{\psi}_n \psi_m\, d\omega = 0$ or 1 according as $n \neq m$ or $n = m$.

Since

$$\sum a_n^2 = 1, \qquad E_0 = \sum a_n^2 E_0.$$

Therefore

$$E' - E_0 = \sum a_n^2 (E_n - E_0).$$

E_n cannot be less than E_0, so that E' cannot be less than E_0. It will be greater than E_0 except in the limiting case where ϕ is the true ground state wave function.

It is now a question of seeing how the minimum energy condition can be usefully applied.

Suppose a trial wave function for the description of a molecule is constructed having the form

$$\phi = c_1 \chi_1 + c_2 \chi_2,$$

where χ_1 and χ_2 themselves are wave functions appropriate to some simpler version of the problem, and c_1 and c_2 are adjustable constants. The energy for the lowest level permitted by the solution for ϕ is given by the expression

$$E' = \frac{\int \bar{\phi} H \phi\, d\omega}{\int \bar{\phi}\phi\, d\omega} = \frac{\int (c_1 \bar{\chi}_1 + c_2 \bar{\chi}_2) H(c_1 \chi_1 + c_2 \chi_2)\, d\omega}{\int (c_1 \bar{\chi}_1 + c_2 \bar{\chi}_2)(c_1 \chi_1 + c_2 \chi_2)\, d\omega}.$$

This last equation is multiplied out and then differentiated with respect to c_1 and c_2 in turn. $\partial E'/\partial c_1$ and $\partial E'/\partial c_2$ are equated to zero. This process leads to the relations

$$c_1(H_{11} - E\Delta_{11}) + c_2(H_{12} - E\Delta_{12}) = 0,$$

$$c_1(H_{21} - E\Delta_{21}) + c_2(H_{22} - E\Delta_{22}) = 0,$$

where, as a result of the differentiation, E is the lowest possible value of E', and

$$H_{11} = \int \bar{\chi}_1 H \chi_1 \, d\omega, \qquad H_{12} = \int \bar{\chi}_1 H \chi_2 \, d\omega,$$

$$\Delta_{11} = \int \bar{\chi}_1 \chi_1 \, d\omega, \qquad \Delta_{12} = \int \bar{\chi}_1 \chi_2 \, d\omega, \quad \text{and so on.}$$

The last two equations in c_1 and c_2 impose a condition which may be expressed in the form of the determinant

$$\begin{vmatrix} H_{11} - E\Delta_{11} & H_{12} - E\Delta_{12} \\ H_{21} - E\Delta_{21} & H_{22} - E\Delta_{22} \end{vmatrix} = 0.$$

The whole process can easily enough be extended to a tentative wave function with a greater number of adjustable constants, $c_1, c_2, c_3, \ldots$.

The method of calculation just outlined can be applied to various structural problems. It is in fact a widely used technique. What at first sight appears somewhat puzzling is how advantage can be derived from it when the values of χ_1 and χ_2 themselves are in most real examples inaccessible to calculation from first principles. The matter is perhaps made clearer by the following example.

Suppose we have a molecule with a conjugated carbon atom skeleton. It is assumed that certain electrons, the σ electrons, are allocated to certain particular bonds and that they retain their places. Others, the π electrons, are assigned to molecular orbitals. What this means mathematically is that each is described by a wave function which is constructed tentatively as a sum of atomic orbitals

$$\phi = c_1 \psi_1 + c_2 \psi_2 + c_3 \psi_3 + \ldots.$$

ϕ, of course, measures the probability that the electron occurs near the point represented by the coordinates of ϕ itself. Each of the ψ terms is connected with a probability that the electron is in the neighbourhood of, or in a sense belongs to, the atom 1, 2, 3,..., according to the subscript of the term. By the principle of the multiplication of probabilities, the wave function of the whole molecule contains the product of the ϕ functions for each of the π electrons.

The condition of minimum energy can now be applied and it leads to values for $c_1, c_2, \ldots$, and so on *in terms of integrals* of the type H_{11}, H_{12}, and so on of the preceding paragraphs. These integrals are not in general determinable, but this does not mean that a useful result cannot be achieved, even with a rather rough approximation. Some of the integrals, namely those relating to pairs of atoms which are not directly bonded in the molecule, are set equal to zero, and others are given a constant standard value, assumed to be the same throughout a whole series of molecules of not too different general type. This removes much of the specificity from the problem, but not all. One very important element remains, that, namely, of the algebraical form of a determinant similar to that above. The character of this determinant, in turn, is governed by the total number of carbon atoms in the molecule under study, and, what is also important, upon the number of neighbours each individual atom possesses in that molecule, this last factor deciding which of the standardized integrals are zero and which not. Relative values of the constants, c_1, c_2,... are now calculable. The use made of them is this: the relative electron distributions in a series of molecules of steadily changing structure can be compared, for example in the series, benzene, naphthalene, anthracene, the successive polyenes, different types of heterocyclic ring, and so on.

ψ_j represents an assignment of an electron to the jth atom of a structure, and c_j^2 is the probability of this state of affairs. $\sum c_j^2$, therefore, taken over all the electrons, may be regarded as expressing the total density of electrons on the jth atom, and in this way the distribution of charge throughout the structure in the different types of compounds can be studied.

In general the procedure is attended with considerable success. What must be borne in mind, however, is that the success of the calculations technically depends upon the neglect of all save what, in the example quoted, is virtually the geometrical factor in the particular structural problem. It is of great interest that the geometry of carbon ring systems should so largely determine their character, but this fact could not, in the present state of knowledge, have been predicted from the outset.

Retrospect

In all the foregoing the only fundamental law of force which has emerged is the inverse square law of electrostatics. The interaction of particles is chiefly regulated by prescriptions of permissible energy states. If the only level into which a combination of particles may enter is lower than corresponds to the sum of their original energies, then energy has to be discarded. The result is a manifestation which can be described as the operation of an attractive force. But it is really something more abstract. If a traveller is not allowed to bring currency into a country, he may discard it on his way there, but it is the law rather than the circumstances of the journey which really compels the sacrifice. Dynamics does not demand that an electron passing from one orbit to another in an atom should radiate energy: what does is the requirement that its new angular momentum shall not exceed the prescription of the quantum rules. And similarly in many other connexions.

Another most potent factor is the selection of alternative energy states imposed by the Pauli principle. This in its turn is based upon abstract requirements about the distinguishability of particles and has nothing to do with the nature of force as such. Chemical valencies are therefore determined more by categorical principles than by dynamical rules.

The general tendency illustrated by these developments is evident throughout physics: gravitation is reduced to a manifestation of the geometry of space and time, electron spin loses its primitive significance and becomes a quality required for relativistic invariance of the wave equation, and, according to the speculations of Eddington, every kind of physical interaction, including gravitation, is ultimately dependent upon some sort of generalized Pauli principle in which multiple occupation of states is impossible.

In its present stage of evolution, chemistry compromises between the abstract principle and the naïve pictorial hypothesis.

XII

INTERATOMIC FORCES AND MOLECULAR PROPERTIES

Introduction

IT will now be expedient to discuss briefly the relation between inter-atomic forces and certain other molecular characteristics which are more or less closely connected with them.

Vibration frequencies and force constants

The forces between atoms are, of course, only indirectly accessible to experimental study. What is most commonly measured is the energy change accompanying a transformation, but this quantity introduces the force as a complicated integral, the constitution of which is seldom clear. The nearest approach to an immediate mani-festation is perhaps in the vibration frequency of a diatomic molecule.

When two masses joined by a spring execute a simple harmonic motion about their equilibrium position, the frequency is given by the equation

$$\nu = \frac{1}{2\pi}\left(\frac{f}{m^*}\right)^{\frac{1}{2}},$$

where m^* is the reduced mass, that is, the harmonic mean of the two individual masses, and f is the force constant, or restoring force for unit displacement.

If the vibrations which a diatomic molecule manifests in its spec-trum are assumed to be simple harmonic, then f may be calculated from ν.

For polyatomic molecules the situation is more complicated, and the vibrations are characteristic not of individual pairs of atoms but of the molecule as a whole. If it contains N atoms, their positions in space are describable by $3N$ Cartesian coordinates which may be written $q_1, q_2,..., q_i,....$ These may conveniently be measured from the equilibrium positions of the respective atoms. The total kinetic energy of the system is $\sum \frac{1}{2}m_i(dq_i/dt)^2$, where m_i is the mass of a representative atom. The potential energy is of the form

$$U = \sum \tfrac{1}{2}a_{ij}q_i q_j,$$

i and j being two representative atoms. If all the displacements were zero except one, U would assume the form $\frac{1}{2}a_{ii}q_i^2$, that is, the ordinary form for the simple harmonic motion of a single mass where the potential energy is proportional to the square of the displacement. But a_{ii} in general would be a function of more than one interatomic force, since the movement of one atom will affect the forces between others. In real problems it is usually uncertain what relative weight should be given to the square terms of the form $\frac{1}{2}a_{ii}q_i^2$ and what to the cross terms of the form $\frac{1}{2}a_{jk}q_jq_k$, but trial-and-error methods can be used to find appropriate potential energy functions for given molecules, and the observed spectrum of vibration frequencies can often be satisfactorily reproduced.

Sometimes the potential energy function can be simplified by representation as the sum of squares proportional to the linear displacements of masses, on the one hand, and to the angular deformations of bonds, on the other:

$$U = \sum \tfrac{1}{2}k_1(\Delta x)^2 + \sum \tfrac{1}{2}k_1'(\Delta\theta)^2.$$

This implies that the stretching of bonds between adjacent atoms or the distortion of the valency angles are the only important factors. It neglects the consideration that a stretched bond probably has a different bending constant and that a number of other mutual influences are at work.

In the more generalized forms of potential energy expression there may be more unknown constants than there are observable frequencies. Various devices must then be introduced for the resolution of the problem. One of the best of these, where it is applicable, is the observation of the change in frequency which occurs when various atoms in the molecule are replaced by isotopes, the substitution of deuterium for hydrogen, for example, being one of the commonest cases where the mass can be changed without change of force constant.

Even when an empirically chosen potential energy function gives satisfactory results for a set of observed frequencies, care has to be exercised in evaluating the conclusions about the interatomic forces. In a first approximation these conclusions will be valid enough, but there is much interest in the exploration of just such matters as the way in which the strength of one bond varies when the character of an adjacent one is changed: in the question, for example, as to how the strength of a C—C link depends upon its environment. There is a not inconsiderable danger of supposing that details which are really a function of the approximate forms assumed for the potential energy may be manifestations of real physical effects. With care and judgement, however, very interesting results may be achieved.

Normal modes of vibration

The way in which the normal frequencies for a complete molecular framework arise is of some interest in itself, and will be illustrated by a somewhat idealized example, namely the linear vibrations of a system of equal masses—which might serve as a model of a straight carbon chain. The method of calculation is typical of that to be applied to more complex cases, and shows quite clearly how the frequencies are characteristic not of individual bonds but of the structure as a whole.

Suppose we have three equal masses bound by elastic forces and susceptible of displacements along the x-axis only, this axis being the one along which they are spaced.

If the displacements are x_1, x_2, and x_3 respectively we shall have, from the equations of simple harmonic motion,

$$k(x_2-x_1) = m\ddot{x}_1,$$

$$k(x_1+x_3-2x_2) = m\ddot{x}_2,$$

$$k(x_2-x_3) = m\ddot{x}_3,$$

where m is the mass and k is the elastic constant.

The restoring force on the first mass is proportional, not to its own displacement, but to the difference between it and that of the adjacent mass. The force on the second depends upon the difference between (x_3-x_2) and (x_2-x_1).

If the vibrations are to be repeated time after time without change in the relative amplitudes of movement of the various masses, these must all move with the same frequency, and this frequency will characterize what is called a *normal vibration* of the system as a whole. Thus if $x = A\sin(nt+\alpha)$, n must be the same for all the masses.

Since
$$\ddot{x}_1 = -n^2x_1, \quad \ddot{x}_2 = -n^2x_2, \quad \text{and} \quad \ddot{x}_3 = -n^2x_3,$$

as may be seen by differentiation, the equations of motion become

$$(k/m)(x_2-x_1) = -n^2 x_1,$$

$$(k/m)(x_1+x_3-2x_2) = -n^2 x_2,$$

$$(k/m)(x_2-x_3) = -n^2 x_3,$$

or, by rearrangement,

$$\left(n^2-\frac{k}{m}\right)x_1+\frac{k}{m}x_2 = 0,$$

$$\frac{k}{m}x_1+\left(n^2-\frac{2k}{m}\right)x_2+\frac{k}{m}x_3 = 0,$$

$$\frac{k}{m}x_2+\left(n^2-\frac{k}{m}\right)x_3 = 0,$$

whence

$$\begin{vmatrix} n^2-\dfrac{k}{m} & \dfrac{k}{m} & 0 \\[2mm] \dfrac{k}{m} & n^2-\dfrac{2k}{m} & \dfrac{k}{m} \\[2mm] 0 & \dfrac{k}{m} & n^2-\dfrac{k}{m} \end{vmatrix} = 0$$

and

$$n^2\left(n^4-\frac{4k}{m}n^2+\frac{3k^2}{m^2}\right) = 0,$$

i.e.

$$n^2\left(n^2-\frac{k}{m}\right)\left(n^2-3\frac{k}{m}\right) = 0,$$

whence $n = 0,$ $\sqrt{\left(\dfrac{k}{m}\right)},$ or $\sqrt{\left(\dfrac{3k}{m}\right)}.$

The solution $n = 0$ corresponds to a translation of the whole set along the axis with no relative displacement of the masses. The other two solutions determine the frequencies of normal modes. The value $(k/m)^{\frac{1}{2}}$ corresponds to relative amplitudes $x_1 = -x_3$, $x_2 = 0$, while $(3k/m)^{\frac{1}{2}}$ corresponds to $x_1 = x_3$, $x_2 = -2x_1$. These modes are shown in (a) and (b) respectively.

(a)   ←—O   O   O—→,

(b)   O—→ ←—O   O—→.

To find the relative amplitudes of the different displacements corresponding to the modes (*a*) and (*b*) we write down the various quantities $\Delta_{12} = x_1 - x_2$, $\Delta_{23} = x_2 - x_3$, and so on, and adjust the absolute magnitudes so that $\sum \Delta^2$ for each normal mode is the same (as required by the equipartition principle).

It is of some interest to see how the modes and frequencies evolve as the system becomes more complex. For a chain of any number

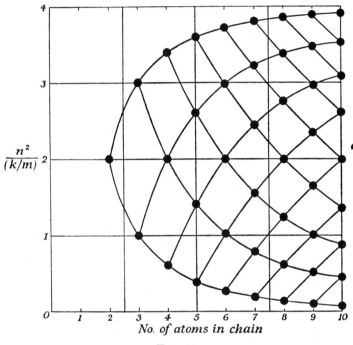

FIG. 25

of masses in a line, the method of calculation is similar to that already exemplified, except that the high-order equations become rather laborious to solve. Fig. 25 gives the relative values of $n^2/(k/m)$ for all the linear modes of a chain composed of any number of equal masses from 2 to 10. These values, as may be seen from the above equations, are proportional to the squares of the frequencies.

The number of modes increases with the number of masses. The lowest value of the frequency diminishes steadily towards zero. It always corresponds to a mode in which two halves of the system vibrate with respect to one another somewhat as though they were two composite heavy masses. For example, in the four- and seven-chains respectively, the modes of lowest frequency are those shown below.

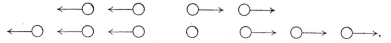

In a sense they are like vibrations of two composite groups, but this is not at all exactly so, since the relative displacements of the various masses moving in a given direction are by no means all equal.

The highest frequency increases towards a limit. It always belongs to a mode in which alternate masses are moving in opposite directions, for example, with the six-chain

If the chain is infinite in length, the influence of the two end masses becomes negligible and each atom, or mass, since it moves in the opposite direction from both its neighbours, is subject to twice the restoring force which it would experience in a system of two masses. The frequency being proportional to the square root of the restoring force, its square, which the numbers in the diagram measure, will be just double for the infinite chain what it is for the chain of two members. The convergence of $n^2/(k/m)$ to a value just twice the initial value is evident in the diagram.

In the linear model which has just been discussed the number of modes is one less than the number of masses. In general, three-dimensional modes have to be considered, and here the relation obeyed is that if there are N atoms in the molecule, there are $3N-6$ normal modes of vibration. This is easily proved. N isolated masses have $3N$ translational degrees of freedom and no others. Into whatever system the masses may be combined, they retain these. But since when N atoms constitute a molecule they must preserve certain relations between their coordinates, it becomes convenient to formulate some modes of motion in common: namely 3 for the translation of the centre of gravity of the entire system and 3 for the rotation of the whole about three axes. This leaves $3N-6$ degrees of freedom for vibration.

When a molecule is set into vibration by some process such as a collision with another molecule, the various normal modes are in general excited in a random way. It then vibrates not with a single mode, but with a superposition of several or all of them. These, naturally, show interference phenomena, and the amplitude of stretching of individual bonds shows secular variations according as the phases of the sundry modes with the separate frequencies reinforce one another or annul one another. In this sense one may speak of an ebb and flow of energy in individual links of the molecule. This effect is of considerable significance in connexion with the theory of reaction velocities.

Dissociation energies and related quantities

The potential energy function is, as will be obvious, not simply related to the force which would exist between two isolated atoms except with a diatomic molecule. Nor will this function be simply related to a dissociation energy.

Even with a diatomic molecule there is no direct proportionality between these two quantities. The energy required to cause a displacement x is $\int_0^x F\,dx$, where F is the restoring force. For small displacements $F = fx$, where f is the force constant previously spoken of, and the energy will be

$$\int_0^x fx\,dx = \tfrac{1}{2}fx^2.$$

But as x increases, f begins to fall and, of course, vanishes for very large separations of the atoms.

The dissociation energy will thus be

$$\int_0^\infty \phi(x)x\,dx,$$

where $\phi(x)$ is a function which decreases according to a very complicated law as x increases. The law in question is not only complicated but highly specific and varies from molecule to molecule.

There will therefore be no precise correlation between dissociation energies and force constants, though there will be a general parallelism. Small force constants will be associated with weak binding and low energies, and large constants with tight binding and high energies, but this is all that can be said.

In hydrocarbons there are certain vibrations identifiable as due mainly to relative displacements of H-atoms and the C-atoms to which they are bound. These vibrations decrease in frequency according as the H forms part of a group CH_3, CH_2, or CH, and from this it is probably correct to conclude that the energy required to detach it would decrease also in that order. A quantitative comparison would not, however, be justified.

As will have become evident in the earlier parts of this account, energies are in general more important than forces, since it is they which appear in the equations of thermodynamics and of the quantum theory. Energies, as has been said, are derivable in principle from forces, but the calculation requires a knowledge of the variation of force with distance. They must therefore be determined in practice from calorimetric or from spectroscopic observations. Even these two methods do not always measure the same quantity. When a molecule AB dissociates under the influence of light, either or both of the atoms may be formed in one of their excited states. Thus, for example,

$$\text{AB} \longrightarrow \text{A} + \text{B} - D_1,$$
$$\text{AB} \longrightarrow \text{A}^* + \text{B} - D_2.$$

$(D_2 - D_1)$ is the energy of the transition $\text{A} \to \text{A}^*$ and must thus correspond to one of the excitation quanta of the atom A. If D_2 and D_1 can be separately determined, the nature of the state in which the atom A is formed in the spectral dissociation can be recognized. Since the atomic levels are fairly widely spaced, a rough value of $D_2 - D_1$ may suffice for the identification.

With diatomic molecules, energies of dissociation may be determined in various other ways. One method depends upon the variation with temperature of the equilibrium constant of the dissociation, and application of the thermodynamic relation $d \ln K / dT = \Delta U / RT^2$. A second method involves determinations, based upon measurements of explosion temperatures, of the apparent specific heat of the partially dissociated gas.

What is usually measured in calorimetric experiments is, however, something rather different from a dissociation energy. For example, in studying the molecule H_2O we might be presented with experimental results in the following form:

$$H_2 \text{ (gas)} \to 2H - Q_1$$
$$O_2 \text{ (gas)} \to 2O - Q_2$$
$$2H_2 + O_2 \to 2H_2O \text{ (gas)} + Q_3.$$

For the perfectly definite but experimentally less accessible reaction of H and O, we have

$$2H + O \to H_2O \text{ (gas)} + Q_4.$$

From the rule known as Hess's law, which is simply a special case of the conservation of energy,

$$Q_4 = \tfrac{1}{2}Q_3 + Q_1 + \tfrac{1}{2}Q_2,$$

since the energy change must be the same whether hydrogen atoms and oxygen atoms unite directly with one another or whether they first form diatomic molecules which subsequently react to give water. Q_4 represents the energy liberated when two O—H bonds are formed. In a purely formal way it may be divided into two equal parts which are then termed the bond energies of the oxygen–hydrogen links in water.

But the energies of the two reactions

$$H + O \rightarrow OH \quad \text{and} \quad H + OH \rightarrow H_2O$$

are not necessarily even approximately the same, since the addition of the first hydrogen atom will, in principle, modify the attraction of the oxygen for the second.

From the heats of the reactions

$$CH_4 + 2O_2 = CO_2 + 2H_2O,$$
$$C_{solid} + O_2 = CO_2,$$
$$2H_2 + O_2 = 2H_2O,$$
$$H_2 = 2H,$$

that of the reaction $\qquad C_{solid} + 4H = CH_4$

may be calculated. If the heat of vaporization of solid carbon to the atomic state may be assumed, the energy of the reaction

$$C_{gas} + 4H = CH_4$$

is calculable. According to a conventional formulation, one-quarter of this energy of formation is called the bond energy of the C—H bond in methane.

It is, however, not equal to the energy of the reaction

$$CH_3 + H = CH_4,$$

since the methyl radical cannot be regarded simply as a methane molecule minus one hydrogen atom. When the fourth atom is removed the remainder of the molecule suffers a reorganization, in this case quite a profound one, since the tetrahedral configuration of the methane molecule gives place to a planar configuration with the three valencies of the methyl group at angles of 120°.

Bond energies might have remained of a purely formal significance

s

were it not for the fact that in a first rough approximation they have been found to be not only additive but constant. In any given molecule the sum of the bond energies must by definition equal the heat of formation from the atoms. For a single molecule this means nothing. The bond energy of C—Cl in methyl chloride is only obtainable by subtraction of three times the bond energy assumed for hydrogen from the heat of formation of the CH_3Cl. But what is found is that a single list of bond energies can be drawn up from which, *approximately*, the heat of formation of any molecule of normal valency structure can be predicted.

This scheme is subject to very distinct limitations, but is of importance in that it provides a norm of behaviour the deviations from which can be studied and compared in various examples.

In the table of bond energies separate values are conveniently listed for singly, doubly, or triply bound atoms, for O in C=O, for O in C—O—C, and so on.

Resonance

When a compound is so constituted that more than one normal valency formula may be used to represent its molecule, as with benzene where the two Kekulé forms and the three Dewar forms are possible, the energy of formation usually proves to be greater than that calculated for any of the possible individual formulae. The molecule thus appears to exist in a state which is more stable than that corresponding to any of the conventional valency-bond representations. Detailed evidence from many sources, indeed, suggests that these formulae are quite often inadequate. Benzene, for example, is best regarded not as possessing three single and three double carbon–carbon bonds, but six equal bonds of order approximately 1·5.

The extra stability in such examples is often said to be derived from a process called *resonance* between the *canonical structures* corresponding to the alternative valency formulae. But there is really no process, and the canonical structures as such do not exist. They are called canonical because they possess the formal simplicity of classical structural chemistry, and it is this that gives them their importance as aids to thought or visualization.

Bond lengths

A highly significant extra datum in the discussion of molecular energies, and in the attempt to assign rational and useful bond energies, is the length of a bond. The distances between the centres of gravity of atoms can be determined, in favourable examples with high accuracy, by the diffraction of X-rays or of electrons by molecules. The length of the CH bond in methane is 1·094 A (Angström units), in ethylene 1·071 A, in acetylene 1·059 A. Here the bond shortens as the force constant increases, but the two effects are not simply related.

The C—C links in ethane, ethylene, and acetylene respectively are 1·55 A, 1·35 A, and 1·20 A. If the *bond orders* are taken as 1, 2, and 3 for the three molecules there appears a well-defined functional relation when order is plotted against length, and, according to this, the value for benzene, 1·40 A, corresponds well enough to an order of 1·5, that is, half-way between a single and a double bond.

Once this functional relation is established, other bond orders can be inferred from the corresponding lengths. Much of the finer detail of structural relationships may be studied in this way.

In more elaborate discussions, closer consideration of the definition of bond orders is needed, along the lines, for example, of the quantum-mechanical theories which have been referred to earlier and which yield information about the average density of electronic charge on the various atoms of a molecule (p. 255).

XIII

FORCES BETWEEN MOLECULES AND BETWEEN IONS

Van der Waals forces

INTERATOMIC forces, as manifested in valency bonds, are essentially electrostatic. They depend upon electron distributions so prescribed that attraction outweighs repulsion. The prescriptions are dictated largely by the need to conform with the condition of an antisymmetrical wave function. It is the fact, moreover, that spin states are defined by simple alternatives which restricts the modes of chemical interaction to the saturation of definite valency linkings. When the considerations resting upon symmetry and spin conditions have no longer to be applied, the property of saturability ceases to be a characteristic of the forces between particles. Two sets of interactions exempt from this limitation are of importance in physical chemistry. They are, on the one hand, the so-called *van der Waals forces* which cause the agglomeration of atoms or molecules to liquids and solids, and, on the other hand, the simple Coulomb forces between charged ions in gases, or, more commonly, condensed phases and especially solutions.

In general the forces which cause the condensation of molecules to solids and liquids are much weaker than those of valency. The heat of the reaction $2H_2 + O_2 = 2H_2O$, which involves the making and breaking of valency bonds, is of the order 10^5 cal., while the latent heat of vaporization of water is of the order 10^4 cal. for a gram molecule.

There is really nothing in the whole theory of atomic and molecular structure which suggests any interpretation of these intermolecular forces as other than electrical. They exist between systems which individually are electrically neutral, and therefore they are not simple ionic forces. But many molecules possess as a whole an electrical fine structure which endows them with a field at points not too far remote.

An ion possesses a field the intensity of which is inversely proportional to the square of the distance. A dipole, which may be deemed uncharged as a whole, still exerts a field, but one which falls off more rapidly, being inversely proportional to a function of the distance approximately representable as a cube.

Suppose we have a dipole as shown:

$$+e \quad l \quad -e \qquad\qquad r$$
$$\longleftarrow\!\!\longrightarrow\!\!\cdots\cdots\cdots\cdots\cdots\cdots\cdots\cdots O.$$

The force on unit charge at a point O is $e/r^2 - e/(r+l)^2$. This is approximately equal to $2rle/r^4$ when r is great compared with l. $el = \mu$, the dipole moment, so that the force is $2\mu/r^3$. If the point O is not on the axis a trigonometrical factor appears, and this, averaged over all orientations to the dipole, leads to a numerical multiplier. The force remains, however, proportional to μ/r^3.

A dipole is detectable in that it swings round to align itself with an electric field, and in consequence molecules with dipolar moments possess special dielectric and other properties. Many molecules possess no such moments, but, even so, their fine structure still permits the existence of an external field. The structure shown below is called a quadrupole

$$+\,-$$
$$-\,+.$$

A simple calculation, similar to that made on the dipole, shows that the field at an external point falls off still more rapidly with the distance from the centre of gravity of the combination.

It is clear, therefore, that ionic forces are more important than dipolar forces, and the latter more important than quadrupolar ones. Ions, obviously, are not always present, but where they are, ionic interactions outweigh the others. At first sight, dipoles seem only to appear in special molecules, and even quadrupoles would appear to be absent from atoms such as those of the inert gases which show complete spherical symmetry in their electron distributions. Since the latter do in fact condense to liquids, there must be a mode of interaction independent of permanent electrical multipoles of any kind. As was first shown by London, the quantum theory predicts such a mode, and it proves after all to be of a dipolar nature.

Any neutral atom or molecule can be schematized in terms of a positive centre surrounded by a cloud of negative electrification. If the positive centre is displaced from its equilibrium position, it will oscillate with a frequency ν_0. According to the quantum theory, even in the lowest possible energy state, an oscillator possesses energy $\frac{1}{2}h\nu_0$. Thus the atom or molecule will, from this cause alone, always show a fluctuating dipolar moment. The average value of this is zero, but at most instants it is finite. The important fact is that this fluctuating dipole will induce similar dipoles in other systems.

That the interaction of the induced and the inducing dipole leads to a lowering of energy is to be seen qualitatively in a very simple way. If two pendulums of frequency ν_0 are coupled, they develop two new frequencies $\nu_0 \pm \Delta \nu_0$. In the same way the two zero-point oscillations of the electrical systems in the molecules develop by their interaction new frequencies, as a result of which their total energy is lowered in a way to be discussed in more detail presently. This is the origin of the van der Waals attraction.

The forces so called into play are sometimes called *dispersion forces*, since the oscillator frequencies entering into the calculations are also those which enter into the theory of the dispersion of light.

The London dispersion forces are the most important cause of van der Waals attraction in so far as they are the only ones exerted generally by all kinds of molecule. In actual magnitude, however, they may be exceeded by other kinds of dipole force in substances which in fact happen to possess a permanent dipolar moment.

Molecules with permanent moments exert two important actions. On the one hand, they induce dipoles in other molecules, the direction of the induced moments being such that attraction results. On the other hand, they cause bodily orientation of such particles present as may themselves bear dipoles. This again results in a running down of potential energy.

The three types of interaction vary in quantitative importance from substance to substance. With carbon monoxide, for example, the London forces account for almost all the interaction, while with water, which possesses a large permanent moment, the orientation forces are estimated to account for about four-fifths of the total effect. The dipole induction forces are, on the whole, much less important.

One extremely significant characteristic of the London forces is that they are additive. One fluctuating dipole, A, induces in another, B, a moment in such a way that the relative phases correspond to attraction; and if a third, C, is brought near, it causes no important disturbance. Suppose C induces in A a moment which causes attraction of C and A. This moment is superposed on that which attracts A to B, but the phases of the two are not necessarily in any special relation. The new component in A interacts only in an irregular fashion with that of B, giving an alternation of attraction and repulsion, the average effect over a period of time being negligible. But the original component of the total moment in A gives rise to a steady attraction by its interactions with B, and in general the appropriate component in each oscillator gives rise to attraction by its interaction with the corresponding component in the others. These considerations extend to the mutual influences of any number of oscillators.

Whether the van der Waals forces arise from the zero-point oscillations and their mutual effects, from the orientation of existing permanent moments, or from the induction of new ones, they are all essentially of the nature of dipole attractions—to which multipole interactions of higher order may be added as correction terms.

For this reason the potential energy of the interaction is in general proportional to the inverse sixth power of the distance between the attracting particles, as may be seen by a more detailed consideration of the various cases. Roughly speaking, the principle is this. The field, F, due to one dipole $\propto 1/r^3$. The moment, μ, induced in another particle, or the orientation impressed upon it, is proportional to the field, and the energy of the second particle in the field is proportional to $\mu' F$. Since $\mu' \propto F$, the energy $\propto \mu' F$, and $F \propto (1/r^3)$, it follows that energy $\propto F^2 \propto (1/r^6)$.

A somewhat more detailed discussion will now be given.

Interaction of zero-point oscillations

The zero-point oscillation of the atom or molecule may be schematized as an elastic vibration of a charge of mass m. The frequency is then given by the formula

$$\nu_0 = \frac{1}{2\pi}\sqrt{\left(\frac{k}{m}\right)},$$

where k is the elastic restoring force for unit displacement. From another point of view the motion may also be thought of as involving the displacement of a charge e through a distance x under the influence of a field F. The equivalence of these formulations is expressed by the equation
$$eF = kx.$$

The moment ex may also be equated to the field F multiplied by a polarizability, α.

Thus $$ex = \alpha F.$$

From the two relations, we have

$$k = \frac{eF}{x} = \frac{e^2}{\alpha}.$$

The kinetic energy of the oscillating charge is $p^2/2m$, where p is the momentum, and the potential energy is $\frac{1}{2}kx^2$. If there are two such oscillators, far enough apart to exert no mutual influence, then the total energy is given by

$$E_1 + E_2 = \frac{p_1^2}{2m} + \frac{kx_1^2}{2} + \frac{p_2^2}{2m} + \frac{kx_2^2}{2}.$$

Suppose now the two approach close enough to interact. In the simplest example we may assume a linear configuration as shown below:

$$+ \; x_1 \; - \qquad\qquad + \; x_2 \; -$$

$$\longleftarrow \qquad r \qquad \longrightarrow$$

The mutual potential energy of the system is

$$e^2 \left\{ \frac{1}{r+x_2-x_1} - \frac{1}{r+x_2} - \frac{1}{r-x_1} + \frac{1}{r} \right\} = -\frac{2e^2 x_1 x_2}{r^3}, \quad \text{approximately.}$$

The total energy is thus

$$\frac{p_1^2}{2m} + \frac{p_2^2}{2m} + \frac{k}{2}(x_1^2 + x_2^2) - \frac{2e^2 x_1 x_2}{r^3}.$$

The coordinates are now changed to

$$u_1 = \frac{1}{\sqrt{2}}(x_1 + x_2) \quad \text{and} \quad u_2 = \frac{1}{\sqrt{2}}(x_1 - x_2),$$

so that $$x_1 = \frac{1}{\sqrt{2}}(u_1 + u_2) \quad \text{and} \quad x_2 = \frac{1}{\sqrt{2}}(u_1 - u_2).$$

The potential energy assumes the form

$$\frac{k}{2}\left\{ \frac{(u_1+u_2)^2}{2} + \frac{(u_1-u_2)^2}{2} \right\} - \frac{2e^2}{r^3}\frac{(u_1^2-u_2^2)}{2}$$

$$= \frac{k}{2}(u_1^2+u_2^2) - \frac{e^2}{r^3}(u_1^2-u_2^2) = \frac{1}{2}\left(k - \frac{2e^2}{r^3}\right)u_1^2 + \frac{1}{2}\left(k + \frac{2e^2}{r^3}\right)u_2^2.$$

This last expression represents the potential energy of two oscillators with coordinates u_1 and u_2 and having two new values of k,

$k \pm 2e^2/r^3$. There are two corresponding frequencies

$$\nu_1 = \frac{1}{2\pi}\sqrt{\left(\frac{k+2e^2/r^3}{m}\right)} \quad \text{and} \quad \nu_2 = \frac{1}{2\pi}\sqrt{\left(\frac{k-2e^2/r^3}{m}\right)}.$$

The original frequency of the unperturbed oscillators was

$$\nu_0 = \frac{1}{2\pi}\sqrt{\left(\frac{k}{m}\right)},$$

so that $\qquad\qquad \nu_1 = \nu_0(1+2e^2/kr^3)^{\frac12}$

and $\qquad\qquad \nu_2 = \nu_0(1-2e^2/kr^3)^{\frac12}.$

The zero-point energy will have changed from

$$\tfrac12 h\nu_0 + \tfrac12 h\nu_0 = h\nu_0$$

to $\qquad\qquad \dfrac{h\nu_0}{2}(1+2e^2/kr^3)^{\frac12} + \dfrac{h\nu_0}{2}(1-2e^2/kr^3)^{\frac12}.$

When the binomials in this last expression are expanded, the first terms in r cancel, but the second terms are added. The higher terms may be disregarded, the result being $h\nu_0(1-e^4/2k^2r^6)$. The lowering of energy resulting from the interaction is

$$\frac{h\nu_0 e^4}{2k^2r^6} = \frac{h\nu_0 \alpha^2}{2r^6}.$$

If the calculation is made for three-dimensional oscillators, the numerical factor comes out to be $\tfrac34$ instead of $\tfrac12$. In any event the interaction energy remains inversely proportional to the sixth power of the distance.

Induction effect

Next the induction effect will be considered.

Suppose that there are in a molecule positive and negative charges susceptible of relative displacement under the influence of a field. The polarization that occurs may be formally represented as the movement of a charge e through a distance x. If there were no field, the displacement would be reversed, so that an elastic restoring force may be formally postulated. The potential energy increase attending the elastic displacement is

$$\int_0^x kx\,dx = \tfrac12 kx^2.$$

But the displacement is due to the field F, and the drop in potential energy caused by movement in this field is $-Fex$. Moreover, the force Fe must equal kx, so that $-Fex = -kx^2$. The resultant fall in potential energy is thus

$$-kx^2 + \tfrac{1}{2}kx^2 = -\tfrac{1}{2}kx^2.$$

It is expedient to define a polarizability, α, by the relation

$$ex = \alpha F.$$

Then, potential energy $= -\tfrac{1}{2}kx^2$

$$= -\tfrac{1}{2}Fex$$

$$= -\tfrac{1}{2}\alpha F^2.$$

This shows that the energy depends upon the square of the field.

The interaction of the two dipoles, that which gives rise to the inducing field and that induced thereby, is thus associated with a potential energy term proportional to F^2. But F itself is proportional to $1/r^3$, so that the interaction energy depends upon $1/r^6$. The attractive force is given by the differential coefficient of the energy with respect to the distance, and is thus dependent upon the inverse seventh power of the latter.

Orientation effects

Dipolar molecules, as explained, not only induce extra moments in one another but tend to assume such orientations as to reduce the potential energy.

At very low temperatures the degree of orientation is nearly complete. The energy of one molecule of moment μ in the field F of another is proportional to μF, where F varies as μ/r^3. Here the potential energy of the interaction is proportional to μ^2/r^3. But this state of affairs changes rapidly as the temperature rises, since thermal agitation destroys the order more and more. When the state of affairs is almost completely random, the potential energy of interaction of two dipoles becomes proportional not only to the field of the first but to the degree of orientation which this can impress upon the second. The latter effect, as in the case of the induced moment, is again proportional to the field. For this reason $1/r^6$ again appears in the interaction energy, together with a term $1/kT$ which measures the resistance to orientation opposed by the thermal motion.

The essential principles of the calculation are contained in the following considerations. If a molecule with a permanent moment

μ makes an angle β with the field F, its potential energy is proportional to $-\mu F \cos \beta$. By Boltzmann's relation (p. 79) the number of molecules at temperature T which possess this potential energy is proportional to $e^{+\mu F \cos \beta / kT}$ and to trigonometrical factors. If kT is not too small, this last expression may be written in the form of an expansion with higher powers neglected, namely, $1 + F\mu \cos \beta / kT$. The average moment is proportional to the integral of a product which includes $-\mu \cos \beta$, the moment in the direction of the field, and $1 + F\mu \cos \beta / kT$, taken over all angles.

The trigonometrical terms lead to numerical factors only, and the mean moment thus depends upon $\mu^2 F / kT$. But the effective polarizability is given by $\alpha F = $ mean moment.

Therefore $\qquad\qquad \alpha \propto \mu^2 / kT.$

The interaction energy, being determined by $\frac{1}{2}\alpha F^2$, becomes proportional to $(\mu^2/kT)(\mu/r^3)^2$ and thus to $\mu^4/r^6 kT$.

Attractions and repulsions

In all important cases, therefore, the potential energy of the attraction varies as r^{-6}, the orientation energy being the only term which depends significantly upon the temperature.

When molecules are brought very close together, attraction changes into repulsion, because the electron clouds begin to overlap. The potential energy now rises steeply as the distance between the centres diminishes. The function expressing the change in the repulsive energy is sometimes written in the form A/r^n and sometimes, better, in the form $Ae^{-r/\rho}$. In the former, n is a rather high power (approximately the ninth), expressing the rapid increase in repulsion with diminishing distance. This steep rise of the repulsive force is represented even more effectively by the exponential formula.

When the repulsive and the attractive potentials are combined, the expression for the energy assumes the form

$$U = Ae^{-r/\rho} - B/r^6.$$

For the equilibrium distance, r_0,

$$dU/dr = 0.$$

The variation of U accompanying displacements from equilibrium determines the elastic properties of the substance, such as its compressibility. From these properties information may be derived about the forms of the various functions in the energy equation and about the values of A and B.

The problem of calculating what equilibria exist in and what motions are executed in general by a close-packed assembly of molecules exerting van der Waals forces upon one another is so complex as to elude precise treatment. Some further reference will be made to the question in connexion with the liquid state in general (p. 318).

Interionic forces, especially in solutions of electrolytes

The law of force between individual pairs of ions is simple, being given by Coulomb's law which postulates proportionality to $e_1 e_2/r^2$, where e_1 and e_2 are their respective charges and r is the distance apart of their centres. In the close-packed assembly presented by many crystals there is an equilibrium between the attractive Coulomb forces of oppositely charged ions (partly masked by the repulsive forces of like ions) and the repulsions due to the interpenetration of electron clouds on close approach. The treatment of this problem is complicated and is similar to that mentioned in the last paragraph. In an electrolytic solution containing highly dissociated salts another type of problem arises. The ions in general are well separated, but the total effect of all the others present upon the potential energy of a given individual is considerable and determines the most characteristic properties of such solutions.

The influence may be calculated by an elegant approximation due to Debye and Hückel which also leads to a qualitative picture possessing many useful applications.

Let the focus of attention be a given positive ion. Any negative ones carried past it by their thermal motion will be deflected towards it, while positive ions will be constrained to swerve away from it. If innumerable instantaneous photographs were taken and superposed, the composite picture would show a spherically symmetrical atmosphere of negative electrification round the central ion.

This ionic atmosphere of opposite sign may for many purposes be regarded as possessing a physical reality, and use may be made of it both for approximate calculations and for qualitative discussions. It is employed in the theory of ionic interactions in the following way.

At a given point distant r from a central positive ion let the electric potential be ψ. If the concentration in regions remote from other charges is n, then, according to the Boltzmann principle, the respective concentrations, n_+ and n_-, at the distance r will be given by

$$n_+ = ne^{-ze\psi/kT} \quad \text{and} \quad n_- = ne^{+ze\psi/kT},$$

where $\pm ze\psi$ is the potential energy at distance r of an ion of valency z and charge $\pm ze$. The concentration of positive ions is smaller, and that of negative ions greater, than the normal for the reason already explained.

If there are various kinds of positive and negative ion of valency typified by z_i and of concentration typified by n_i, the electric density, ρ, at the distance r will be represented by

$$\rho = e \sum_i n_i z_i e^{-z_i e\psi/kT}.$$

If $ze\psi$ is small compared with kT, the first term in the expansion of the exponential may be taken, and we have

$$\rho = e \sum n_i z_i \left(1 - \frac{z_i e\psi}{kT}\right) = e \sum n_i z_i - \frac{e^2\psi}{kT} \sum n_i z_i^2.$$

Electrical neutrality of the solution as a whole demands that

$$\sum n_i z_i = 0,$$

so that $\qquad\qquad \rho = -\frac{e^2\psi}{kT} \sum n_i z_i^2.$

Now in so far as a physical reality may be attributed to the atmosphere of electrification, ρ may be inserted in the classical electrostatic relation between density and potential, Poisson's equation. For a spherically symmetrical system this is:

$$\frac{\partial^2\psi}{\partial r^2} + \frac{2}{r}\frac{\partial \psi}{\partial r} = -\frac{4\pi\rho}{D},$$

D being the dielectric constant of the medium. Therefore

$$\frac{\partial^2\psi}{\partial r^2} + \frac{2}{r}\frac{\partial \psi}{\partial r} = K^2\psi,$$

where $\qquad\qquad K^2 = \frac{4\pi e^2}{DkT} \sum n_i z_i^2.$

The solution of the differential equation is

$$\psi = \frac{Ae^{-Kr}}{r} + \frac{Be^{Kr}}{r}.$$

When $r = \infty$, $\psi = 0$, so that $B = 0$. When $r = 0$, $\psi = z_i e/Dr$, since in the immediate neighbourhood of a given ion the potential is determined by its own charge, and the influence of the other ions becomes negligible in comparison. Thus $A = z_i e/D$ and

$$\psi = \frac{z_i e}{Dr} e^{-Kr}.$$

If the central ion were present alone, the potential at r would be $z_i e/Dr$. The difference, representing the effect of the atmosphere, is

$$\frac{z_i e}{Dr} e^{-Kr} - \frac{z_i e}{Dr} = -\frac{z_i e}{D} \left(\frac{1 - e^{-Kr}}{r} \right).$$

If the exponential is expanded to the first term, the result is found to be
$$\psi_i = -z_i eK/D.$$

ψ_i represents the potential at the point $r = 0$ due to the ionic atmosphere, that is to say, the potential which the other ions impose upon the central ion.

The energy of a charge Q raised to the potential V being $\frac{1}{2}QV$, the electrostatic energy acquired by the central ion in virtue of its atmosphere is
$$\tfrac{1}{2} z_i e\psi_i = -\tfrac{1}{2} z_i^2 e^2 K/D.$$

The energy per gram ion is thus $-\tfrac{1}{2} z_i^2 e^2 KN/D$.

It is reasonable to suppose that the electrostatic energy constitutes a simple addition to the free energy of the collection of ions. If such an hypothesis is made, then important properties of the solution become deducible by purely thermodynamic means.

Activity of electrolytes

If the ions were far enough removed from one another to exert no mutual electrostatic forces, they would follow the laws of ideal solutions. The free energy could be expressed in the form

$$\bar{G}_i = \bar{G}_{0i} + RT \ln c_i,$$

where c_i is the concentration. In fact an empirically determined function, the activity, must be introduced in place of c_i (p. 68):

$$\bar{G}_i = \bar{G}_{0i} + RT \ln a_i$$

and
$$a_i = f_i c_i,$$

where f_i is the *activity coefficient*. Thus

$$\bar{G}_i = \bar{G}_{0i} + RT \ln c_i + RT \ln f_i.$$

The term by which the free energy differs from the ideal value is equated to the electrostatic energy, so that

$$RT \ln f_i = -z_i^2 e^2 KN/2D,$$

$$\ln f_i = -z_i^2 e^2 KN/2DRT = \frac{-z_i^2 e^2 N}{2DRT} \left(\frac{4\pi e^2}{DkT} \sum n_i z_i^2 \right)^{\frac{1}{2}}$$

$$= \frac{-z_i^2 e^2 N}{2DRT} \left(\frac{4\pi e^2}{DRT/N} \sum \frac{Nc_i z_i^2}{1000} \right)^{\frac{1}{2}},$$

since n_i is expressed in ions/c.c. and c_i in gm. ions/l. Thus finally

$$-\ln f_i = \frac{z_i^2 e^3 N^2}{(DRT)^{\frac{3}{2}}} \left(\frac{\pi}{1000} \sum c_i z_i^2 \right)^{\frac{1}{2}}.$$

The sum $\frac{1}{2} \sum c_i z_i^2$ is known as the *ionic strength*. The formula just derived shows, therefore, that the *activity coefficient depends upon the square root of the ionic strength* in a solution of sufficient dilution.

It is customary to define an activity coefficient of a salt in terms of the separate activity coefficients of its constituent ions according to a convention which for a uni-univalent salt takes the form

$$a_{\pm} = (a_+ a_-)^{\frac{1}{2}},$$

whence

$$f_{\pm} = (f_+ f_-)^{\frac{1}{2}}.$$

If the electrolyte dissociates into ν_+ positive ions and ν_- negative ions, the mean activity coefficient is defined by the relation

$$f_{\pm} = (f^{\nu_+} f^{\nu_-})^{1/\nu},$$

where

$$\nu = \nu_+ + \nu_-.$$

Thus

$$-\ln f_{\pm} = -\frac{\nu_+ \ln f_+ + \nu_- \ln f_-}{\nu} = \frac{(\nu_+ z_+^2 + \nu_- z_-^2)}{\nu} \frac{e^3 N^2}{(DRT)^{\frac{3}{2}}} \left(\frac{\pi}{1000} \sum c_i z_i^2 \right)^{\frac{1}{2}}.$$

For a uni-univalent electrolyte the relation reduces to the form

$$-\ln f_{\pm} = 0.51 \sqrt{c},$$

when the appropriate numerical values are inserted in the equation.

There will be further occasion to apply these results on the electrostatic attractions and repulsions of the ions in explanation of various specific properties of electrolytic solutions.

Having learnt something of the motions of molecules, the statistics of their assemblages, and of the forces by which they are formed and in virtue of which they interact with one another, it will now be expedient to devote some attention to certain more detailed properties of matter in bulk.

PART V

THE FORMS OF MATTER IN EQUILIBRIUM

SYNOPSIS

THE antagonism of ordering forces and primordial motions leads to equilibria between gases and condensed phases. The rich display of forms and structures in the latter arises from the mode of operation of the forces and especially from the regulating ordinances of the quantum code.

The rule about the kind of distinguishability characterizing electrons in atoms (antisymmetry of wave function, Pauli principle), together with the other rules about quantum numbers, fixes the constitution of complete electron groups possessing maximum stability (inert gas structure). Atoms normally depart from the stability maximum in that they have either excess or defect of electrons relatively to the nearest inert gas. Those with excess may achieve greater stability by shedding electrons or by transferring them to other atoms: those with defect by sharing electrons or by capturing them from elsewhere. The two sets of possibilities are not symmetrically related, whence comes the first major differentiation of substances.

When electrons are simply shed, the metals result. These consist of a regular array of positive ions with a system of free electrons held communally and obeying special statistical laws. Metals, in consequence, possess characteristic electrical, optical, mechanical, and, sometimes, magnetic properties.

When electrons are transferred, positive and negative ions are formed: when they are shared covalent compounds result. Both ionic and covalent compounds form in the solid state extended arrays (space lattices) with a geometric order that allows an approach to minimum potential energy. Since valencies are discrete and spatially directed, molecules possess shapes, and the force fields around them have characteristic forms which give rise to a whole range of different space lattices.

Univalent atoms united by covalencies in molecules such as Cl_2 have no bonds left, but polyvalent atoms can form lattices in which each atom is joined to one or more neighbours by a covalency, making the whole array into a giant molecule. The molecules or ions in other lattices are held by van der Waals or Coulomb forces. The physical characteristics of the varied types of solid show very wide variations which reflect these different modes of assemblage.

In condensed phases a minimum potential energy is not the sole consideration. The molecules all execute motions of various kinds, consistently with their structure and the quantum rules, and room must be found in the space lattice for movements of the required amplitude. Rise in temperature increases the motions and leads to increased entropy. Sometimes this is compatible with the maintenance of the original lattice, and then the entropy changes are manifested in the specific heat. Sometimes, however, a new lattice must be formed to accommodate the livelier and more diverse movements, and then there is a change of phase, the entropy increase being now revealed in the absorption of latent heat.

Restraints on motion may be relaxed in respect of some coordinates and not of others: and considerable degrees of order may persist even when rigidity of the structure has disappeared. Very varied relations of mobility and order are, in fact, met with in liquid crystals, in liquids, in substances with rubber-like properties, and in condensed helium.

Interpenetration of condensed systems leads to solutions which have their own special conditions of formation and stability.

Extended phases of liquid or solid are more stable than droplets or minute crystals. Yet the highly dispersed phases which play so important a part in nature (foams, emulsions, gels, and so on) may in certain circumstances achieve a relative degree of permanence. The tendency of phase boundaries to reduce their area to a minimum is compensated in some degree by their capacity for taking up foreign substances which partially neutralize the unbalanced forces responsible for the contractive urge. These boundary effects manifest themselves in different ways, and dominate that part of the subject called colloid chemistry.

XIV

DISPOSAL OF ELECTRONS IN ATOMIC ASSEMBLAGES

Forms of matter

ANYONE who has sought in chemistry a road to the understanding of everyday things will probably have been impressed by the apparent gulf separating the substances with which simple chemical experiments are done in the laboratory and the materials of which the ordinary world seems largely to be made. Trees, rocks, alloys, and many other common objects and substances are of evident complexity, and this is not all: even the simpler chemical bodies seem to be extraordinarily diverse, and the problem of their classification is a formidable one. Among the major questions of physical chemistry is that of the connexion between the electrical theory of matter, the kinetic theory, quantum mechanical and statistical principles, and the forms assumed by the various systems accessible to normal experience.

The survey of the general scene begins with certain material assemblies which are remote at any rate from terrestrial concern. According to our conception of atomic structure the nucleus is small and dense. Stripped of their electrons at immensely high temperatures, nuclei constitute systems in which enormous concentrations

T

do not preclude the kind of mobility normally characteristic of gases. Matter in this state probably exists in the interior of stars, and models of it play their part in astronomical and astrophysical theories. Extraordinary relations of star size and density and the peculiar dynamics of stellar bodies bring such unfamiliar forms of substance within the range of scientific observation.

The temperatures prevailing inside certain stars are believed to be of the order of millions of degrees. Collision energies, proportional to kT, are great enough to make nuclear reactions possible, and stellar alchemy accompanied by nuclear transformations must contribute largely to the energy output of the great suns. One interesting scheme which has been built upon a knowledge of mass defects is that by which helium nuclei are supposed to be synthesized from hydrogen, not directly, but in a kind of catalytic cycle:

$$^{12}C + {}^{1}H = {}^{13}N + \text{radiation}$$
$$^{13}N = {}^{13}C + \text{positive electron}$$
$$^{13}C + {}^{1}H = {}^{14}N + \text{radiation}$$
$$^{14}N + {}^{1}H = {}^{15}O + \text{radiation}$$
$$^{15}O = {}^{15}N + \text{positive electron}$$
$$^{15}N + {}^{1}H = {}^{12}C + {}^{4}He.$$

This sort of thing lies outside the boundaries of what we arbitrarily call physical chemistry, but it is well to observe what lies on the frontiers of the conventional domain.

In the cooler, though still very hot, surface layers of stars like the sun, atoms in less violent states of ionization are detectable by spectroscopic means. Equilibria of the type

$$M \rightleftharpoons M^{+} + \text{electron}$$

are established, and are in some measure accessible to study. They may indeed be treated theoretically by thermodynamic rules, if appropriate assumptions are made about the relevant properties of free electrons, and formulae for thermal ionization have been worked out on this basis by Lindemann and by Saha.

Thermal ionization is observable in flames, so that the gap between celestial and terrestrial conditions is in a certain measure bridged.

What is called chemistry in the traditional sense only begins when primordial matter has cooled sufficiently to allow the nuclei to retain possession of their electrons—except in so far as atoms share or interchange them. The chemical properties of substances are indeed largely determined by the manner in which the external electrons of the atom are disposed of.

This subject has already been dealt with to some extent in connexion with atomic structure. The major landmarks of the periodic system are, of course, the inert gases, whose properties show clearly that they possess completed electron groups. Their lack of chemical reactiveness provides a measure of the stability of such groups, and of the categorical nature of the Pauli principle which imposes the rules of constitution.

In a general way it may be said that when there are few electrons in the outermost group they are readily shed to leave a positive ion, and when they are many they readily make their number up to that of the next inert gas. A quantum group which is nearly filled counts in fact not as well supplied but as defective.

On this basis the main distribution of electropositive and electronegative elements in the periodic system may be easily understood.

But electrons lost or gained must be accounted for, and it is the *variety of ways in which this balance may be struck which so greatly diversifies the picture of chemical types.*

If an atom with an excess transfers its electrons to one with a deficiency, positive and negative ions are created. These may either build themselves into a continuous crystal lattice, as occurs in simple salts, or else they may fall apart, when in a medium of high dielectric constant, to give electrolytic solutions. At higher temperatures the salts may exist as gases with an equilibrium between ion-pairs and free ions.

When, on the other hand, two atoms which both count as defective, are brought together, they may complete their groups by sharing electron pairs, and the characteristic covalency results.

The simplest covalent compounds are the diatomic molecules formed from electronegative atoms. The variety and complexity of covalent structures depend essentially upon the fact that certain polyvalent elements can form stable chains of atoms, the most notable being of course those which occur among the derivatives of carbon. They are responsible for those compounds of high molecular weight which can constitute fibres and sheets and which therefore play so important a part in the structure of living tissues. Scarcely less notable are the extended patterns of silicon and oxygen which form the basis of silicate rocks and clays.

Another and very characteristic mode of disposition of the electrons occurs when atoms of electropositive elements are brought together. In the vapour state these elements are not infrequently monatomic, though spectroscopic and other evidence shows the existence in small concentration of molecules such as Na_2, or NaK. In the solid state, however, they form structures which possess the well-defined and peculiar properties of metals.

Electron transfers and the formation of stable ions depend upon the Coulomb forces, and upon the regulating character of the Pauli principle. The nature of atomic stability has already been discussed, and it can be said that an ion is simply a more stable form of atom. The problem of how it disposes itself with other ions to achieve an overall electrical neutrality is, from the point of view of the theory of atomic structure, a secondary matter: but from another point of view it presents us with a quite fundamental question. From what has been said so far it cannot be concluded that the nature of the metallic state is at all obvious, and yet this is one of the commonest conditions which matter assumes. The constitution of the metallic state therefore calls for special consideration.

Metals

The more obvious and striking properties of metals are their opacity and lustre, their mechanical characters, such as malleability and ductility, and their very high electrical and thermal conductivity.

Much of this can be explained by a quite crude form of the theory that metals contain a high proportion of free electrons scattered among an array of positive ions.

In the first place, the metallic elements are in fact those which form positive ions by shedding valency electrons, and these latter, without escaping wholly from the field of the positive ions, could wander about among a collection of them without remaining firmly attached to any individual. In the second place, metallic conduction, unlike electrolytic conduction, occurs without any transfer of matter, and can very plausibly be ascribed to the movement of free electrons under a potential gradient. In the third place, when a metal is heated it emits electrons which give rise under an appropriate potential difference to a thermionic current. The magnitude of the latter increases with temperature according to the law, $C \propto e^{-A/RT}$, which at once suggests that the emission is determined by the evaporation of something present in the metal with the usual kind of statistical energy distribution.

If there is a characteristic concentration of electrons in each metal, then when two metals are placed in contact there will be a certain tendency for diffusion from one to the other. Movement of electrons will occur until it is checked by the opposing potential difference which the redistribution sets up. Hence the contact potential and the possibility of galvanic cells.†

When a current crosses the junction of two metals there occurs a change in electron concentration analogous in some ways to the expansion or contraction of a gas. This will be accompanied by

† There is a change in free energy when electrons are transferred from one metal to another, and at the surface of contact of two metals there is a corresponding potential difference. A noble metal, offering lower levels for the occupation of electrons, assumes a negative charge with respect to a less noble metal. (In the equilibrium state, of course, the charges modify the levels themselves so that the work of transfer becomes zero.)

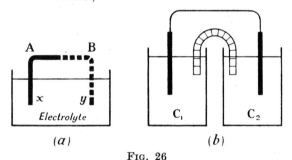

FIG. 26

There is correspondingly a potential difference between metals and solutions in which they are immersed. Of two metals connected as in Fig. 26 (a) to form a cell with an electrolyte providing ions of both kinds, the one will dissolve and the other acquire fresh substance by the discharge of ions. There will be potential differences at x and y such that their sum is equal to E, the electromotive force of the cell.

In such a case the free energy of the cell is that of the process

$$A^{+}+B = A+B^{+},$$

if we assume that the free energy of the actual electrolyte is unchanged by the replacement of one kind of ion by the other.

In certain cases, however, the free-energy changes occurring in the solution itself are important, and may even become the dominant factor.

This last case is illustrated by the so-called concentration cell, which is represented in Fig. 26 (b). Two electrodes of the metal A dip into solutions of A ions of differing concentrations, c_1 and c_2, the former being greater than the latter. This combination exhibits an electromotive force for reasons which have nothing to do with the total energy, or with the affinities of metals for electrons. If A ions dissolve into the right-hand solution and are discharged from the left-hand solution, the total distribution of electrons among metal atoms is unaltered. But there is a concomitant transfer of material from a more concentrated to a less concentrated solution, and therefore an entropy increase. In the process positive charge is given to the left-hand electrode and negative to the right. Thus the system develops an electromotive force and constitutes a cell.

We will calculate the electromotive force for the simple case of a univalent metal and a uni-univalent salt in solution. Silver and silver nitrate will serve as examples. If one Faraday of electricity passes, the following is the balance-sheet of the happenings:

More concentrated solution	*Less concentrated solution*
1 gram ion Ag^+ discharged: n gram ions Ag^+ gained by migration from less concentrated solution in transport of current.	1 gram ion Ag^+ enters solution from electrode: n gram ions Ag^+ lost by migration into more concentrated solution in transport of current.
Net result: $(1-n)$ gram ions Ag^+ lost.	Net result: $(1-n)$ gram ions Ag^+ gained.

It may easily be shown that the changes in NO_3^- concentration exactly parallel those in the Ag^+ concentration. Thus, if the salt is completely dissociated, $2(1-n)$ gram ions are transferred from concentration c_1 to concentration c_2. The osmotic work is $2(1-n)RT \ln(c_1/c_2)$, and this must equal the electrical work which is EF. Thus

$$E = 2(1-n)\frac{RT}{F} \ln\frac{c_1}{c_2}.$$

n is the *transport number* of the silver ion.

We have now seen two extreme cases, in one of which the source of the free energy is an electron transfer from one metal to another, while in the other it is an equalization of concentration. In the limit, there need be no heat of dilution for this second case, and any electrical energy is generated at the expense of the heat which is absorbed while the process of dilution goes on.

In the example of the cell: copper, copper sulphate solution, zinc sulphate solution, zinc, the total electrical energy represented by the product (electromotive force × valency × Faraday) is almost exactly equal to the heat which would be released if metallic zinc precipitated metallic copper in a calorimeter. The entropy changes associated with dilution factors are negligible. On the other hand, almost all the energy of a silver nitrate concentration cell is provided by the heat which the cell is authorized to absorb from the surroundings in virtue of the accompanying entropy increase.

In general, both kinds of effect play their part in varying degrees.

Their relative importance can be judged from the effect of temperature on the electromotive force. In the general free-energy equation (p. 67)

$$\Delta F - \Delta U = T\frac{\partial(\Delta F)}{\partial T},$$

ΔU is the calorimetric heat, measured under conditions where there are no electrical effects. ΔF is the product of valency, Faraday, and electromotive force. If ΔF and ΔU are equal, then the electromotive force is independent of temperature: if ΔU is zero it becomes directly proportional to the absolute temperature. In some cases the cell warms or cools as it works. The reason is that the transfer of electrons to more stable states is accompanied by other alterations in the system (such as establishment of more or less favourable concentration relations) which correspond to increased or lowered probability and favourable or adverse entropy changes.

energy and entropy changes, and an absorption or emission of heat which manifests itself in the *Peltier effect*. The *Thomson effect* is the related phenomenon whereby the application of heat to the junction of two metals gives rise to an electromotive force (that, namely, which is exploited in the measurement of temperatures by thermocouples).

Similarly naïve, but on the whole satisfying, pictures can be drawn of the mechanical and optical properties of metals. The lubrication of the lattice of ions by numerous minute and highly mobile electrons could well be imagined to confer special ease of deformation and rearrangement and thus to explain the phenomena of slip and extension.

The opacity and reflecting power are attributable to the influence of free electrons on the propagation of electromagnetic waves. Sufficiently mobile electrical particles annul the electric field of the waves and thus prevent their propagation. The surface of the metal should therefore constitute a node or plane in which the displacement vanishes. This requirement can only be met if the reflected wave is equal in amplitude to the incident wave and differs from it in phase by π, a condition implying perfect reflection. Electrons are not, however, infinitely mobile and, although they can nearly enough annul the field of light waves of low frequency, their response is not lively enough to do the same to waves of high frequency. Hence a certain degree of transparency, as for example with alkali metals in the ultra-violet region, the imperfect reflecting power and the specific colours exhibited by various metals.

The simplest assumption to make in the development of a more detailed theory is that the electrons of a metal form a sort of gas. The strength and weakness of this hypothesis is well illustrated by the consideration of electrical and thermal conductivity.

The electrons are assumed to possess a mean free path, l, and a root mean square velocity, $\bar{u}$, determined by the relation

$$\tfrac{1}{2}m\bar{u}^2 = \tfrac{3}{2}kT \qquad (\text{p. 17}).$$

The thermal conductivity will then be proportional to $l\bar{u}$, as for an ordinary gas.

If an electric field F acts upon the metal it will produce in each electron an acceleration Fe/m during a time interval which on the average is $l/\bar{u}$. At the end of this time the acquired velocity, $(Fe/m)(l/\bar{u})$, will be lost in a collision with an atom. The mean excess velocity in the direction of the field is therefore $\frac{1}{2}Fel/m\bar{u}$, which is $\frac{1}{2}Fel\bar{u}/m\bar{u}^2$. The electrical conductivity is proportional to this quantity and thus to $l\bar{u}/kT$. Since the thermal conductivity is proportional to $l\bar{u}$ (p. 20) there follows the relation

$$\frac{\text{thermal conductivity}}{\text{electrical conductivity}} = \text{constant} \times T.$$

This law is in fact well obeyed.

The hypothesis of the electron gas breaks down, however, in its application to specific heats. It implies that the thermal energies of electrons are equal to those of atoms, by the equipartition principle. But the specific heats of metals can be almost entirely accounted for by the atomic motions alone. Dulong and Petit's law, and indeed the Einstein and Debye relations, ignore any contribution from the electrons to the energy, and yet in their respective spheres give a good enough account of the facts.

That the discrepancy was to be explained in terms of a quantum phenomenon of some kind was first suggested in Lindemann's theory that the electrons constitute not so much a gas as a solid lattice interpenetrating that of the positive ions. If the vibration frequency is high enough, then, in accordance with Einstein's equation, the specific heat of the electron lattice will vanish at normal temperatures, just as that of the atomic lattice itself vanishes in the region of the absolute zero. An interesting possibility suggested by this picture is that at very low temperatures where the thermal vibrations of the ionic lattice no longer cause it to engage and entangle with the electron lattice, the latter could slip unopposed through the solid. In this way the extraordinarily high conductivity, or *supraconductivity*, shown by some metals in the neighbourhood of the absolute zero might be explained.

That the peculiar properties of metals are indeed manifestations of the quantum laws is no longer in doubt, but the evolution of ideas has led to a rather more sophisticated conception than that which has just been outlined.

Two major facts point the way. In the first place, electrons contribute to the conductivity without adding significantly to the specific heat. In the second place, the difference between metallic conductors and insulators attains more nearly to the character of an absolute distinction than the primitive theories can account for.

Electrons, as is easily seen, can acquire a certain freedom to move in virtue of the fact that the force exerted by one positive ion is largely balanced by that of neighbouring ions. A similar effect should be present, even if in smaller degree, in any regular array of atomic structures, and differences in binding energies alone do not account for the whole orders of magnitude which separate the conductivities of various types of solid.

Some kind of categorical law seems to be involved, and once again the role of censor is played by the Pauli principle. This rule, generalized in what is called the Fermi–Dirac statistics, states that no two electrons in a system can ever rely upon mere particle identity for distinguishability and that a given energy state may be occupied by two electrons only, and then only if the two have opposite spins.

The first development of the older electron gas theory is in Sommerfeld's conception of a metal as a system in which electrons possess quantized translational energies but with each possible level filled by two electrons only. If the number of free electrons is roughly equal to that of the atoms, the filling up of the states is such that the higher levels correspond to considerable energies. Conduction is thus provided for. But, according to the Fermi–Dirac statistics, precisely when the states are thickly occupied the distribution becomes largely independent of temperature. Thus the energy of the electrons does not change with the energy of the atoms and there is no contribution to the specific heat.

This view of the matter is still far from completely satisfactory and does not explain the wide gap between conductors and insulators. The conception of electrons in a metal as rather like so many particles in a box is far too much idealized, and account must be taken of the potential field of the positive ions in which these electrons move. This field is periodic with the same periodicity as the lattice itself, and the electron velocity distribution in such a region is susceptible of mathematical study in a more complete way.

The result of the calculations may be anticipated by the statement that the energies of the electrons prove no longer to form a continuous series, but to fall into a group of bands separated by ranges in which no possible states exist. In a general way this might be expected. If the atoms were very far removed from one another, each electron would be bound in a sharply defined quantum level.

If the electrons, on the other hand, were free to move in a uniform field formed by the complete averaging of all the ionic forces, they would have a complete range of closely spaced translational states. In the intermediate condition they occupy bands of closely crowded energies separated by forbidden regions.

This being so, the distinction of conductors and insulators can be very sharp. If a band is only partially filled, electrons can easily move to other and higher translational levels within it, and these faster electrons contribute to the current. If the band of energies is full, the electrons cannot contribute to an effective transport of electricity unless they receive enough energy to jump the forbidden zone into one of the levels of a higher zone. In these circumstances we have an insulator or semi-conductor in which current only passes under enormous electrical stress or as a result of considerable thermal activation.

The regions of permitted energy can be marked out in a solid diagram, in which the three rectangular axes are the components of the momentum. The permitted regions in this *momentum space* are called *Brillouin zones*. Since they depend upon the periodicity of the potential energy, they are determined by the lattice constants of the crystal. The degree to which they are filled is a function of the number of valency electrons possessed by the metal, but since the various zones may on occasion overlap, the relation of the conductivity to the valency of the metal and to the crystal structure is a complex one.

It is now important to give a somewhat more detailed consideration to the matters which have just been outlined, since the ideas, apart from their quantitative mathematical expression, have a limited significance only, and translations of quantum-mechanical formulations into everyday language have a meaning which is largely metaphorical—and not infrequently convey the illusion of understanding rather than understanding itself.

Fermi–Dirac statistics

Something must first be said about the Fermi–Dirac statistics, which, indeed, are most appropriately introduced here, since the theory of metals is the field in which they find their principal application.

The principles according to which the distribution of particles among states is calculated are quite similar to those which have been employed already (p. 135) except for the additional postulate that one particle only may be allocated to each level. If the possible states are duplicated by the existence of two opposing spins, then two particles, one of each spin, may be placed in each translational level.

Now a given translational energy ϵ_j corresponds to a multiplicity of states, since each rectangular component of the momentum is itself quantized, and numerous values of p_1, p_2, and p_3 can satisfy the relation
$$p_1^2 + p_2^2 + p_3^2 = p^2 = 2m\epsilon.$$

All values of p satisfying this condition lie on a sphere of radius $\sqrt{(2m\epsilon)}$ in a diagram constructed with the components of p as axes. The volume of the sphere is $\frac{4}{3}\pi(2m\epsilon)^{\frac{3}{2}}$. The particles are scattered through a geometrical volume V, so that the volume of what is called *phase space* (that space of which the element is $dp_1\,dp_2\,dp_3\,dx\,dy\,dz$) for the particles whose momenta do not exceed p is
$$\tfrac{4}{3}\pi(2m\epsilon)^{\frac{3}{2}}V.$$

Both the older quantum theory and the wave-mechanical formulation of the quantum laws specify the parcelling of phase space into elements such that $dp_x\,dx = h$, and in a three-dimensional problem what constitutes a state is a volume of phase space equal to h^3 (compare p. 156). The *number* of states corresponding to momenta *up to p*, or energies up to ϵ, is
$$\frac{4\pi}{3}\frac{(2m\epsilon)^{\frac{3}{2}}V}{h^3},$$
and the number corresponding to energies between ϵ and $\epsilon + d\epsilon$ is
$$\frac{2\pi(2m)^{\frac{3}{2}}V}{h^3}\,\epsilon^{\frac{1}{2}}\,d\epsilon.$$

All these, since the distribution is not in fact continuous, and the differentiation is a convenient approximation, correspond to an energy ϵ_j. Thus we may write for the multiplicity
$$g_j = \frac{2\pi(2m)^{\frac{3}{2}}V}{h^3}\,\epsilon^{\frac{1}{2}}\,d\epsilon.$$

The problem is to calculate the number of ways in which N_j particles may be assigned to these g_j states, not more than one being permitted in each. This is simply a form of the elementary question of the number of ways in which N_j objects (the filled states) may be chosen, without regard to order, from a total of g_j objects (all the states). The answer is $_{g_j}C_{N_j}$ or $g_j!/\{N_j!(g_j-N_j)!\}$. The total number of ways in which distributions can be made in all the energy ranges is the product of similar expressions for all values of j. Converting products to sums by taking logarithms, we find

$$\ln P = \sum_j \left\{ \frac{g_j!}{N_j!(g_j-N_j)!} \right\}. \tag{1}$$

For statistical equilibrium

$$\delta \ln P = 0, \tag{2}$$

subject to the further conditions

$$\delta \sum N_j = 0, \tag{3}$$

$$\delta \sum N_j \, \epsilon_j = 0. \tag{4}$$

Equation (1) is simplified by the introduction of Stirling's approximation, and (2), (3), and (4) are solved by the method of undetermined multipliers (p. 29).

The result of the calculation follows in a straightforward way and is

$$N_j = \frac{g_j}{e^{\alpha+\beta\epsilon_j}+1},$$

where α is determined by the condition

$$\sum \frac{g_j}{e^{\alpha+\beta\epsilon_j}+1} = N.$$

To understand the nature of the constants α and β we will anticipate and assume that in appropriate circumstances $e^{\alpha+\beta\epsilon_j}$ is great compared with unity. The above results then reduce to

$$N_j = g_j e^{-\alpha} e^{-\beta\epsilon_j}$$

with
$$\sum g_j e^{-\alpha} e^{-\beta\epsilon_j} = N.$$

In other words we have returned to the Maxwell–Boltzmann distribution. This will naturally be indistinguishable from the Fermi–Dirac distribution when g_j is very large compared with N_j, that is, at high enough temperatures. This limiting case shows us that β will be $1/kT$ as before (p. 33), so that we have

$$\sum g_j e^{-\alpha} e^{-\epsilon_j/kT} = N.$$

As a good approximation we may replace the sum by an integral

$$e^{-\alpha} \int_0^\infty g_j e^{-\epsilon_j/kT} d\epsilon = N.$$

Introducing the value of g_j from above we have

$$\frac{1}{e^\alpha} \frac{2\pi(2m)^{\frac{3}{2}}}{h^3} V \int_0^\infty \epsilon^{\frac{1}{2}} e^{-\epsilon_j/kT} d\epsilon = N.$$

The integral is a standard one and equal to $(kT)^{\frac{3}{2}} \sqrt{\pi}/2$, so that

$$e^\alpha = \frac{V}{Nh^3} (2\pi mkT)^{\frac{3}{2}}.$$

If T is great enough, e^α in turn is great enough to make $e^{\alpha+\beta\epsilon_j}$ outweigh unity by as much as we please. The basis of our calculation is then justified and the distribution law followed is in fact similar to the Maxwell–Boltzmann. When, however, T is small e^α drops and eventually it becomes so small that $e^{\alpha+\beta\epsilon_j}$ is itself small compared with unity. In these circumstances N_j tends to become independent of temperature. This is because the states are so few that there are hardly any alternatives about filling them. The distribution of the particles now differs sharply from the classical one and the system shows what is sometimes spoken of as degeneracy.

An ordinary gas should, if it follows the Fermi–Dirac statistics, show degeneracy at low enough temperatures. But the effects cannot be detected, since they are masked by deviations from the gas laws due to van der Waals forces.

Electrons, however, are in a different case. e^α, as shown by the formula given above, depends upon $m^{\frac{3}{2}}$. Since the mass of an electron is several thousand times smaller than that of an atom or molecule, an electron gas would remain degenerate up to temperatures several thousand times higher. Expressed in another way this means that the density of states is much lower for electrons, g_j being proportional to $m^{\frac{3}{2}}$, so that they remain filled completely even at temperatures where quite large quantities of energy are available. In the ordinary temperature range, therefore, the energy distribution is determined mainly by the requirement of complete filling, and the change with temperature is small. Hence the low specific heat of the electron component of the metal.

Quantum-mechanical theory of metals

The conception of an electron gas explains certain major properties of metals. The application to this gas of the Fermi–Dirac statistics removes some grave difficulties, but for a fuller understanding the energies of electrons in a periodic potential field must be studied. This problem is one which the application of the wave equation is adapted to solve.

To simplify matters we shall consider the translational motion of electrons along the axis of x only.

In the absence of a potential field the Schrödinger equation has the form

$$\frac{d^2\psi}{dx^2} + \frac{8\pi^2 m E}{h^2}\psi = 0.$$

This is satisfied by the solution

$$\psi = e^{ikx},$$

according to which $\qquad k^2 = 8\pi^2 m E / h^2$

and if $E = \frac{1}{2}mv^2$, $\qquad k = 2\pi m v / h.$

k is thus proportional to the momentum, and may be referred to as momentum if we understand the appropriate units to be employed. Moreover, since $h/mv = \lambda$, $k = 2\pi/\lambda$, where λ is the electron wavelength.

If the length of the metal in which the electrons move is L, and if we wish ψ to satisfy the correct boundary conditions, L must equal $n\lambda$, where n is an integer. This condition would give us the quantization of the momentum in the x-direction. It follows that

$$k = 2\pi n / L.$$

Analogous considerations apply to the three-dimensional problem. The arrays of k-values are closely spaced but unbroken series.

Now let a periodic potential field be introduced, such as would exist in the presence of positive ions placed at uniform distances in a space lattice. The wave equation now becomes

$$\frac{d^2\psi}{dx^2} + \frac{8\pi^2 m}{h^2}(E - V)\psi = 0,$$

where V is a periodic function of x.

It is reasonable to guess—and the guess is confirmed by formal mathematical analysis—that ψ now assumes the form

$$\psi = e^{ikx}u,$$

where u is a function of x with the same periodicity as V.

The essential nature of the problem is illustrated in a simple version (due to Kronig and Penney) where V is assumed to be of the form shown below, and to consist of rectangular barriers of height V_0 and width b separated by intervals of length a.

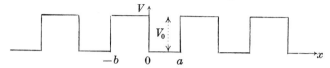

We then have from $x = 0$ to $x = a$

$$\frac{d^2\psi}{dx^2} + \frac{8\pi^2 m}{h^2} E\psi = 0, \quad \text{or} \quad \frac{d^2\psi}{dx^2} + \beta^2\psi = 0, \tag{1}$$

and from $x = 0$ to $x = -b$

$$\frac{d^2\psi}{dx^2} + \frac{8\pi^2 m}{h^2} (E - V_0)\psi = 0, \quad \text{or} \quad \frac{d^2\psi}{dx^2} + \gamma^2\psi = 0. \tag{2}$$

The expression $\psi = e^{ikx}u$ is substituted first in (1) and then in (2), when the following conditions become apparent:

From $x = 0$ to $x = a$

$$\frac{d^2u}{dx^2} + 2ik\frac{du}{dx} - (k^2 - \beta^2)u = 0 \quad \text{with} \quad \beta^2 = \frac{8\pi^2 mE}{h^2}, \tag{3}$$

and from $x = 0$ to $x = -b$

$$\frac{d^2u}{dx^2} + 2ik\frac{du}{dx} - (k^2 + \gamma^2)u = 0 \quad \text{and} \quad \gamma^2 = \frac{8\pi^2 m(V_0 - E)}{h^2}. \tag{4}$$

The solutions of (3) and (4) are of the form $u = Me^{mx} + Ne^{nx}$, and substitution shows that the values of the constants must be as follows:

$$u = Ae^{(-ik+\gamma)x} + Be^{-(ik+\gamma)x}, \tag{5}$$

$$u = Ce^{i(-k+\beta)x} + De^{-i(k+\beta)x}. \tag{6}$$

At the points $x = 0$, $x = a$, and $x = -b$, the values of u and of du/dx given by (5) and by (6) respectively must naturally be consistent with one another.

Thus $$A + B = C + D,$$

to fit u at $x = 0$ in (5) and (6).

$$(-ik+\gamma)A + (-ik-\gamma)B = i(-k+\beta)C + i(-k-\beta)D,$$

to adjust du/dx for $x = 0$ from (5) and (6).

$$Ae^{(ik-\gamma)b} + Be^{(ik+\gamma)b} = Ce^{i(-k+\beta)a} + De^{-i(k+\beta)a}$$

for u at $-b$ from (5) and u at a from (6).

$$(-ik+\gamma)Ae^{(ik-\gamma)b}+(-ik-\gamma)Be^{(ik+\gamma)b}$$
$$= i(-k+\beta)Ce^{i(-k+\beta)a}+i(-k-\beta)De^{-i(k+\beta)a}$$

for du/dx at $-b$ from (5) and at a from (6).

These relations constitute four simultaneous equations in A, B, C, and D which may be eliminated from them (most easily by equation to zero of the appropriate determinant). a, b, β, γ must satisfy the relation

$$\left(\frac{\gamma^2-\beta^2}{2\beta\gamma}\right)\left(\frac{e^{\gamma b}-e^{-\gamma b}}{2}\right)\left(\frac{e^{i\beta a}-e^{-i\beta a}}{2i}\right)+\left(\frac{e^{\gamma b}+e^{-\gamma b}}{2}\right)\left(\frac{e^{i\beta a}+e^{-i\beta a}}{2}\right)$$
$$=\frac{e^{ik(a+b)}+e^{-ik(a+b)}}{2},$$

that is

$$\frac{\gamma^2-\beta^2}{2\beta\gamma}\sinh\gamma b\sin\beta a+\cosh\gamma b\cos\beta a=\cos k(a+b). \qquad (7)$$

It is now convenient to make V_0 very large and b very small, while preserving a finite value for the product, or, what amounts to the same thing, for $\gamma^2 b$. This makes the potential peaks high and narrow, and reduces the period of V_0 to a instead of $(a+b)$. (In proceeding to the limit the following points are to be observed:

$$\sinh\gamma b=\tfrac{1}{2}(e^{\gamma b}-e^{-\gamma b})$$
$$=\frac{1}{2}\left(1+\frac{\gamma^2 b}{\gamma}+...-1+\frac{\gamma^2 b}{\gamma}-...\right)=2\gamma^2 b/2\gamma=\gamma b,$$

when V_0 and thus γ increases without limit, while $\gamma^2 b$ reaches a finite value.

$$\cosh\gamma b=\tfrac{1}{2}(e^{\gamma^2 b/\gamma}+e^{-\gamma^2 b/\gamma})=\frac{1}{2}\left(1+\frac{\gamma^2 b}{\gamma}+...+1-\frac{\gamma^2 b}{\gamma}+...\right)=1,$$

as the same limiting conditions are reached.)

In the limit condition (7) becomes

$$\frac{\gamma^2}{2\beta\gamma}\gamma b\sin\beta a+\cos\beta a=\cos ka,$$

or
$$\frac{\gamma^2 ba}{2}\frac{\sin\beta a}{\beta a}+\cos\beta a=\cos ka,$$

or
$$P\frac{\sin\beta a}{\beta a}+\cos\beta a=\cos ka. \qquad (8)$$

$P=\tfrac{1}{2}\gamma^2 ba$ and is a measure of the potential barriers, the product $\gamma^2 b$ being by hypothesis finite.

The total energy of the electron in this system is proportional to β^2, since
$$\beta^2 = 8\pi^2 m E/h^2.$$

The relation (8) has important properties which are the key to the whole situation.

In the first place, k must be a real quantity. If it were imaginary, the product ik in the fundamental equation $\psi = e^{ikx}u$ would be real and ψ could become infinite as x increased indefinitely. This would be contrary to the requirements which a wave function has to satisfy.

According to (8), however, certain values of E, the total energy, namely those which would make βa nearly a multiple of π, make $\cos \beta a$ nearly unity, and when to this is added $P(\sin \beta a)/\beta a$ the result gives a value of $\cos ka$ which exceeds unity. The cosine cannot exceed unity for any real value of k. The values of E which demand it are therefore impossible.

Here we have in its simplest form the fundamental result that energy states corresponding to certain values of the momentum are excluded. The forbidden regions occur periodically and are separated by regions crowded with permitted states.

The alternation of allowed and impossible levels depends, as the above formulae show, upon the value of a, the periodicity of the potential energy. In the corresponding three-dimensional problem there are three components of k, and three periodicities determined by the geometry of the lattice unit cell. The values of k_x, k_y, or k_z for which the forbidden energy levels exist depend upon the direction of movement of the electron through the lattice. When the three momentum components are plotted in momentum space, the permitted regions can be marked out and constitute the Brillouin zones. In view of their relations to the periodicity they are closely dependent upon the form of the unit cell as revealed by X-ray analysis of the crystal.

It will be noted that in (8) if P is made very large, that is, if the potential barriers become very high, no solution is possible at all except in so far as $\sin \beta a = 0$. Thus $\beta a = n\pi$ and therefore $\beta^2 a^2 = n^2 \pi^2$ or $E = n^2 h^2/8ma^2$. The energy levels become discrete and the electrons are confined.

The great importance of the Brillouin zones is that the number of possible states in each is limited. In certain circumstances, therefore, they may be entirely filled with the electrons present and none

U

of these can pass into a state where it can participate in conduction phenomena unless it is given enough energy to carry it across the forbidden zone into a higher zone. The energy required for this may be prohibitive, and then an insulator results.

The number of *states in a zone* is supposed to be equal to *the number of atoms in the metal*. The argument upon which this statement is based is as follows. In virtue of the factor u in $\psi = e^{ikx}u$, ψ itself is periodic with period a, where a is a periodicity of the lattice. The periodicity of e^{ikx} must be that of some multiple of a, and in order that the boundary conditions at 0 and L shall be satisfied, the form must be $e^{2\pi inx/L}$, which is $e^{2\pi inx/N_x a}$, where N_x is the number of spacings along the axis. n may now have the values $0, \pm 1, \pm 2, ..., \pm \frac{1}{2}N_x$. The value 0 gives $e^0 = 1$, the value $\frac{1}{2}N_x$ gives $e^{\pi ix/a}$. The number of values is $(2N_x/2)+1 = N_x+1$, which equals the number of atoms spaced along the axis. This defines the possible states in the zone.

In the three-dimensional problem the number of states comes out equal to the product of three sets of numbers of spacings, and thus to the total number of atoms in the metal.

Specific properties of metals and non-conductors

In the lattice of a univalent element belonging to group 1 of the periodic system there is one valency electron for each atom. There is thus one electron for each state in a given Brillouin zone. But according to the Pauli principle each level accommodates two electrons of opposite spin. There are thus twice as many possible billets as there are electrons. If an electron is offered an excess velocity in one or other direction by the solicitation of an electric field, it can easily find adjacent to its own a vacant translational level in which it can respond.

The bivalent metals possess two valency electrons for each atom, and since these should fill the lowest zone entirely, the conductivity might have been expected to show a very sharp fall. While it is quite true that group 1 contains the best conductors known, the power of other metals to carry current is also quite considerable. What has to be postulated, and what can be supported by semi-quantitative calculations, is that with certain atoms the three-dimensional Brillouin zones for the p electrons partially overlap with those of the s electrons, so that there can be a response to an accelerating field by a passage from the one type of zone to the other. The further discussion of this matter involves detailed consideration of zone structure and approximate estimates of the actual energies.

In the higher groups of the periodic system there is no such ambiguity. Vacant levels are certainly not available. In diamond, for example, each carbon atom is linked by a covalent electron pair to four other atoms arranged tetrahedrally about it. In this symmetrical structure all the valency electrons are equally shared and each pair is held in balance between two atoms. On purely energetic grounds, therefore, there is no good reason why they should not display a modicum of mobility. The highly insulating character of diamond is in fact due to the complete filling of the Brillouin zones and to the absence of permitted levels in which electrons can display an excess velocity in the direction of an applied potential difference.

Although, as we have seen, some of the differences between insulators and conductors are of a categorical nature, the existence of metallic properties sometimes depends upon quantitative factors of a less definite kind. While carbon and silicon are insulators and give crystal lattices of the covalent giant molecule type, lead and tin in the same group of the periodic system exhibit metallic conduction. The outer shells of these elements consist of two s electrons and two p electrons, the former constituting a sub-group which is in some degree saturated. It appears, with tin often and with lead usually, to be stable enough to remain aloof from covalency formation and to play no part in the building of the metallic crystal. Lead and crystalline tin, therefore, behave as bivalent metals and owe their conductivity to this fact.

When permitted and forbidden zones are separated by a gap of a certain moderate width, rare transitions are possible for thermally excited electrons. The substances in which this happens are semi-conductors. They show a small conductivity which, unlike that of pure metals, increases as the temperature rises. Most semi-conductors owe their property to impurities which create fresh energy levels bridging the gap between the zones. These levels may, according to the nature of the impurity, furnish electrons which can conduct in the higher zone, or else may provide homes for electrons from the lower zone, thereby freeing levels in which other electrons of that zone can show response to the accelerating field.

Such, in general, is the sort of account which can be given of the nature of metals and of the contrast between them and the non-metallic elements.

Essentially it rests upon the fact that while completion of electron groups by sharing is simple enough for two atoms lacking only one or two electrons, a similar manœuvre for those which lack five, six, or seven would lead to peculiarly cumbrous structures, such as a cluster of eight sodium atoms. The communal holding of electrons in a positive ion lattice is then preferred.

The whole theory hangs upon the mathematical conceptions which this communal system suggests. They are not without certain arbitrary characters, and it is therefore of importance that the underlying ideas should find further confirmation in another major phenomenon, namely that of ferromagnetism.

Magnetism in general: ferromagnetism

Since a magnetic field is produced by an electric current, which consists in a flow of electrons along a conductor, the motion of free electrons in atomic orbits may fairly be supposed to give rise to a similar effect. It is also a reasonable hypothesis that the spin of an electron should be associated with a magnetic moment, and so it proves.

In most molecules with symmetrically disposed orbits and paired spins the effects cancel out, but where there is an unbalanced moment a substance shows what are called *paramagnetic* properties, and orientates itself in line with a magnetic field. The *susceptibility*, χ, of a body is defined by the relation $\chi = I/H$, where H is the applied field and I is the magnetic moment per unit mass. The magnetic moment is called forth by the field in so far as this orientates the permanent moments. Orientation becomes less easy as thermal motion increases, and consequently the susceptibility decreases with increase of temperature, sometimes in accordance with the law $\chi \propto 1/T$.

Although paramagnetism is confined to substances with incomplete groups of electrons, a property called *diamagnetism* is universal. In any material a magnetic field will induce a moment in such a direction that it opposes the inducing force. The diamagnetic body sets itself at right angles to the field. All substances are in principle diamagnetic, but if they possess natural moments the influence of these outweighs that of the induced moments, so that in effect paramagnetism is observed.

The phenomenon of *ferromagnetism* long remained mysterious. It is confined to a few substances, iron, cobalt, nickel, and certain of their alloys and compounds, and is characterized by being enormously more powerful than paramagnetism.

The moments are called forth by the magnetizing field applied from outside, but do not disappear completely when the field is removed—a phenomenon known as hysteresis. The development of the observable magnetism seems to depend upon the alignment of small domains of order in the solid substance (which, it appears, are not the microcrystalline units of which the macroscopic crystal is usually built up). The domains themselves possess the inherent and fully developed property, and it is the nature of the magnetism within the individual elements rather than the question of the relation of these to the whole crystal which is of fundamental interest.

The formal theory of Weiss represents the field within the substance by the equation

$$H_i = H_{\text{external}} + \lambda\sigma,$$

where λ is a constant and σ is the intensity of magnetization. $\lambda\sigma$ is the so-called molecular field. It depends upon some kind of coupling of the elementary magnets within the domain, but the major problem is to determine what this coupling involves.

In the first place, it appears from delicate measurements on the mechanical moment acquired by a body when it is magnetized that the spin moments rather than the orbital moments of electrons are those chiefly responsible for ferromagnetism. This finding points to some hypothesis about the mode of coupling of electron spins. The ordinary magnetic interaction of the spin moments is much too small to account for the powerful mutual effect.

A much more drastic sanction resides in the requirement that the total wave function of the system shall be antisymmetrical, because in certain circumstances this imposes on the electrons the condition of parallel spins. In the hydrogen molecule the electrons possess opposite spins in virtue not of any mutual force which they exert directly upon one another, but of the condition that the lowest energy state demands an orbital wave function of the symmetrical type. The categorical requirement of overall antisymmetry then dictates the antiparallel spin function. According to the calculation of Heisenberg, there are certain crystals for which the lowest energy state involves the parallel alignment of the spins. These crystals are ferromagnetic. In this theory also the electrons coordinate their spins not, as it were, by their own efforts, but to conform to the general symmetry rules of quantum mechanics.

The calculations which are made to determine which is the state of lowest energy in a given example envisage an extended molecule with a large number of communal electrons. The wave function ψ is the product of two factors ϕ and u. $u = u_\alpha$ for spins of the same kind.

If the spins are parallel, ϕ must be antisymmetrical in the space coordinates of all the electrons. The form which satisfies this condition is expressed by the determinant

$$\begin{vmatrix} \phi_1(r_1) & \phi_1(r_2) & \cdot & \cdot \\ \phi_2(r_1) & \phi_2(r_2) & \cdot & \cdot \\ \cdot & \cdot & \cdot & \cdot & \cdot & \cdot \end{vmatrix},$$

r_1, r_2,... being coordinates of electrons and the serial numbers attached to ϕ indicating the assignment of the electrons.

By the general theorem of wave mechanics (see p. 252) the energy is given by

$$\frac{\int \bar\psi H\psi \, d\omega}{\int \bar\psi\psi \, d\omega},$$

the denominator being normalized in the usual way. The numerator contains *inter alia* a series of terms of the type

$$\int \bar\phi_1(r_1)\bar\phi_2(r_2)... H\phi_1(r_1)\phi_2(r_2)... \, d\omega$$

with each $\bar\phi$ balancing the ϕ of the same subscript. These terms collectively contribute an amount to the integral which may be written roughly $N\epsilon_0$, where N is the number of electrons. There are other terms of the type

$$\int \bar\phi_k(r_1)... H\phi_l(r_1)... \, d\omega$$

where k and l are different (exchange integral). It is assumed that the contribution of all such terms is zero unless k and l refer to *nearest neighbours* in the crystal (the extended molecule). The total energy then assumes the form

$$W_0 = N(\epsilon_0 - ZI),$$

where Z is the number of nearest neighbours and I is one of the exchange integrals.

Whether or not the crystal is ferromagnetic now depends upon the sign of I. If, as the equation is written, it is positive, the chosen combination with ϕ antisymmetrical and u corresponding to parallel spins will in fact correspond to the lower energy and be the stable one.

A positive value for I does in fact demand special conditions, so that ferromagnetism can be seen to be rare, The conditions required are also in qualitative conformity with those in fact applying to the metals iron, cobalt, and nickel.

Inspection of the details of the calculation shows that the positive contributions to I arise from electron–electron or nucleus–nucleus interactions in the energy term of the operator H. Thus they will be most evident when there is a considerable overlap of electron clouds, which occurs most markedly in atoms possessing d and f electrons (quantum number $l = 2$ and 3). This factor tends to locate ferromagnetism in transition elements. For electron overlap to outweigh electron–nucleus interaction, the nuclei should not be too close. Nor, on the other hand, should they be too far apart, or all interaction of any kind becomes feeble. This factor makes for further specificity, and in fact for the elements iron, cobalt, and nickel the ratio (interatomic distance/radius of d electron shell) does lie within a special rather narrow range.

Qualitative as the above considerations are, they illustrate further the importance of the communal electrons in the interpretation of metallic properties.

X V

EXTENDED ARRAYS OF MOLECULES

Types of assemblage formed by atoms

THE communal metallic electrons come into their own when private sharing between pairs of individuals becomes too cumbrous for stability. It predominates when the valency electrons are few, as in groups 1, 2, and 3, and in the transition elements, or where some tend to remain in inert sub-groups, as in the heavier elements of group 4.

Covalent bond formation becomes practicable when not more than four neighbours have to be involved in the sharing. Carbon (group 4) and tin in its grey non-metallic modification form such links with four tetrahedrally disposed neighbours, antimony (group 5) with three close neighbours, while selenium and tellurium (group 6) complete their octets by sharing with two neighbours. In all these examples what is called a giant molecule is formed. It varies from the well-knit diamond structure to the less evident spiral chains of the group 6 elements.

With the elementary halogens the sharing of electrons is confined normally to a single pair. The diatomic molecules so formed have no valencies left to knit the lattices of the solids into continuous frameworks, and van der Waals forces are left to dictate the structure of the crystals.

In such a manner the general disposition of metallic properties and the variation in the mode of linking throughout the periodic system of the elements can be explained. On the overall pattern there are many embroideries, and highly specific influences play their parts.

Oxygen and nitrogen, for example, form diatomic molecules which do not, in the solid state, participate in more extended covalent arrays like the continuous spirals of selenium. This is because, for specific reasons, the diatomic molecules are very stable. The double link of the oxygen molecule is in fact more than twice as strong as the single link. Thus a large number of separate O_2 molecules are more stable than a long chain—O—O—O—O—O—O—.... .

That the pictures of covalent bonds, on the one hand, and of the communal electrons, on the other, are not necessarily quite so different as might at first sight appear is suggested by the views of Pauling on the nature of the bonds in metals. He postulates a state of affairs where covalent bonds are indeed formed, but are shared in a special way between any given atom and all its neighbours. This is sometimes interpreted in terms of the process which has already been referred to as resonance, and a vivid though essentially incorrect idea of it may be formed by imagining the bonds to alternate between the various pairs of atoms. But there is no real process of alternation. What quantum mechanics envisages is not a switch from A—B C to A B—C but a state of affairs intermediate between the two. This being so, the Pauling view does not so much constitute a rival to the hypothesis of the communal electrons as offer an alternative technique for handling it—and one which for many of the purposes of chemistry may well be more convenient.

The crystalline state

In solids, then, the forces which tend to impose order on the individual chemical units may be van der Waals forces, as with the inert gases, with elements which form diatomic molecules, and with organic substances; they may be Coulomb forces between ions, as in many simple salts and with the positive ion–electron interaction in metals; and, finally, they may be the covalencies binding atom to atom throughout extended regions of space.

While it is not possible to predict behaviour in each individual example, the reasons for this general classification and the trend in character through the periodic system are explicable in terms of the electrical theory of matter.

Whichever kind of interaction prevails, the molecular or ionic units must tend to set themselves into arrays which possess a minimum of potential energy. Hence the existence of the crystalline state and its characteristics of symmetry. Symmetrical orderings naturally allow potential energies lower than the unsymmetrical arrangements which would result from their distortion. To represent a possible spatial configuration of ions or molecules the system need not possess a potential energy which is an absolute minimum. Several relative minima may be separated from one another and from the absolute minimum by intervening maxima.

Thus several spatial configurations which correspond to relatively but not absolutely stable minima may have to be taken into consideration. Each has certain elements of symmetry, but some have more than others. Hence the existence of *polymorphic modifications*.

If the molecular force field is highly unsymmetrical, two or more molecules can orient themselves into a sub-system which then arrays itself with other similar sub-systems to give an extended configuration of minimal potential energy. The number of modes in which the extended configuration can be built up is large, and the analysis of the various possible cases is dealt with in the science of crystallography.

The potential energy minima can be achieved in patterns which repeat themselves throughout extended portions of space—in principle indefinitely—and which constitute *space lattices*. The smallest complete unit of pattern represents the *unit cell* of the lattice. The piling together of the unit cells gives the crystal. In order that they may be repeated indefinitely in all dimensions the unit cells must possess the form of parallelepipeds. The shape of these governs the symmetry of the crystal as a whole, though it does not unambiguously dictate the external form, since various geometrical figures are compatible with the same elements of symmetry.

Various kinds of symmetry are distinguished. In the first place, there are planes, axes, and centres of symmetry. A structure possesses a plane of symmetry when what lies on one side of a given plane is a mirror image of what lies on the other side. It possesses an n-fold axis of symmetry when rotation through an angle of $360/n$ degrees brings it into a condition indistinguishable from the original. For a centre of symmetry there must correspond to each point in the structure another point such that the lines joining the respective pairs are all bisected at the centre.

The combination of symmetry elements defining a crystal form is referred to as a *point group*. There are thirty-two such combinations encountered among real crystals. They fall into classes according to the form of the unit cell. In general the latter has three sides a, b, c and three angles α, β, γ. In ascending order of symmetry the crystal classes are: the triclinic with a, b, and c unequal and one axis perpendicular to the other two; rhombic with three unequal but mutually perpendicular axes; hexagonal with $a = b$ at 120° and c unequal to them but at right angles; rhombohedral with equal sides, and angles equal but not right angles; tetragonal with $a = b \neq c$, and the angles all right angles; and finally, cubic with $a = b = c$ and $\alpha = \beta = \gamma = 90°$.

Two further elements of symmetry enter into the definition of the extended space lattice, namely glide planes and screw axes.

If by reflection in a plane and simultaneous linear displacement the array may be brought into self-coincidence, it possesses a glide plane, and if this same effect is achieved by rotation through a given angle and simultaneous linear displacement, there is a screw axis.

The complete set of symmetry elements which define the geometrical relationships between all the individual constituents of the three-dimensional repeating pattern is called the *space group*.

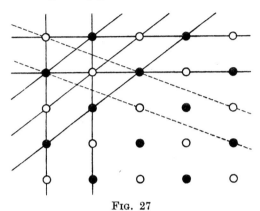

FIG. 27

Purely geometrical analysis shows that there are 230 space groups divided unequally among the thirty-two point groups, which in turn are shared unequally by the seven crystal systems.

Macroscopic crystallography can discover the point group, but only X-ray analysis reveals the space group. These matters will not be treated here. All that will be said is this: a regular array of atoms or molecules such as occurs in a space lattice may be traversed by numerous planes passing through two-dimensional arrays of points. According to the nature of the lattice, the density of points in a given plane may be greater or smaller and in general varies from one type of plane to another in a given lattice. In an ionic lattice, moreover, a given plane may contain positive ions or negative ions or both, and the chemical and electrical character of the layer varies with the way in which the section through the lattice is taken. The general principle is illustrated in Fig. 27.

These crystal planes reflect X-rays and interference occurs according to the relation
$$2d \sin \theta = n\lambda,$$
where d is the distance between successive planes of the same type,

and θ is the angle of incidence. λ is the wave-length and n is an integer. From the various values of d the dimensions and angles of the unit cell can be calculated. From its volume, the density of the solid, and the molecular weight, the number of ions or molecules in each unit cell can be determined. Detailed study of the actual intensities of the various X-ray reflections allows conclusions to be drawn about the distribution of electric density in the lattice and hence about the precise spatial pattern. We shall not, however, enter into the technique of such matters.

In principle, the space lattice is determined by the symmetry of the force field of the individual molecule or ion, the way in which several molecules or ions may reduce their potential energy by forming groups of higher symmetry, and the way in which the primary or secondary units then reduce their own potential energy by forming the repeating spatial pattern.

All this, however, has ignored the influence of the thermal motions. Forms of lattice which do not allow room for the vibrations appropriate to the temperature, even if the potential energy relations are exceedingly favourable, are impossible. The lattice form chosen by a given substance is that corresponding to the minimum potential energy compatible with the dynamical degrees of freedom of the constituent molecules.

As the temperature rises a form of lattice which allows room for feeble vibrations frequently has to change into another with greater tolerance. In a general way, polymorphic transformations occur in such a sense that more compact structures are stable at lower temperatures and more open structures at higher. Exceptions to this rule do indeed occur, but can sometimes be explained in terms of special circumstances, as for example when increasing thermal energy leads to the rupture of special chemical bonds (such as hydrogen bonds) which maintain an open structure in the forms stable at lower temperatures.

In these general respects polymorphic changes in the solid state resemble the transition from solid to liquid (p. 100): and once again the energy-entropy motif is dominant.

The change from one possible lattice form of a given substance to another obviously makes a finite and indeed profound difference to the size and shape of the unit cell. Units of one lattice type are geometrically incompatible with units of the other, and the new polymorphic form must constitute a separate phase. This being so, for thermodynamic and kinetic reasons which have already been discussed (p. 71), there is a definite *transition temperature* at which the change of phase occurs.

Order–disorder transitions

The foregoing considerations become modified for certain systems, especially those of more than one component, such as alloys, and here a special kind of change, known as an *order–disorder transition*, can occur. The phenomena shown by the alloy of copper and zinc known as β-brass will introduce us to a matter of some general importance. At low temperatures the alloy consists of a regular lattice of copper atoms, one at each corner of a series of cubes, and of a similar lattice of zinc atoms, so disposed that each cube of the copper lattice has a zinc atom at its centre and each cube of the zinc lattice a copper atom. The two interpenetrating simple cubic lattices thus give what is called a body-centred cubic lattice.

The X-ray reflections for layers of zinc and copper atoms respectively are separate, distinct, and recognizable. As the temperature increases the character of the reflections changes and comes to correspond more and more to randomly mixed atoms of the two sorts. The ordered configuration of the lower temperatures gives place to the random configuration of the higher without any change in the lattice itself. What occurs constitutes the order–disorder transition.

A quantitative criterion for the degree of order can be laid down. Imagine $2n$ lattice points all unoccupied. For the perfectly ordered state n specific points are reserved for copper and n for zinc. In the actual state let a fraction p of the zinc atoms occupy their own reserved points, the remainder intruding into the places reserved for copper. For perfect order, $p = 1$; for complete randomness $p = \frac{1}{2}$, since there is then an equal chance for the zinc to find one of its own sites or a copper site. The formula $\sigma = (p-\frac{1}{2})/(1-\frac{1}{2})$ then gives a convenient measure of the order, becoming 1 or 0 for the two extremes of configuration.

The more ordered the configuration the lower the potential energy: the lower also the entropy, and the relation of these two is important. The energy change, ΔU, accompanying a given transfer of atoms from ordered to random positions (at approximately constant volume) is a continuous function of σ itself, since, for example, there is no change in potential energy when atoms are moved from a given random configuration to a neighbouring one, so that $\Delta U \to 0$ when $\sigma \to 0$. In an ordinary phase change at constant volume the equilibrium is defined by $\Delta F = \Delta U - T\Delta S = 0$. ΔU and ΔS being constant characteristics of a given pair of phases and independent of their amount,

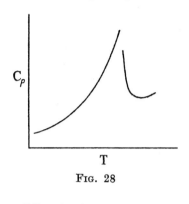

C_p

T

FIG. 28

T_{equil} is fixed and definite. In the transitions from order to disorder at a given temperature ΔU is positive but *alters as the change proceeds*. ΔS is also positive, so that neither order nor disorder need always become complete. As T increases, $T\Delta S$ overcomes ΔU more and more easily, and there comes presently a range in which ΔU cannot balance $T\Delta S$ at all for any value of σ, so that complete disorder sets in.

What is of very wide interest here is that the entropy change which in a phase transition would have occurred at a fixed temperature has in the order–disorder transition been spread out over a range of temperature. The increase in potential energy which in the former would have manifested itself as a latent heat absorbed at the constant transformation temperature is in the latter absorbed over a finite range and thus manifests itself as an anomalously great specific heat. In the region of temperature where such phenomena are in process of evolution the specific heat generally follows a curve of the form shown in Fig. 28.

Gradual transitions

Many of the changes which occur in solids are not profound enough to impose a new space lattice and thereby to reveal themselves as polymorphic phase transformations. They may depend upon alterations of configuration of the statistical kind exemplified by the copper-zinc alloy; and the abnormality in the specific heat with which they are associated is connected with the increased potential energy imposed by the more random arrangement. The heat absorption is due primarily, not to the excitation of new degrees of freedom, but to the increase in configurational entropy.

In other examples new modes of motion appear, not disruptive enough to destroy the original lattice. The study of specific heats at low temperatures has revealed the existence of many of these gradual transitions. They are shown by the ammonium halides, by methane, by the hydrogen halides, and many other substances.

The precise nature of the change in the motions of the molecules or ions is not quite certain. It probably varies from one example to another. Sometimes torsional oscillations may give place to free rotations. Sometimes vibrations about ordered axes may be replaced by vibrations about disordered axes.

Types of solid lattice and the properties of solids

The calculation of the energy of solid structures is possible in principle, but in practice is difficult except in very simple examples. The geometrical constants of the lattice must first be known and the magnitude of the forces acting in different directions between the elements which constitute it. For reasons which ultimately go back to the Pauli principle, different kinds of binding between these elements exist. The various types of lattice may be roughly classified in the following way. First, there are those in which some small number of complete molecules form the content of the unit cell, the interaction between them being due to van der Waals forces. The binding energy of such an array is not very high. Secondly, there are the simple ionic lattices formed typically by salts. Here the important interactions are Coulomb attractions which are balanced by the repulsive forces preventing interpenetration of electron clouds. Finally, there are those lattices in which covalencies spread throughout the crystal.

van der Waals interactions are not susceptible of very precise calculation. The ionic lattices have, however, been subjected to successful quantitative treatment. Their energy is expressible in the form

$$U = -Ae^2/r + B/r^n.$$

$-e^2/r$ is the potential energy of two univalent ions at a distance r A a numerical constant (Madelung constant) which comes from an averaging by integration over each possible pair of ions in the system, and B/r^n is a term which represents the repulsion between ions at small distances.

For equilibrium $dU/dr = 0$ when $r = r_0$, r_0 being known from the geometry of the structure. n may be determined from the compressibility of the solid and the energy thus estimated.

Some of the conditions governing the existence of metallic lattices have already been discussed, but a little more may be said about the compactness of the structures formed by various elements. The alkali metals all form body-centred cubic lattices, that is, structures in which one ion occurs at each of the eight corners of a cube and one at the centre. This is a relatively open formation and one which allows for the low density and comparative softness of these elements. Copper, silver, and gold form face-centred lattices, that is, structures in which there is an ion not only at each corner of the cube but in the centre of each face also. This is much more compact. The densities are in fact much greater.

Transition metals in general have greater bonding, according to the point of view of Pauling. These elements belong to the regions of the periodic system where the group of 8 electrons is expanding to 18. In the first long period, for example, there occur electronic states with $n = 3$, $l = 2$. These are d-states and there are $2l+1 = 5$ of them, each accommodating two electrons. They are filled in competition with the s- and p-states of the $n = 4$ group. There is one $4s$-state for two electrons and three $(2l+1)$ of the $4p$-states $(l = 1)$ for six electrons. Electrons from a number of these states may be concerned in metallic bonds. The structures are thus much more compact than those of the alkali metals. Detailed correlations have been made between the bonding of the so-called resonating systems and the bond lengths or interionic distances.

The lattices in which covalencies link atoms through many unit cells are themselves of various kinds. The simplest is perhaps that of diamond, in which each carbon is joined by tetrahedral covalencies to four others. The interatomic distances correspond to those between carbon atoms linked by single bonds in the molecules of organic compounds, and the total energy of the lattice is the sum of all the bond energies.

Diamond possesses a structure which is continuous in three dimensions. In some solids the covalent unions extend over two dimensions, or simply stretch along one axis. Silicates provide examples of all types, from the simple ionic lattices of orthosilicates such as Mg_2SiO_4 to the three-dimensional networks of the various forms of silica itself.

The characteristic forms and properties of the substances met in daily life depend to a large extent upon the lattice properties. Simple molecular and ionic structures are not remarkable for hardness or stability. They show cleavage, and appropriate solvents can usually be found for their dispersion. Metals, on the other hand, have special properties which, as has been explained, they owe to the free electrons which determine their electrical, thermal, optical, and mechanical peculiarities. It is, however, necessary to remember that some of the mechanical properties of metals, as indeed of other ionic crystals, are also determined to a considerable extent by the cohesion between the microcrystals of which the large specimens are built up rather than by the atomic or molecular constants. This fact turns the study of mechanical character into a highly complicated special subject.

Many of the qualities upon which natural form, on the one hand, or applicability in the arts, on the other hand, depend derive from the special structure of covalent lattices which adapts them according to circumstances to form sheets, fibres, or extended arrays of greater or smaller hardness, softness, compactness, or porosity.

The silicates, already mentioned, provide examples of special importance since they make up so large a portion of the earth's crust. Orthosilicic acid is $Si(OH)_4$. By loss of water it gives rise to meta-silicates with chains of any length

$$
\begin{array}{cccc}
OH & OH & OH & OH \\
| & | & | & | \\
-Si-O-Si-O-Si-O-Si-. & & & \\
| & | & | & | \\
OH & OH & OH & OH
\end{array}
\qquad (a)
$$

As the length increases, the composition tends towards the limit H_2SiO_3 from which the salts are derived. The sodium silicate of 'water glass' belongs to this type. The long chains with their possibility of becoming intertwined or randomly linked together by the formation of fresh Si—O—Si bridges are probably responsible for the stickiness of the solutions and for the firm jellies to which these set when acidified at even quite low concentrations. The solid meta-silicates possess a more or less rigid backbone of covalently linked silicon and oxygen atoms running right through their lattices. This has ionic charges spaced uniformly along it, in the neighbourhood of which the metallic cations are set.

Further elimination of water can occur between two chains of the type illustrated above, (a), and this process, which is called cross-linking, gives rise to extra strength and toughness. When it is confined to two chains the structures produced are fibrous, and the peculiar physical properties of asbestos are supposed to be due to the fact that it is a silicate of this variety. The mode of linking is illustrated in (b).

(b)

The chains are easily separated from one another, but are difficult to break. Thus asbestos is easily split into fibres, but is none the less tough and refractory. Unlike the simple metasilicate chains these double chains are rigid. The limiting composition of long chains of the metallic slats corresponds to $H_6Si_4O_{11}$.

Further cross-linking can occur and gives rise to planar or at least two-dimensional surface structures as shown in (c). The corresponding metallic derivatives constitute silicates such as mica, remarkable for its easy cleavage into thin laminae. The limiting composition for infinite arrays of this kind is $H_2Si_2O_5$.

(c)

Here again the silicon-oxygen structure is continuous and the metallic cations are inserted according to the requirements of electrical neutrality, and also, it must be added, according to conformity of size. This last factor explains the occurrence of isomorphous replacements which give rise to what at first sight may be very puzzling variations in composition. Talc, for example, is $Mg_3(OH)_2Si_4O_{10}$. The two Si_2O_5 units need to be balanced by four positive charges, here represented by the six positive charges of the three magnesium ions and the two negatives of the hydroxyls.

Clays also contain silicon-oxygen sheets alternating with alumi-- nium-oxygen sheets. It appears that the whole structure falls into successive layers between which only relatively weak forces exist, so that the soft and yielding structure results. The plasticity of such materials is of great importance in the economy of nature.

Very stable three-dimensional structures analogous to diamond exist in silica itself. Cristobalite is in fact rather similar in structure to diamond, each silicon being surrounded by four oxygens and each oxygen lying midway between two silicons, a position forcing the oxygen valencies to assume an angle of 180° which is not the pre- ferred angle. For this reason, probably, cristobalite is not so refrac- tory as diamond. The tendency of the oxygen bonds to lie at a smaller angle explains in some measure the existence of the alterna- tive form of silica which occurs in quartz. The kind of symmetry which is established in quartz involves a helical disposition of atoms, and there are in fact right- and left-handed screw structures which act differently upon polarized light traversing the crystals.

The variations in hardness, in the tendency to form sheets and fibres, plasticity, and so on which are manifested by these various inorganic structures and which have their importance in explaining the properties of rocks and soils, minerals, and metals, appear in an even more remarkable degree among complex organic compounds, which in their turn serve as the bases of living tissues, or of sub- stances with properties of great value in the industrial arts.

Organic compounds may interact to form polymers or polycon- densation products of enormous molecular weight. The condition that they should do so is the presence in each molecule of more than one functional group. Ethylene, which may react as $--CH_2CH_2--$, forms polymers containing from two to many thousand units: gly- cols form with dibasic acids polyesters with chains of any length: hexamethylene diamine and adipic acid form polyamides of high molecular weight which constitute one of the varieties of 'nylon', and organic silicon compounds lead to condensation products such as methyl silicones. Among naturally occurring substances, proteins consist of long chains of —CHR CO NH— units, polysaccharides, such as cellulose, of long chains in which the units are the rings derived from pentoses and hexoses.

When the original molecules or monomers contain two functional groups only, the conditions favour single straight chains, but if they contain extra functional groups, cross-linking may occur with the production of sheets and three-dimensional covalently linked structures.

When the molecule consists of a long chain, this constitutes a tough backbone traversing many unit cells of the lattice. In other dimensions the binding is less strong than that due to the covalencies and depends upon van der Waals and dipolar forces which are more easily overcome. Hence the prevalence of thread-forming properties among macromolecular compounds.

The study of the relation between structure and properties in these substances of high molecular weight constitutes an important chapter of chemistry. The character of the materials is determined partly by the chemical nature—hydrocarbon chains repel water, hydroxyl groups tend to confer solubility in water, or at least the power to absorb water—but also by the molecular weight and the degree of polymerization, by the degree of cross-linking, and, in more subtle ways, by the actual distribution of molecular weights among the molecules making up a given preparation, which is seldom homogeneous.

Sufficient length of chain is necessary to give strength to threads, while cross-linking confers rigidity, toughness, and insolubility. Qualities such as plasticity and susceptibility to cold drawing depend upon the flexibility of the individual chains and also upon the ease with which they slip past one another in the lattice. The elastic properties will also depend in an important way on the readiness with which rotation about the valency bonds of the main chain can occur, and the hindrance to this rotation opposed by the geometrical form of attached groups or side chains.

When the solid preparation consists of a medley of chains of different lengths, their ends will not conform to any regular pattern. A given chain will pass from crystal to crystal, and in fact there will be a rather curious state of affairs in which a number of virtually separate crystals are united by threads of longer molecules passing from one to another in a way shown diagrammatically in Fig. 29. Regions of crystalline regularity will be separated from one another by amorphous regions, and the phase relationships as well as the mechanical properties will be appreciably influenced thereby.

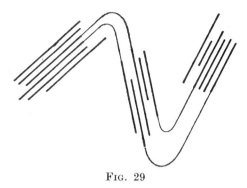

FIG. 29

It has been shown that certain protein chains may exist in straight or in folded forms in the crystal, and this circumstance probably determines some of the elastic properties of living tissues.

The details of these various matters will not be discussed here, but it is very obvious that the different combinations to which known principles of structure and arrangement can give rise constitute a set of remarkable scope and versatility. How these combinations work themselves out is a subject for detailed and specialized study. But in general it can be said that the picture of the world with the tough fibres of its woods, the laminae of its rocks, the elastic tissues of its living beings, its burnished and resonant metals, its hard diamonds, and its friable salts can be referred back to a fundamental motif of which it is only an elaboration. Molecules and ions form patterns of minimum potential energy, in so far as their motions allow them to do so. These patterns are determined by the charges and the shapes: the shapes depend upon the linking of the co-valencies, while both charges and covalencies differ from atom to atom because of two categorical laws admitting no compromise. These are, namely, that the spin of an electron has either one or the other of two possible values, and that the wave function of an atomic system is antisymmetric. After this interpretation the spectacle of nature may seem more uniform: it hardly seems less mysterious.

XVI

FLUID SYSTEMS

The liquid state

IN the study of the solid state the guiding theme is that of order and of the mode of ordering. In the liquid state some of the order characteristic of the solid has been lost, and the first theories of liquids assumed them to possess the random configurations of gases while still being subject to cohesive forces of considerable magnitude. This view is, however, far from completely satisfactory. The primary quality of a liquid is not its disorder but its fluidity, namely its tendency to yield continuously under stress and to conform to the shape of its container without necessarily filling it. X-ray reflections reveal that in fact some degree of order does exist in liquids, and the kinetic and thermodynamic relations of the various states of matter are most easily understandable in terms of the hypothesis that order is relaxed in stages of which melting is not the last.

Let us consider the possible changes in entropy as a solid with a regular space lattice is raised in temperature. At first the mean positions of the molecules are constant, the vibrational energy increasing and the entropy varying according to the expression $dS = C_p \, dT/T$. New modes of motion, such as rotations, may appear and C_p itself increases. Further, in solids such as alloys, interchange of particles between lattice sites may occur with increase in potential energy and further increase in entropy which is continuous over a range of temperature (p. 310).

If new degrees of freedom or growing amplitudes in existing ones are incompatible with the old lattice configuration, a new lattice corresponding to a higher potential energy has to be formed. Small regions of this new lattice cannot, for geometrical reasons, normally remain disseminated through the old and a fresh phase has to develop. The growth of this new phase, for thermodynamic and kinetic reasons dealt with earlier, imposes a constant temperature. The increased potential energy and the associated entropy change now manifest themselves, not as a contribution to specific heat, but as a latent heat.

Before the phase change, however, there has been the possibility of a considerable relaxation of order. When molecules rotate on their axes extra configurational complexions arise. An angular coordinate becomes freely disposable for each unit of the lattice. Whether or not this has repercussions upon the other coordinates depends upon the molecular shape, the lattice dimensions, and the intermolecular forces. Were the molecules highly symmetrical, they could acquire freedom of rotation without interfering with their neighbours: were they in the form of long rods, they could not rotate without disturbing the centres of gravity of all those around them. This is an extreme and obvious case, but the interrelations of coordinates are quite general and often subtle.

Let us consider in general a reference molecule and also a second molecule with Cartesian coordinates relative to the first of x, y, and z, and with polar coordinates relative to the first of r, θ, and ϕ. The mean value of r can only increase to that characteristic of the gaseous state when the kinetic energy is raised considerably. Changes in θ and ϕ, however, may become easy for adjacent molecules long before changes in r. Shear will then be possible and the substance acquires fluid properties. In principle, the restraints on the variation of the different coordinates may be relaxed separately. Three-dimensional separation corresponds to vaporization, angular displacement in any direction to liquefaction. When restraint in one particular direction weakens, a solid becomes susceptible to cold drawing. When the orienting forces in liquids retain their effect sufficiently to align certain kinds of molecule along the x-, y-, or z-axis, there arises the anisotropic liquid or liquid crystal formed by various substances of elongated structure.

The various kinds of relaxation of restraint are all attended with increases of potential energy and also of configurational entropy. It depends upon their geometrical character whether or not they force a phase change and so complete themselves at constant temperature. If a few molecules could indulge in mutual displacements of the kind involved in shear, a solid would no doubt simply acquire liquid-like elements which increased in number according to Boltzmann's law as the temperature rose. But the only lattice which allows these (without strong restoring forces) differs too much from that of the original solid. Hence all the new entropy is associated with a latent heat.

A liquid, then, would appear to be a lattice so mobile under shear that it exists only as a time average. It might perhaps be likened to a flight of birds attempting to keep formation in a gale. They are

continually blown into confusion, but as continually strive to re-
establish their order.

One of the more remarkable properties of liquids is their high
specific heat. This suggests strongly what the X-ray reflections confirm, that they still have configurational order to lose, and thus
configurational entropy to gain: and this without enough disturbance
of their geometry to provoke a further phase change until cohesion
is finally overcome by kinetic energy, and they pass into the state
of vapour.

That order and mobility are by no means very closely correlated
is evident from the existence of glasses, which represent highly super-
cooled liquids. They are hard and brittle, but possess no definite
crystalline structure. The randomness of the molecular arrangement
is about the same as that in liquids, but they are not necessarily
entirely devoid of certain kinds of order, as is suggested by the
characteristic conchoidal fracture which is often shown.

Rubber-like properties

A special kind of ordering and disordering is believed to occur in
substances which show the elastic properties typified in rubber. The
molecules of rubbery substances are long, and are probably in some
degree coiled up in the normal condition. One view, which contains
a good deal of truth though it may well be oversimplified, is that the
ends of the molecules occupy quite random positions in the unstretched state and that the molecules are brought more nearly into
alignment by the stretching. A crude picture of this relationship is
shown in Fig. 30.

If the chains are composed of singly bound carbon atoms, the
tetrahedral valency angle at each link in the chain permits a whole
cone of orientations, so that the position in space of the nth atom
relative to the first can vary widely. From a knowledge of the
valency angle, the bond length, and the number of atoms, the most
probable linear distance between the ends of the chain can be calculated, and the probability of particular distances estimated. A collection of chains has a calculably greater entropy when randomly
coiled than when parallel, and the change in S corresponding to a
given average increase in effective length, that is, distance between
ends, can be worked out. To stretch the rubber at constant temperature requires expenditure of work. The increase of free energy

determines the force which must be applied to effect the elongation. When the tension is relaxed the chains assume their random configuration once more. According to circumstances ΔU, the change in the internal energy, may or may not contribute to ΔF. In rubber itself it contributes little, and the entropy changes are the major factors, as may be inferred thermodynamically from the influence of temperature on the contractile force of the stretched material. Here is the argument.

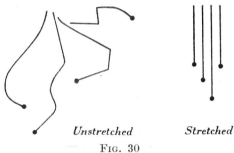

Unstretched   *Stretched*

FIG. 30

In a perfect gas the expansive force originates in the tendency to assume a state of greater entropy, and $\partial U/\partial V$ is zero. In rubber the contractile force originates in what is essentially the same way, namely in the tendency of the molecules to pass to a state of higher entropy. In the two cases there is the same law of temperature variation. Gas pressure on the one hand and contractile force on the other both increase in direct proportion to the absolute temperature. $F = U - TS$, so that

$$\frac{\partial F}{\partial V} = \frac{\partial U}{\partial V} - T\frac{\partial S}{\partial V}.$$

For the gas $\partial F/\partial V = -p$, and $\partial U/\partial V = 0$, so that

$$p = T\frac{\partial S}{\partial V}$$

(though here we must be careful to avoid any apparent logical contradiction if we have originally defined T in terms of p). For rubber of length l, and contractile force P, we have

$$\frac{\partial F}{\partial l} = P, \qquad \frac{\partial F}{\partial l} = \frac{\partial U}{\partial l} - T\frac{\partial S}{\partial l},$$

$$P = \frac{\partial U}{\partial l} - T\frac{\partial S}{\partial l}.$$

Now since P for a given elongation is found experimentally to vary directly as T, $\partial U/\partial l$ cannot contribute in any important way. In other cases, of course, there is no reason why internal energy changes accompanying the distortion should not be the major factors in causing the appearance of the contractile force. Here the temperature dependence would become quite different.

The simple picture of coiling and uncoiling chains in rubbery substances is highly idealized, but in all real examples there is probably some form of entropy change depending upon varying constraints on the succession of valency angles in a chain. The energy-entropy relations are, of course, more general than the simple model of the coiling chains.

Whether rubber, in the light of the foregoing discussion, would be better described as a liquid or a solid is one which would no doubt have appealed to the scholastic philosophers. What is really more significant is that rubber provides another example of the way in which certain combinations of the variables defining configurations cease to be fixed while others remain subject to control. At low temperatures rubber-like substances freeze, in the sense that the molecular motions characteristic of the condition cease to be possible.

Condensed helium

The most remarkable, or more correctly the least familiar, kind of behaviour resulting from the interrelations of order, entropy, and mobility is perhaps that exhibited by condensed helium. Helium is light and the interatomic forces are feeble. Therefore the condensation occurs in a region near the absolute zero where the thermal energy is small. The low mass of the atoms corresponds to a high frequency of any oscillations in which they may engage and a correspondingly high value of $\frac{1}{2}h\nu_0$, the zero-point energy. The ratio of the zero-point energy to the thermal energy is thus of a different order of magnitude from anything known in comparable examples.

The matter may be regarded from the point of view of the *uncertainty principle*. The behaviour of particles which is defined by the wave equation is equivalent to an indefiniteness in what may be known of their dynamical coordinates. If p and q are the momentum and position coordinates, Heisenberg's principle states that both cannot be known simultaneously except with a range of uncertainty given by the relation $\Delta p \Delta q = h$, approximately. In the temperature range of condensed helium, p is very small, so that Δp and Δq represent ranges of uncertainty of unusual relative magnitude. If Δp is defined to within a reasonably small fraction of p itself, then Δq will have an abnormally great value. These circumstances peculiar to helium might be expected to give rise to some special properties, and so it proves. The uncertainty in Δq is probably responsible for the extraordinary phenomena connected with the transport of energy and momentum in helium at the lowest temperatures, and the high zero-point energy may well account for the coexistence of mobility with what is probably a considerable degree of order.

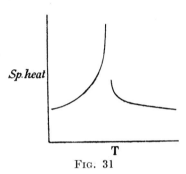

Fig. 31

That condensed helium should have unusual qualities is not surprising and is indeed to be expected. What is surprising is how these qualities manifest themselves in terms of phenomena, such as conductivity and viscosity, of which our mental pictures are formed by observations in higher ranges of temperature.

Some of the important facts about condensed helium will now be summarized. The gas first condenses to a liquid known as helium I, the properties of which are not specially remarkable. Below about $2°$ absolute helium II is formed. This shows a specific heat–temperature relation of the form represented in Fig. 31. The specific heat rises to a sharp peak at $2·19°$ (38 mm. pressure), the so-called λ-point, the excess over the normal in the neighbourhood of this point suggesting an ordered state for helium II, with a rapid decrease in order and increase in entropy as the temperature rises. The general type of behaviour here referred to has already been discussed (p. 310). According to one view, for which, in the light of the earlier discussion, there is much to be said, helium II possesses an atomic arrangement which has a certain crystalline character.

In spite of this ordered structure, the mobility is high and abnormal in character. The viscosity of helium II is low and the viscous flow is independent of the pressure gradient under which it takes place. The substance cannot be confined in a vessel in the ordinary way but flows in the surface films with a facility unlike that shown by anything else known. The thermal conductivity is greater than that of copper.

At higher pressures helium can be constrained into a crystalline form possessing the mechanical characteristics of a normal solid.

Viscosity of liquids

Although liquids possess a relatively high degree of mobility, the movements of their parts are by no means unopposed. They exhibit in fact the quality of viscosity.

The coefficient of viscosity, η, is defined as with gases, by the equation:

$$\text{force per unit area opposing shear} = \eta \times \text{velocity gradient.}$$

It is usually determined by measurement of the rate of flow of liquid through a capillary tube of length l and radius r under a pressure head p, the volume, v, of liquid delivered in unit time being given by the formula

$$v = \pi p r^4 / 8 \eta l.$$

η varies over a very wide range from liquid to liquid, and shows a general tendency to increase in parallel with the molecular weight—a relation exploited in approximate determinations of the molecular weights of polymers.

Viscous resistance has not the same origin in liquids and in gases. In the latter it depends upon the transfer of momentum from faster to slower moving layers (p. 20), and increases with temperature as the thermal exchange becomes more lively. In liquids it falls. The inverse of the viscosity, the fluidity, increases with temperature according to the law

$$\frac{1}{\eta} = A e^{-\lambda/RT},$$

where A is a constant and λ is an energy which is usually in the neighbourhood of one-third the latent heat of vaporization of the liquid, and shows a distinct parallelism with it from liquid to liquid.

This law of temperature variation is of the same form as that representing the proportion of molecules with energy greater than λ, and suggests very strongly indeed that the condition for movement is that molecules should possess enough kinetic energy to push others out of their way. This is sometimes referred to as creating holes in the liquid. That the creation of a hole should require an amount of energy which is a more or less constant fraction of that required to dissipate the liquid as vapour is wholly reasonable.

Apart from the general parallelism with molecular weight there is no simple relation between viscosity and structure.

Solubility

The forms observable in the world about us depend in an important degree upon the ways in which molecules remain free in the gaseous state or agglomerate together, and upon the kinds of order and mobility possessed by the condensed systems which they form. Only less important is the degree in which these condensed systems themselves are able to interpenetrate and mix.

All gases are completely miscible, liquids are more selective, and solids more selective still. Nevertheless, solid solutions are not uncommon, and occur especially among metals, where they constitute an important class of alloys.

The conditions governing miscibility in the solid state are fairly well understood. The atoms and molecules which enter into the mixed lattice must not differ by more than a limited margin in size. Furthermore, the detailed study of alloys has revealed that the possible solid phases are determined by certain definite electron ratios, and that in fact the structure is mainly governed by the concentration of valency electrons.

With liquids, the degree of order being much lower, conformity of size is of far less importance. The solubility of A in B is mainly a question of the mutual attractions AA, BB, and AB. If AA and BB very much exceed AB, then the liquids remain as separate phases. If the AB attractions prevail strongly, solubility is complete. In intermediate cases limited miscibility is possible, because the tendency of A to separate from B as a distinct phase depends not only upon the AA attractions but upon the frequency of encounter. The treatment of the phase equilibria is very similar to that of solid miscibility discussed on p. 75.

If the AB attractions greatly exceed the AA–BB types, heat will be evolved on mixture. But solution is frequently, indeed usually, accompanied by absorption of heat. The mixture of A molecules and B molecules involves a considerable increase in entropy, so that ΔG, which is $\Delta H - T\Delta S$, may remain negative and thus correspond to a spontaneous process in spite of a considerable positive value of ΔH, which represents heat absorption.

The interaction terms of the AA, BB, and AB types are very varied and very specific, but one major classification exists, namely that into polar and non-polar interactions. Substances with dipoles tend to be soluble in other dipolar liquids, but to be insoluble in non-polar media. In the same way, solid salts dissolve in liquids which in virtue of their own dipoles possess high dielectric constants.

Solutions of electrolytes in water

Since the polar compounds of metals with non-metals are both frequent and, from the point of view of their elementary chemistry, simple, and since water, the commonest liquid of nature, possesses a high dielectric constant, it happens that solutions of salts in water not only are important in practical life but have played a very prominent role—perhaps more prominent than they really deserved —in the history of physical chemistry. Matters which fall into their true perspective at the present stage often appear in rather too strong relief at the outset of elementary courses in the subject.

The application of thermodynamic methods to the determination of molecular weights showed salts to be dissociated in solution, a result which helped to establish the accepted views about their structure. If there is an equilibrium between molecules and ions of the type

$$MX \rightleftharpoons M^+ + X^-,$$

then, on condition that the species present obey the gas laws in the sense already considered,

$$\frac{[M^+][X^-]}{[MX]} = K.$$

If one gram molecule of the compound MX has been dissolved in V litres and if α is the fraction dissociated, then

$$\frac{\left(\frac{\alpha}{V}\right)\left(\frac{\alpha}{V}\right)}{\frac{1-\alpha}{V}} = K \quad \text{or} \quad \frac{\alpha^2}{(1-\alpha)V} = K.$$

This formula expresses what was called *Ostwald's dilution law*, and was at one time supposed to apply to all electrolytes which dissociate into two univalent ions. It does in fact apply to what are called *weak electrolytes*, a class of substances of which organic acids are the commonest representatives.

In the historical evolution of the subject the variation of electrical conductivity with increasing dilution was for some time attributed to the gradual rise of α towards unity, and α itself was computed from the well-known relation of Arrhenius, $\alpha = \Lambda_V/\Lambda_\infty$. Λ_V and Λ_∞ are the equivalent conductivities at dilution V, and at infinite dilution respectively. Equivalent conductivity is specific conductivity (reciprocal of resistance of a centimetre cube) multiplied by the volume in cubic centimetres which contains one gram equivalent, so that Λ_V/Λ_∞ would in fact measure the degree of ionization if the inherent conducting power of the individual ions depended only on themselves and not on the presence of others.

This last condition is fulfilled when the ionic concentrations are very low, as they are in fact in dilute solutions of weak electrolytes. The dissociation constants of substances such as weak organic acids can be determined by a combination of the formulae of Ostwald and Arrhenius, but the procedure is quite inadmissible for salts. Here the degree of dissociation is large. In fact the value of α is often indistinguishable from unity, and the mutual influences of the ions are considerable. They are calculable in principle by methods due to Debye and Hückel, and operate differently on different properties. The procedure outlined on p. 276 allows the calculation of the activity coefficients. In general the thermodynamic properties of the salt in solution correspond to those of a system with apparently incomplete dissociation, not because the concentrations of the ions are reduced by molecule formation but because the activity coefficients are lowered by mutual ionic influences.

The equivalent conductivity at finite dilutions is less than Λ_∞, not on account of incomplete dissociation but because the motion of each ion in the electric field is interfered with by the others. An approximate correspondence between Λ_V/Λ_∞ and the apparent degree of dissociation determined by thermodynamic methods is fortuitous in the sense that the mechanisms underlying the reduction in activity coefficient on the one hand and the lowering of the equivalent conductivity on the other are different. Conductivity of electrolytes has lost some of the fundamental significance which it appeared to possess in the days of Arrhenius, but it remains an interesting property of one of the most important classes of solutions.

Electrical conductivity of solutions

Some of the principal facts about electrolytic conductivity will be briefly summarized. Conductivity depends upon the number of ions in the solution, upon their charges, and upon the speed with which they move under a potential gradient.

We consider a uni-univalent salt which is completely dissociated giving c gram ions of each kind in unit volume. Let there be a potential gradient of E volts per centimetre. The absolute mobilities of the ions are defined as the speeds in cm./sec. with which they move under unit potential gradient. These are u and v for cation and anion respectively. Across unit section of the solution perpendicular to the gradient the number of positive ions moving in unit time in one direction corresponds to Ecu gram ions and the number of negative ions moving in the other direction to Ecv gram ions, since all the positive ions within a volume $u \times 1$ or negative ions within a volume $v \times 1$ reach and pass the cross-section. Since one gram ion of a univalent element according to Faraday's law carries the charge F, the total transport of electricity through the section is $EcF(u+v)$ in one second. This is the current in amperes, i:

$$i = EcF(u+v),$$

but $i = E/\rho$, where ρ is the resistance per cm. of a solution of 1 sq. cm. in cross-section. $1/\rho = \sigma$, the specific conductivity. The equivalent conductivity, Λ, is given by

$$\Lambda = \sigma \times \text{dilution} = \sigma/c,$$

$$\sigma = \Lambda c \quad \text{and} \ i = E\Lambda c.$$

Therefore $E\Lambda c = EcF(u+v)$

and $\Lambda = F(u+v).$

When the dilution is great enough $\Lambda = \Lambda_\infty$, and the mutual interference of the ions is negligible. u and v are now characteristic properties of cation and anion respectively and of the solvent.

Λ_∞ is in fact expressible as the sum of two independent terms, one for the positive ion and one for the negative. These may be written U and V respectively, so that

$$U+V = F(u+v),$$

and $U/F = u \quad \text{and} \quad V/F = v.$

U and V are contributions to equivalent conductivity expressed in reciprocal ohms: u and v are absolute speeds expressed in cm./sec. under a potential gradient of 1 volt/cm.

u and v may be determined by the direct observation of the movement of coloured ions—or ions which have any measurable effect on the optical properties of the solution: U and V from the measurement of Λ_∞, once the separate values have been found in any single example.

The principle of the method for finding individual mobilities is as follows. Λ_V is determined as a function of the dilution and Λ_∞ obtained by extrapolation. $\Lambda_\infty = U + V$. The ratio $U/(U+V)$, which is called the *transport number* of the cation, is also obtainable, and with a knowledge of this ratio together with the sum, the separate values are calculable.

The transport number itself is found from a special type of experiment, which will be exemplified by the case of silver nitrate. Suppose a solution of this salt is electrolysed in an apparatus where the cathode and anode compartments are so arranged that the contents of each can be subjected separately to chemical analysis. If one Faraday of electricity passes, one gram ion of silver is deposited at the cathode and, in consequence of the discharge of nitrate ion, one gram ion of silver dissolves at the anode. The total current is proportional to $U+V$ and is made up of fractions of $U/(U+V)$ of positive current towards the cathode and of $V/(U+V)$ of negative current towards the anode. Thus $U/(U+V)$ gram ions of silver migrate from anode compartment to cathode compartment and $V/(U+V)$ gram ions of nitrate migrate in the opposite sense. The balance-sheet is thus

	Cathode		Anode	
	Ag^+	NO_3^-	Ag^+	NO_3^-
Gain .	$U/(U+V)$	0	1	$V/(U+V)$
Loss .	1	$V/(U+V)$	$U/(U+V)$	0
Balance .	$-V/(U+V)$	$-V/(U+V)$	$+V/(U+V)$	$+V/(U+V)$

There is a net transport of $V/(U+V)$ gram molecules of silver nitrate from the cathode compartment to the anode compartment. This is measured by analysis, so that the transport number is determinable.

The separate values of U and V for silver and nitrate ion are thus calculable from Λ_∞. If now Λ_∞ is measured for, say, sodium nitrate, by subtraction of the known value for nitrate we obtain U for sodium: measurements on sodium chloride then give V for the chlorine ion, and so on.

As the concentration of ions in a solution increases, u and v, and correspondingly U and V, diminish. The ionic atmosphere of opposite sign with which, according to the arguments of Debye and Hückel (p. 276), any given ion is effectively surrounded, impedes its motion in a field. The major effect is due to the finite time required for the establishment and dissipation of the atmosphere, the so-called time of relaxation. If the central ion moves, the new equilibrium configura-

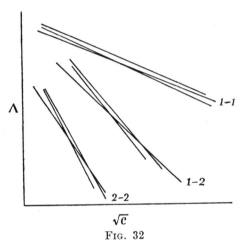

$$\sqrt{c}$$

Fig. 32

tion is not at once established. The atmosphere continues transitorily to exist as a charge of opposite sign which opposes the departure from its midst of the migrant. Calculations show that Λ varies according to a law which at low concentrations assumes the limiting form

$$\Lambda = \Lambda_\infty - a\sqrt{c},$$

c being the concentration of the electrolyte and a a constant.

This law had been discovered empirically by Kohlrausch long before its interpretation was understood. The constant a, while in some degree specific for each salt, is to a major extent determined by the valencies of the constituent ions. Thus uni-univalent, uni-bivalent, and bi-bivalent salts fall into well-marked groups as illustrated (schematically) in Fig. 32.

The dominant influence of the ionic charges shows clearly that the decrease in conductivity in the more concentrated solutions is caused by electrostatic interactions between the ions rather than by the specific molecule formation which occurs in weak electrolytes. It might have pointed the way to the more modern theory earlier than it did.

Many substances occupy an intermediate position between the highly ionized salts and the weak electrolytes. They are not fully dissociated, yet the concentration of the ions which they form is high enough to give rise to an important degree of mutual interference.

One of the most remarkable illustrations of the pictorial utility of the ionic atmosphere theory is provided by the variation of electrical conductivity with frequency. If a strong electrolyte is acted upon by an alternating current, each ion may be imagined to oscillate about a mean position. When the frequency is low the oppositely charged atmosphere keeps on being dissipated and re-formed, but with a time-lag which allows it to offer resistance to the migration of the central ion. But when the frequency is high enough the ion oscillates too rapidly for the atmosphere to suffer much change or for much asymmetry to be created, so that the conductivity rises.

Some other properties of electrolytic solutions

It is, moreover, on account of the ionic atmospheres that the viscosity of very dilute solutions of salts is greater than that of pure water. When a velocity gradient is continuously maintained in the liquid the ionic atmosphere becomes distorted, since it does not reach the equilibrium configuration instantaneously. If a given positive ion is at O and there is a positive velocity gradient in the direction BOA, then the velocities relative to that at O are as shown in the diagram. Excess negative electricity is carried forward at AP and a similar excess lags behind at BQ. The resulting electrostatic attractions tend to reduce the velocity gradient and thus to manifest themselves as contributions to the viscosity.

Salts dissolve in water and other polar solvents in virtue of the powerful interaction between their own charges and the dipoles present in these media. Round each ion the molecules of the solvent probably form loosely patterned configurations with some degree of order. The more rigidly defined is this pattern the lower is the entropy of the solution. On the other hand, the greater is the running down of potential energy which accompanies its establishment and the greater the energy released.

Solubility varies with temperature according to the formula

$$\frac{d\ln s}{dT} = \frac{\Delta H}{RT^2},$$

whence $\quad s = A e^{-\Delta H/RT} = e^{\Delta S/R} e^{-\Delta H/RT}.$

$-RT\ln s$ is the free energy of solution and equal to $\Delta H - T\Delta S$. From $d\ln s/dT$, ΔH is calculable, and thence ΔS when s itself is known. An inverse correlation between the energy and entropy terms in the sense expected is in fact often in evidence.

In connexion with the question of solvent orientation there has always been a good deal of discussion as to whether definite ion hydrates exist in aqueous solution, but this has lost much of the significance which it seemed to possess before the idea of patterned configurations in liquids became current. Indeed the problem tends to resolve itself into one of those slightly tiresome matters of definition. There is a striking gradation in the ionic mobilities of the alkali metals. Lithium, the lightest and in itself presumably the smallest ion, moves slowest and caesium, the heaviest and largest, the fastest. If the ions were free spheres moving through an ideal continuous viscous medium, they would suffer resistances proportional to the squares of their radii, and lithium would be the most mobile. It follows that the water in some way impedes the motion of lithium more effectively than that of caesium. The water dipoles can close in more tightly on the smaller ion and give a more rigid configuration of lower mobility. Whether or not this is called hydration is a matter of choice. If salt solutions are electrolysed with membranes partitioning the solution, or with reference non-electrolytes present, a differential transport of water by the two ions can often be demonstrated. Evidently, then, the ions do not move without causing some displacement of water molecules in the same direction, and to an extent which varies specifically from one ion to another.

Aqueous media and hydrogen-ion concentration

Water is the commonest solvent, and it is dissociated to a small extent in accordance with the equation

$$H_2O + H_2O = H_3O^+ + OH^-,$$

which may be formally written

$$H_2O = H^+ + OH^-$$

The rules of thermodynamic equilibrium require, in so far as the ions obey the gas laws at very low concentrations,

$$[H^+][OH^-] = K_w,$$

the concentration of the water itself being constant.

If acid or alkali is added to the water, the ionic product must still remain constant, except in so far as the concentrations are replaced by activities

$$a_{H^+}a_{OH^-} = \text{constant}.$$

The *ionic product of water* is a constant of very great importance for the following reasons.

First, water is the medium which bathes all living tissues, which consist largely of proteins containing ionizable acid and basic groups. The balance of their ionization (which determines their properties to an important extent) depends upon the hydrogen and hydroxyl ion concentration of the medium, and these two concentrations are connected permanently by the value of K_w.

Secondly, a great many chemical reactions are catalysed by substances which can either receive or donate (unhydrated) hydrogen ions, so that the influence of a medium upon changes occurring in it is often largely determined by the hydrion concentration.

There is a well-established convention according to which the state of the medium is described by what is called the pH. This function is simply the negative logarithm of the hydrion concentration. At ordinary temperatures K_w is of the order 10^{-14}, so that in pure neutral water, $[H] = [OH^-] = 10^{-7}$ (gram ions/l.) and the pH is 7·0. N/100 strong acid, in which the hydrion concentration is 10^{-2}, has pH equal to 2, with the hydroxyl ion concentration equal to 10^{-12}. N/100 alkali has pH 12.

The pH of a medium is best maintained at a standard value by the use of what is called a *buffer solution*. This is one in which the hydrion concentration is defined by an equilibrium between species present in large enough amounts not to be seriously influenced by the addition of impurities. The equilibrium

$$\frac{[H][Ac]}{[HAc]} = K, \quad \text{or better,} \quad \frac{a_H a_{Ac}}{a_{HAc}} = K_a,$$

defines the hydrion concentration, or activity, in terms of the ratio of acetate ion to acetic acid. If large concentrations of sodium acetate and acetic acid are mixed they define a pH which is not disturbed by small additions of anything else in the way which a minute concentration of a single pure acid could be.

The various arts and devices for preparing and using buffers and for measuring the pH are outside the scope of this discussion. We should, however, indicate briefly the method by which K_w itself is determined.

In a hundredth-normal solution of sodium hydroxide the hydrion concentration is too small to affect the numerical value of [OH] which as nearly as may be is 10^{-2}. If then the hydrion concentration of this solution is found by any indirect method, the product of the answer with the known value of [OH] gives K_w directly. The minute value prevailing in the alkaline solution, 10^{-12}, can be measured by the use of a concentration cell (p. 285). A platinum electrode surrounded by gaseous hydrogen behaves like a metal electrode reversible to a cation, in this case hydrion. Two such electrodes immersed respectively in acid and alkali give a concentration cell from the electromotive force of which the ratio of the two hydrion concentrations can be calculated. That in a solution of dilute acid is known by chemical analysis (if the acid is dilute enough to be all dissociated while still strong enough to be analysed): hence that in the alkali is calculated. All data for evaluating K_w (apart from various somewhat difficult corrections) are now available. In all such determinations the choice of conditions and the manipulation of the results in such a way as to obtain the most accurate values is a matter for special art.

Another method which is interesting in principle is to find K_w from the conductivity of pure water. Given that the molecular conductivity is known, and that the mobilities of the two ions are measured separately by the use of acid or alkali, the concentrations of the ions may be calculated and K_w worked out. The difficulty is to know when the water is pure, since normally it contains dissolved substances which contribute far more to the conductivity than its own ions do. The problem was solved by a special device. The temperature coefficient of the dissociation of water is high, since it depends upon the displacement of an equilibrium: moreover, the numerical value may be known from the heat of the dissociation (which is nothing other than the heat of neutralization of strong acid by strong alkali) by the application of the thermodynamic equation $d \ln K / dT = \Delta H / RT^2$. The temperature coefficient of the conductivity due to the impurities is low, since it does not depend upon an equilibrium shift. Therefore, as water is progressively purified, the conductivity falls, while the temperature coefficient rises. The one quantity can be plotted against the other, and the curve extrapolated to show what conductivity would be possessed by water of the (unattained) degree of purity corresponding to the theoretical temperature coefficient. From this conductivity the degree of ionization and K_w are calculated.

There are other methods, one at least of which is technically easier than those mentioned, but these are the most interesting in principle.

XVII

MATTER IN DISPERSION

Disperse phases

EXTENDED masses of homogeneous or nearly homogeneous phases are common enough in nature. They occur in the air, in the sea, and in the crystalline rocks and minerals. But equally conspicuous are forms in which dispersion seems to be the order of the day, from clays and muds, foams and latexes, to the intricate and tenuous structures of living cells and their conglomerations.

In so far as a condition of minimum potential energy is sought, massive phases are favoured, and small particles or droplets tend to fuse together into larger ones. If, for example, a drop of a liquid A is surrounded by another liquid B, the condition that it should not dissolve is that the attractions between the molecules of A should outweigh those between molecules of A and molecules of B. This being so, molecules in the surface layer of A are subjected to a pull into the interior of the drop. The greatest response to this pull is made when the surface between the two liquids assumes its minimum area.

The work done by the forces when the interfacial area is reduced by dA may be written $\sigma\, dA$, where σ defines the *surface tension* of A in contact with B, and the work measures a change in surface energy. The surface of a sphere being proportional to the square of the radius, r^2, and the volume to the cube, r^3, the ratio of surface to volume varies as $1/r$. The surface energy of a given mass of liquid is a minimum, therefore, when it forms one drop of large radius rather than many drops of small radius.

The tendency of small drops of liquid to coalesce to large ones is manifested in an increase of vapour pressure with diminution of radius. The relation between vapour pressure and drop radius is easily calculated. When a small amount of liquid, volume dV, evaporates from a drop of radius r, the change in surface area is dA. We have

$$V = \tfrac{4}{3}\pi r^3, \qquad dV = 4\pi r^2\, dr,$$
$$A = 4\pi r^2, \qquad dA = 8\pi r\, dr.$$

Therefore
$$dA = \frac{2\,dV}{r}.$$

The diminution of surface energy due to the contraction of area is given by

$$\sigma \, dA = \frac{2\sigma \, dV}{r}.$$

The vapour is obtained at vapour pressure p, which is greater than that, p_0, corresponding to an infinite mass of liquid with a plane surface. When the vapour is evaporated from the drop at p, expanded till the pressure drops to p_0, and condensed into the large mass, the work obtained (cf. p. 61) is $dx \, RT \ln(p/p_0)$, where dx is the number of gram molecules corresponding to dV. We have also $M_0 \, dx/dV = \rho$, where M_0 and ρ are molecular weight and density respectively. The work obtained from the expansion of the vapour is derived from the energy yielded up in the contraction of the surface during the evaporation. Equating the two free-energy terms we find

$$\frac{2\sigma}{r} = \frac{\rho RT}{M_0} \ln \frac{p}{p_0}.$$

When $r \to \infty$, $\ln(p/p_0) \to 0$, and $p/p_0 \to 1$. The formula expresses quantitatively the tendency of large drops to grow at the expense of small ones, and thus for bulk phases to be produced.

Similar relations hold for small particles in contact with a solution, if vapour pressure is replaced by solubility. Larger crystals of solids, in virtue of their lower vapour pressure and solubility, tend to grow at the expense of smaller ones. For qualitative purposes small crystals of solids may be treated as spheres to which the above formula is roughly applicable. In fact, however, each face of a crystal has its own specific surface energy, and the condition for equilibrium is that the total surface energy shall be a minimum. This condition involves not a minimum surface area but a compromise in which the faces of higher energy are reduced and those of lower energy are increased. For a given mass there is thus an equilibrium shape. It still remains true that one large crystal has a lower energy than several smaller ones of the same total mass.

These influences make for uniformity and continuity in the distribution of matter, but an opposing tendency is also observable. Ordinary crystals consist, in general, not of single perfect blocks but of a mosaic of smaller ones with planes of easy fracture between them. This structure is partly the result of the conditions prevailing during growth. A minute inclusion of impurity—which is never wholly absent—is enough to deflect the planes of deposition so that invisible faults and cracks result. Another powerful influence must be the irregular temperature gradients in which all real systems growing at a finite rate evolve. Even in the most carefully controlled thermostats they still exist, while outside the laboratory the relation of earth and sun makes temperature inequalities a major factor in determining the course of natural phenomena. Alternate heatings and coolings set up strains even in crystals which initially are perfect. The same agency helps to denude rocks.

But these effects are manifestations of the lack of equilibrium in the world, and such processes as the attrition of sand by the action of the wind contribute in a humble way to the degradation of solar energy. It remains true that the bulk phases are the stabler. In metals the large crystals grow by annealing, and by suitable mechanical and thermal treatment perfect single crystals are obtained. Yet the disperse systems come into existence and not infrequently achieve a relative degree of permanence.

That new phases should originally be formed in a disperse state is a natural consequence of growth from nuclei. In precipitation, whether from the gaseous state or from liquid, the original nucleus formation is usually a matter of chance. Minute centres are produced in a random way throughout the original phase, and these grow until the transformation is complete. The result is a disperse system of particles which constitute a fog or a suspension. How fast these coalesce is a matter which depends upon circumstances having nothing to do with their formation.

When solutions of gold salts are reduced, suspensions of metallic particles known as gold sols are produced. Some reducing agents favour formation of many fresh nuclei; others are unable to do this, but can cause deposition of fresh gold on those already formed. If small nuclei produced by the first kind of reducing agent are added to a solution containing a gold salt mixed with the second kind of agent, precipitation occurs steadily on a constant number of nuclei until the supply of gold is exhausted. A suspension of particles of uniform size results. With reducing agents which produce new nuclei throughout the course of the reduction, suspensions of very uneven particle size result.

In this and other examples the initial dispersion depends upon the mode of formation. The stability depends upon quite different factors. Gold sols are relatively stable. The thick jellies of calcium carbonate formed by mixing very concentrated solutions of calcium bromide and sodium carbonate change in a few minutes to a coarsely crystalline form. Fogs, foams, and emulsions vary in stability as widely as sols.

Stabilization of disperse systems

The factors which make for the stabilization of disperse forms are of great importance. They operate in virtue of a process called *adsorption*, which is the preferential concentration of certain kinds of molecule at the boundary surface between two phases.

It is illustrated by the behaviour of a soap (which is the alkali salt of a long-chain fatty acid) at the boundary of benzene and water. Groups such as —COONa favour solution in the water, as evidenced by the properties of sodium formate or acetate, while the hydrocarbon chains favour solution in benzene. The soap molecules make the best of both worlds when they become concentrated in the interfacial zone so that their carboxylic groups, with or without their associated alkali ions, are in contact with the water, and the rest of the molecule penetrates into the benzene. In the state of equilibrium the concentration of soap at the boundary exceeds that in either of the liquid phases.

The enrichment of the interfacial layers is attended by a decrease in free energy which is the greater the larger the area involved. The adsorption, therefore, stabilizes the finely dispersed system of droplets which constitutes an emulsion.

Oil and water having been agitated together normally separate rapidly, but in presence of various agents with the requisite adsorptive properties form stable emulsions. Substances which draw these agents back into solution in either phase will break the emulsion.

In the system which has just been discussed the adsorption occurs in virtue of the specific affinity of the parts A and B of the adsorbed molecules for phases I and II respectively.

A—B

Phase I   A—B   Phase II

A—B

A similar effect would be produced by an attraction between B and the molecules of phase II and a mutual attraction between the A groups themselves. Phase I might well then be a relatively indifferent medium such as air, and the considerations just applied to explain the stability of emulsions could be transferred to foams and froths.

Chemical inhomogeneity at interfaces can manifest itself in numerous ways. If molecules of a type A are strongly attracted by others of type M but not powerfully enough to overcome the mutual forces between the individuals of their class, then adsorption of A by M will occur but no solution.

The forces which hold A to the free surface of a continuous mass of M may be of any kind—van der Waals forces, whether of the London type or of the dipolar type, interionic forces, or covalencies. The adsorption of gases by charcoal at low temperatures depends upon van der Waals forces. At high temperatures oxygen is held by covalencies. Oxygen and hydrogen may, according to circumstances, be taken up by metals as molecular layers or as surface films of oxide or hydride.

In the stabilization of disperse systems ionic forces play a specially important part. When arsenic sulphide is precipitated from an arsenical solution by hydrogen sulphide a stable sol is obtained, the particles of which can be shown by observation of their migration in an electric field to bear a negative charge ascribable to adsorbed ions. Metal sols, whether formed by precipitation or by the passage of a discharge between metal electrodes under water, also possess negative charges. Ferric hydroxide sols are positive. The adsorbed ions have the important effect of creating a repulsion between the particles in the sol and so hindering their agglomeration and precipitation.

The addition of electrolytes to a sol, by offering the opportunity for a compensating adsorption of ions opposite in sign to those which stabilize it, cause precipitation. The efficacy of various salts is in some degree specific, but governed by one overriding principle, namely, that in the coagulation of a negative sol, positive ions of high valency are specially powerful and in that of a positive sol, negative ions. To cause precipitation within, say, one minute of addition to a positive sol, the amounts required of sodium chloride, sodium sulphate, and sodium citrate would be of the orders of magnitude $1,000:50:1$. For a corresponding action on a negative sol the amounts of sodium chloride, barium chloride, and aluminium chloride would be in somewhat similar ratios.

Quantitatively the problem is a complex one, since the effect depends upon the differential adsorption of the two ions contributed by the salt. But if the condition for coagulation is that a given charge should be neutralized, then the number of univalent ions required is three times as great as the number of tervalent ions and the proba- bility that the necessary adsorptions shall occur is much smaller.

In solutions of compounds like soaps, particles of a special kind make their appearance. These consist of a central core of non-polar material, such as hydrocarbon chains, with a periphery of ionizable groups such as carboxyl groups. The particle may effectively consti- tute a very large ion with a high charge. Since the viscous resistance to the motion of such an ion varies as the square of its radius and thus as the two-thirds power of its volume, while the force acting upon it varies with its total charge which can be considerable, the electrical conductivity of the solution is sometimes very high. Substances which form such solutions are referred to as colloidal electrolytes.

The application of the usual equilibrium law to the dissociation of colloidal electrolytes gives in rough approximation

$$[R^{n-}][Na^+]^n = \text{constant.}$$

If this product is exceeded precipitation occurs. The solubility is thus very sensitive to the concentration of the cation. This general principle explains the precipitation of such bodies as proteins by salts. The individual relationships are, however, of great specificity and complexity and will not be further dealt with here.

Changes in concentration at interfaces not only play a considerable part in regulating the forms assumed by disperse systems: they are of importance in themselves in connexion with such phenomena as the adsorption of gases, vapours, or dissolved substances by charcoal and by various catalytic agents.

The Gibbs relation

Negative adsorption, such as the depletion of the dissolved sub- stance at the boundary of a solution, may occur as well as positive adsorption. The condition is that the surface layers of uncontami- nated solvent should be more stable than layers into which solute penetrates. This might at first sight appear to imply also the condi- tion of insolubility. But the boundary layers of a solvent differ quite a lot from the bulk phase in that they are often oriented and possess a distinctive structure of their own. If solvent–solvent interactions in the specialized interfacial regions are more powerful than solvent–solute or solute–solute interactions, then relative displacement of solute into the interior will occur.

Positive and negative adsorption are closely connected with changes in surface tension. If the entry of solute into the boundary layer gives a more stable structure, then the surface energy is lowered and the tendency of the surface to contract is weakened. Thus the condition for positive adsorption is that the surface tension is reduced by the solute. Conversely the condition for negative adsorption is that it is enhanced.

There is a thermodynamic relation between the adsorption and the surface-tension changes. Creation of concentration differences by accumulation of molecules in a boundary layer would, in itself, represent an increase in free energy, but it is compensated by the fact that the surface free energy is correspondingly lowered, since σ is decreased. An equilibrium between the two effects is maintained. The simplest derivation of the well-known *Gibbs relation* which expresses the balance will now be given.

Suppose a solution is reversibly diluted by the addition of dV of solvent, the area of the surface of the liquid remaining constant. The change in free energy is $-\Pi\, dV$, where Π is the osmotic pressure. Now let the surface area be increased by dA (for example by allowing the liquid to flow into a shallower vessel). The increase in free energy is

$$\left(\sigma + \frac{\partial\sigma}{\partial V}\, dV\right) dA,$$

the surface tension, which was σ before the dilution, having now changed. The total change in free energy accompanying the dilution and the surface alteration is thus

$$\left(\sigma + \frac{\partial\sigma}{\partial V}\, dV\right) dA - \Pi\, dV.$$

The same result could be achieved by carrying out the operations in the reverse order, namely with increase in area first and then addition of more solvent osmotically. The expression for the change of free energy in the second procedure is

$$\sigma\, dA - \left(\Pi + \frac{\partial\Pi}{\partial A}\, dA\right) dV.$$

The two expressions must be equal by the second law of thermo-dynamics. Therefore,

$$\frac{\partial \sigma}{\partial V} = -\frac{\partial \Pi}{\partial A},$$

or

$$\frac{\partial \sigma}{\partial c}\frac{\partial c}{\partial V} = -\frac{\partial \Pi}{\partial c}\frac{\partial c}{\partial A}.$$

$c = n/V$, where n is the number of gram molecules of solute present in the whole system. Thus

$$\frac{\partial c}{\partial V} = -\frac{n}{V^2} = -\frac{c^2}{n}.$$

Also, if the solution is dilute enough for activity to be taken as equal to concentration, $\Pi = cRT$.

It follows that

$$\frac{c}{RT}\frac{\partial \sigma}{\partial c} = \frac{n}{c}\frac{\partial c}{\partial A} = V\frac{\partial c}{\partial A}.$$

The coefficient $\partial c/\partial A$ is the change in the number of gram molecules in unit volume of the solution caused by unit increase of area. $V(\partial c/\partial A)$ is therefore the amount of solute from the whole solution which must have passed into some interfacial region when the surface underwent unit increase. It must correspond to the quantity usually called Γ, the surface excess. Thus

$$\Gamma = -V\frac{\partial c}{\partial A},$$

or

$$\Gamma = -\frac{c}{RT}\frac{\partial \sigma}{\partial c}.$$

From experimental measurements of the influence of a given substance on an interfacial tension its tendency to accumulate in or to avoid the boundary region may thus be inferred.

Boundary regions and bulk phases have their own special structures and their own special energies. That is why forms of delicacy and intricacy are possible in nature; or at least an important part of the reason.

Adsorption isotherms

Equations which express, for a constant temperature, the relation between the amount of a substance occupying unit area of an interfacial region and the concentration in the continuous phase are called adsorption isotherms.

The simplest is represented by the *Langmuir isotherm* which will be derived for the simple example of a gas adsorbed on a solid, the derivation being, however, applicable with minor changes to other examples. It is assumed that there are on the surface a definite number of sites which are capable of accommodating adsorbed molecules, and that when these are occupied the surface is saturated.

When the pressure of the gas is p, the fraction of the sites filled with adsorbed molecules is x.

For equilibrium the rate of condensation of molecules on to vacant sites equals the rate of evaporation from occupied sites. Thus

$$k_1 p(1-x) = k_2 x,$$

$$x = \frac{p}{p + k_2/k_1}.$$

x rises from zero to unity as p rises from zero to infinity, but for suitable values of k_2/k_1 very nearly reaches unity at moderate finite pressures.

The assumption of a defined number of sites for adsorption is consistent both with experimental evidence and with the very short range of action of molecular forces, which in general are not transmitted through one adsorbed layer to a second one. Multiple layers probably occur in the adsorption of vapours when they are near to their saturation pressures. A solid adsorbent then forms a base on which the first layer is taken up and this itself forms the base for a second, but in virtue of its own attractive forces rather than those of the underlying solid. We are dealing in such cases with an anticipation of the liquefaction process which would set in at a somewhat higher pressure even without the help of the solid surface.

The Langmuir isotherm represents the simplest possible case, but it is of considerable practical utility. It usually describes observed behaviour qualitatively, and quite often with a reasonable quantitative success. The over-simplification which it involves is essentially the disregard of the mutual interactions of the adsorbed molecules themselves. The presence of molecules on a surface may, according to circumstances, either facilitate or impede the adsorption of others, so that much more complicated relations of p and x result. The appropriate equations to express them must in the nature of things involve more constants than the Langmuir isotherm. They constitute a specialized study.

The form of isotherm expressed by the Langmuir equation is shown by curve *a* in Fig. 33. Curve *b* is an isotherm for a system in which a strong *co-operative effect* exists between the adsorbed molecules. The field due to adsorbed molecules already on the surface contributes to the holding of fresh adherents. Such effects foreshadow liquefaction or crystallization, but sometimes only remotely.

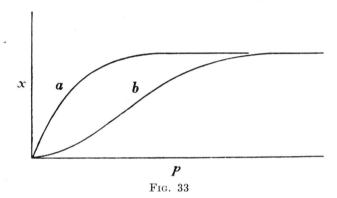

FIG. 33

Other complications may be contributed by the nature of the adsorbent itself. If it contains capillaries and narrow crevasses, condensation of liquid from vapours near their saturation pressures will occur, and a strongly sigmoid isotherm will result.

The condensation of a vapour into a wide vessel would take place abruptly at the saturation pressure, and if the amount of liquid in the vessel were plotted as a function of the pressure of the vapour, a curve of the form shown in Fig. 34 would be obtained. In this diagram the height of *a* would be simply a measure of the capacity of the vessel. p_0 is the saturation pressure. If the radius of the vessel were reduced to capillary dimensions, p_0 would fall very considerably, as is shown by the thermodynamic calculation already given (p. 337). A mass of an adsorbent such as active charcoal may be regarded as equivalent to a series of vessels of varying radius and capacity. (Narrow laminar spaces between planes have the same effect as capillaries for this purpose.) In such a system the idealized form of Fig. 34 becomes that of Fig. 35. From the slope of the curve at different points the distribution of effective pore sizes could be calculated. Some vapours, notably that of water, are in fact adsorbed by active charcoal according to curves of the shape shown in Fig. 35: others give isotherms approximately of the Langmuir

z

type. Broadly speaking, the differences in behaviour depend upon the relative importance of the interactions between surface and adsorbed molecules on the one hand, and the contribution made by the mutual forces between the adsorbed molecules themselves on the other.

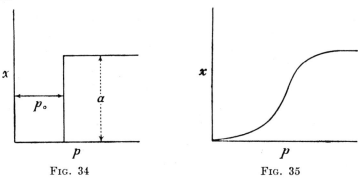

FIG. 34   FIG. 35

Another factor affecting the form of adsorption relations is the geometrical one that the number of molecules which the surface can accommodate varies according to the regularity of their packing. A random occupation of sites by irregularly oriented molecules will effectively block further adsorption before more than a fraction of the total sites is filled, whereas an orderly accession might have left room for many more. Complex time-lags and hysteresis effects may result from circumstances such as these.

The various influences of the molecules already present on the adsorption of fresh recruits are reflected in functional relations between x and the heat of adsorption, which is seldom constant over any wide range.

Surface films of sparingly soluble substances

Sparingly soluble substances, such as compounds with a long hydrocarbon chain and an active end-group, spread on the surface of water to give unimolecular films. The molecules are anchored by the penetration of groups such as hydroxyl into the water, but they do not dissolve bodily. Such films constitute what is virtually a two-dimensional state of matter, and they are of special interest in that many of the characteristic properties of three-dimensional systems reappear with appropriate modifications in this restricted world, which has been rather thoroughly explored by Rayleigh, Pockels, Devaux, Langmuir, and Adam.

The key experimental method is the measurement of the surface pressure F, that is. the number of dynes acting on 1 cm. length of a mechanical barrier by which the film can be compressed. The extent of the water surface which the film covers can easily be made visible, so that the area, A, may be determined as a function of F, and the equation of state of the two-dimensional phase may be discovered.

Different types known as gaseous, condensed, and expanded films are distinguished. In the gaseous films there appears to be free motion of the molecules over the surface, and in certain examples an equation $FA = kT$ has been verified. This is the analogue of Boyle's law, and k itself has approximately the value to be expected from a variant of the kinetic theory calculation of gas pressure. The equation holds only for large values of A. As the pressure increases, FA passes through a minimum, just as pV does with an imperfect gas. At certain pressures condensation occurs to a film which is very resistant to further compression.

In some films there must be a powerful lateral adhesion between molecules, since the area remains small even at zero pressure. These are the condensed films and correspond to matter in bulk in the liquid or solid state. In them actual polymorphic changes may occasionally be observed to occur at definite temperatures, so that the analogy is quite a far-reaching one.

In some examples the transition from gaseous to condensed films has been observed as a function of temperature. At some temperatures there is a collapse to the condensed state when the pressure exceeds the two-dimensional analogue of the vapour pressure, but above a critical temperature this no longer occurs.

Just as in other phase relationships, there is the usual complex specificity. The energy and entropy conditions prescribe various configurations for the two-dimensional array of molecules, which cannot be so closely packed as to be incapable of executing the motions required by the temperature and by their own dynamics. Hence arise varying degrees of covering by the condensed films, varying angles of tilt of the chains with respect to the water, and so on.

The molecules concerned in the formation of surface films are usually dipolar, so that the interface acquires special electrical properties. These are susceptible of rapid measurement and thus provide one method for the investigation of occurrences in labile systems such as those undergoing chemical reactions.

A greater variety of specific interactions can arise at or near the boundary of two phases than in the bulk of any single one. Peculiar combinations of mobility with orientation can exist, in which the character of a gas is in some degree harmonized with that of a crystal. Structures not at all possible in a three-dimensional continuum can be built by appropriate relations of surfaces. It is not surprising, therefore, that surface films play so prominent a part not only in the catalytic reactions of the inorganic world but in biology. The scheme of things depends greatly upon its regions of transition.

Colloid chemistry

Many of the disperse systems which are commonly observed in nature or in the laboratory owe their origin, as we have seen, to the unbalanced forces which act at phase boundaries. Others, however, depend upon the existence of molecules so large that they must be deemed to count in a macroscopic sense as particles themselves. Such are the molecules of proteins like gelatine, polysaccharides like starch, and the polycondensation products formed in the laboratory from substances with several functional groups.

In solution these substances scatter light, they exhibit high viscosity and low diffusion rates, and they enter into complex structural relations with the solvent. In some of their physical properties the solutions, although they are true solutions by many criteria, simulate the sols and gels of the more truly heterogeneous systems. Owing their stability, however, to the interactions between their own molecules and the solvent, they are less subject to coagulation and precipitation. In so far as they form solutions they are called lyophilic, in contradistinction to the easily precipitable sols of inherently insoluble substances such as metals or arsenic sulphide in water, which are called lyophobic.

The famous distinction made by Graham between crystalloids and colloids was based primarily upon ease of diffusion through membranes in the process known as dialysis. The non-diffusible colloids, as is now realized, owe their property to a wide variety of circumstances, and what came to be called colloid chemistry has grown into a vast and miscellaneous subject.

Substances often tend to assume colloidal properties in virtue simply of a very great molecular weight. Polymerization or poly-condensation reactions which build up such bodies are seldom so exactly controllable that all the molecules formed are of equal size. If, for example, the condensation of a dibasic acid with a glycol gives an ester with an average molecular weight of 5,000, the product will normally contain many molecules larger and many smaller than the average. It will be precisely characterized, not by its molecular weight alone, but by the frequency distribution of various molecular weights among its constituents. Chemically its behaviour may conform well enough to that of a single compound, but physically it will constitute a system of many components, a fact which may be reflected in lack of crystallinity, indefiniteness of melting-point, and in such mechanical properties as plasticity. The way in which physical and mechanical properties are governed by average molecular weight and by molecular weight distribution in macromolecular compounds of any given class constitutes another elaborate and specialized study which has come to assume no little importance.

Colloid chemistry can also be deemed to include the study of the structure and properties of various extended phases which are solid but non-crystalline, such as gels. A few words about the relation of these to other forms of material may not be inapposite at this stage. As we have seen, continuous solid lattices may be built up from small units when these are held by van der Waals forces, or when they become linked one to another by covalencies. We know that mixed crystals may be formed. Sometimes this is due to simple replacement of similar molecules one by another, sometimes, no doubt, to specific interactions of the two components. If the size relations are suitable, very unlikely-seeming molecules may room together. In an extreme case we have the *clathrate* compounds, where molecules of aromatic substances form *cages* which hold in the solid lattice large quantities of inert gas atoms. In the compound of quinol and argon four out of five of the cages made by the former contain atoms of the latter. Size, on the one hand, and interaction forces, on the other, interplay, in general, in a complex way. We know that liquids, though mobile, have a residue of ordered configuration, and we know that liquids may bring solids into solution. It is hardly surprising, therefore, that when a liquid, possessing mobility and a degree of order, interacts with molecules of a polymerized substance, some very original architectural combinations may result. The long molecules may form frameworks, into which the liquid, already needing but little inducement to form ordered arrays, fits. If the girder-like structure provided by one component is deformable, as it may well be, then the natural mobility of the liquid content allows it to conform, and special elastic properties result.

It is hardly reasonable to expect a general theory of such systems. All that can be said is that the factors which govern their properties are already operative in simpler examples, and that the more complicated types must be understood in terms of analogies drawn from various sources. That is why the subject remains on the whole at the qualitative level. What does emerge in a striking way is the wealth of forms which arise from the interplay of relatively few fundamental motifs. This is specially significant for the understanding of the way in which natural forms originate and of the merging of physical chemistry into the related parts of geology and biology.

PART VI
PASSAGE TOWARDS EQUILIBRIUM

SYNOPSIS

THE world, not being in equilibrium, presents a complex spectacle of changes varying from the almost instantaneous to the imperceptibly slow. The rates of chemical transformations offer a more intricate problem than equilibria. If the speeds of direct and inverse reactions are known, equilibria can be calculated, but the converse proposition does not hold. Infinitely numerous pairs of values for the rates are consistent with the same equilibrium constant. In fact, alternative routes to the same chemical equilibrium are not only possible in principle but followed in practice, often simultaneously.

No theories which liken chemical reactions to processes of hydrodynamic flow, or which introduce conceptions such as friction and lubrication, are of much help. Chemical reactions require a statistical interpretation. Molecules capable of even transient existence represent configurations with a minimum potential energy. The products of a reaction correspond to a lower minimum than the initial substances, and the two minima are separated by a maximum. This maximum corresponds to a transition state, access to which is possible only for those molecules which acquire *activation energy* (E). If the activation energy is known, the probability that molecules acquire it by collision or otherwise is calculable from the statistical distribution laws. The need for activation explains the factor $e^{-E/RT}$ occurring in all expressions for reaction rate, and determines the characteristic form of the temperature-dependence. A survey of many reactions reveals numerous correlations between variations of rate and changes in E.

There is a possibility, indicated by wave-mechanical theories, that microscopic systems may pass from one state to another separated from the first by an energy barrier without actually acquiring the high energy corresponding to the intermediate region. This so-called tunnel-effect appears to operate in the escape of α-particles from nuclei, but for systems with the masses, energies, and distances usually involved in chemical reactions it appears unimportant.

Rates of transformation are governed by the need that the requisite molecular encounters should occur, that activation energy should be available, and that the orientations and internal conditions of the colliding molecules should be correct. Or, according to an alternative statement, the rate may be related to the statistical probability of a *transition state* having a specified configuration.

Activation energies are calculable in principle from interatomic forces, and are easily determined by experiment. With certain tentative assumptions, the problem of estimating absolute reaction rates may then be attempted on the basis of kinetic and statistical theories. In some simple examples the estimates are reasonably successful. In the simplest cases the rate is equal to the number of collisions in which activation energy is available, but usually much more complex conditions have to be fulfilled.

In bimolecular reactions all conditions must be satisfied at the moment of encounter: in unimolecular reactions they may be satisfied at any time between the collision which imparts the activation energy and the next one— in which the energy is likely to be removed again. For this reason the absolute rates of unimolecular reactions tend, for a given value of E, to be much higher.

Very many chemical reactions take place in a series of steps, each one of which satisfies certain criteria of simplicity, often consisting in a transfer of electrons, the breaking of a single bond, or the exchange of a single atom between two molecules. A limit to the simplification of mechanism is set by the high activation energy which the most primitive steps, such as resolution into atoms, would demand. In related series of reactions there is often an inverse correlation between the effects on the rate of the activation energy (low values of which correspond to high rates) and of the so-called entropy factor (low values correspond to small rates). Roughly speaking, the more primitive processes require more energy but are more probable in other respects.

Not infrequently, however, a difficult initial formation of free atoms or radicals leads to the propagation of a chain reaction which greatly multiplies the effect. Sometimes the chains may branch, when special phenomena of in-flammation and explosion may occur at sharply defined limits of concentration.

The addition of foreign substances to a reaction system may open the possibility of alternative reaction mechanisms of lower activation energy (or occasionally more favourable transformation-probability). The resulting increase in the speed of attainment of equilibrium constitutes catalysis, but there is no single theory of this phenomenon, which is practically coextensive with the whole of reaction kinetics.

Chemical reactions are propagated in space as well as in time. Flames and explosions travel with definite speeds, new phases grow, and interdiffusion phenomena may lead to periodic precipitation effects.

The linking of reactions in space and time manifests itself in the growth and functioning of the living cell. This is an autosynthetic system which possesses adaptive and other properties which in a considerable degree depend upon the principles of chemical kinetics.

The structure of the organic world is ordered, but the maintenance of the order is compensated by concomitant increases in entropy. From one point of view living systems are by-products of degradative processes, but this point of view is far from being the only one, or even the most important.

XVIII

THE STATISTICAL NATURE OF CHEMICAL CHANGES

Passage to equilibrium

IF the world reached equilibrium it would be a sterile and ungracious place: winds and rivers would become quiescent, fires burnt out, and life extinct. All the events which give vitality and movement to the scene are transitions towards equilibrium from the condition of violent unbalance in which the universe was found at the beginning of the present cosmological era—whenever and whatever that incomprehensible point of departure was.

Among these happenings chemical transformations, nuclear, atomic, and molecular, play their titanic and their subtle roles. Nuclear reactions control the rate of release of energy from stars, and thus in turn everything of interest to humanity: and the cerebral mechanisms by which humanity is enabled to take an interest in anything at all are controlled by intricate molecular changes in chemical compounds of high molecular weight.

The routes to equilibrium are manifold and tortuous, and the theory of the processes of change more complicated than that of equilibria themselves. Apart from a passing consideration of nuclear changes we shall be concerned only with chemical reactions in the ordinary sense of the term.

At the outset the principles which govern the rate of establishment of equilibrium were by no means easy to discern. Obviously much of the matter in the world is separated by large distances from other matter with which it might react; and evaporation, solution, and diffusion are the factors which limit the occurrence of many possible changes. But there is a real chemical inertia of some kind which slows down, often to a negligible speed, the reactions even of substances perfectly mixed in the gaseous state.

There arises naturally enough the question whether the rate of a given transformation should not be a function of its free energy, and indeed the equation:

$$\text{rate of reaction} = \frac{\text{free energy}}{\text{chemical resistance}}$$

was once proposed by analogy with Ohm's law, and with the expression for the terminal velocity of a body moving against a viscous resistance. This formulation does not in fact contribute seriously to the understanding of the problem. In the first place, there is no means of defining the chemical resistance except in terms of the equation itself. This logical difficulty might have been circumvented had there proved to be any general parallelism between free energy and reaction rate, of a kind which would allow the resistance, though undefined, to be regarded as roughly constant. But in fact many reactions with very large free energies, such as the combination of hydrogen and oxygen, occur extremely slowly in comparison with others of low free energy. Only in certain particular series of related reactions is there any correlation between rate and affinity, and this comes about for special reasons which will appear.

Light dawned on the matter only when the statistical nature of molecular happenings came to be realized. A slow chemical change is not analogous to a uniform hydrodynamic flow. It is an affair where molecules one after another, in random places and at random times, do something which some have already done and others have yet to do. This idea is inherent in the notion of the chaotic movements of molecular systems and in the conception of the laws of energy distribution. It evolved, as things happened, chiefly from the need to explain the law connecting reaction rate and temperature.

This law is expressed, with good approximation, by the equation

$$k = A e^{-E/RT}$$

(where k = rate constant, R = gas constant, and A and E are constants), which resembles the expression for the probability that an amount of energy equivalent to E per gram molecule should be collected in a molecule.

In certain simple examples of gaseous reactions the rate proved to be calculable in order of magnitude at least from the equation:

number of molecules reacting = number of collisions $\times e^{-E/RT}$.

The statistical idea thereby gained a status which it might in any case have achieved on its own merits. The subsequent developments proved less simple, but never fundamentally out of harmony with this beginning.

Classical and quantum-mechanical principles

What might have transformed the whole conception of chemical reaction rates would have been new principles derived from quantum mechanics. This, however, did not happen. Calculation of entropies and many related problems, such as the derivation of distribution laws, were profoundly affected by the changed ideas about the counting of states. Methods of estimating interatomic and intermolecular

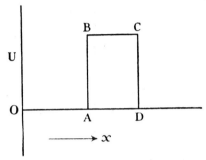

Fig. 36

forces, and indeed the whole theory of molecular structure, depend upon quantum mechanics, but, given the molecular properties so determined, the theory of the rate of attainment of equilibrium can be developed in terms of ideas not so far removed from those called classical as the conceptions needed in some other parts of chemistry and physics.

The principle which might have made so much difference is that which is believed to govern the slow escape of α-particles from atomic nuclei. It may be explained in simple terms as follows. Suppose the potential energy of a particle is represented by the line $OABCD$ (Fig. 36). If the particle has a kinetic energy which is less than AB, and if its position (x) is to the left of AB, it cannot, according to classical mechanics, pass to the right of $ABCD$ which constitutes a potential barrier. This barrier can only be surmounted by a particle with sufficient kinetic energy. According, however, to the equations of wave mechanics there is a finite probability that the particle will be found to the right of the barrier, and the barrier is said to have been penetrated rather than surmounted. The phenomenon is also referred to as leakage or tunnelling.

It is believed to explain how α-particles having escaped from nuclei are sometimes found to possess less kinetic energy than they would have acquired in being repelled by the Coulomb forces from a distance corresponding to the top of the potential barrier, which they are therefore supposed to have penetrated below its summit. This rather rough statement will be amplified later, but the important matter here is that occurrence of phenomena of this sort might have made reaction rates follow laws very different from those indicated by the ordinary kinetic and statistical theory. That in fact they do not is a consequence of the relative magnitudes of the potential barriers encountered in molecular phenomena and of the masses of the particles concerned.

We shall find, therefore, that in interpreting chemical reaction rates there will not be much need to invoke more than the familiar kinetic and thermodynamic principles, in which of course quantum-mechanical considerations are already to a large extent embodied.

Penetration of potential barriers

The principle of the so-called tunnel mechanism will now be outlined, partly because of its probable significance in nuclear trans-formations—a subject which borders closely on physical chemistry—and partly because it emphasizes the general blurring of the conception that a particle is something as strictly localized in space and time as primitive theories had suggested. This may help to remind us that even if rather rough mechanical pictures serve well enough for the interpretation of chemical changes, they are, nevertheless, only convenient modes of representation.

Suppose that in Fig. 34 the origin is at A and that the potential energy of a particle would be U anywhere from $x = 0$ to $x = a$, and zero when $x < 0$ or when $x > a$; that is to say, there is an energy barrier of height U and width a. If particles start to the left of the barrier (x negative) with energy E, they can reach $x = 0$ without change of kinetic energy. From $x = 0$ to $x = a$, however, the kinetic energy is $E - U$. According to classical mechanics if $E < U$ the particles cannot pass to the right of the barrier.

Quantum mechanics formulates matters quite differently. Its equations do not deal with localized individuals but only with amplitude functions, and it proves that the amplitude function on the far side of the barrier need not be zero even when $E - U$ is negative.

With the conditions postulated, the wave equation gives, for all regions except between $x = 0$ and $x = a$,

$$\frac{\partial^2\psi}{\partial x^2} + \frac{8\pi^2 m}{h^2} E\psi = 0,$$

and between $x = 0$ and $x = a$

$$\frac{\partial^2\psi}{\partial x^2} + \frac{8\pi^2 m}{h^2} (E - U)\psi = 0,$$

where $E - U$ is negative.

These two equations may be written

$$\frac{\partial^2\psi}{\partial x^2} + A^2\psi = 0, \qquad \text{except from } x = 0 \text{ to } x = a, \qquad (1)$$

$$\frac{\partial^2\psi}{\partial x^2} = B^2\psi, \quad \text{from } x = 0 \text{ to } x = a, \qquad (2)$$

where A^2 and B^2 are positive, that is A and B are real.

The solution of (1) is easily seen by substitution to be $\psi = e^{\pm iAx}$. The amplitude function is in any case combined with the time-variable function $e^{2\pi i \nu t}$, and thus it is seen that the two alternative values of $e^{i(2\pi\nu t \pm Ax)}$ represent waves travelling in opposite directions. When $x > a$ there will be only a forward wave so that $\psi = e^{iAx}$, while when x is less than zero there will be a forward and a reflected wave, the latter corresponding to particles which have been unable to penetrate the barrier.

Thus we have

$$\psi = e^{iAx} + Me^{-iAx} \quad (x < 0), \qquad (3)$$

where M is a constant,

$$\psi = Ne^{iAx} \quad (x > a). \qquad (4)$$

The solution of (2) is

$$\psi = Pe^{Bx} + Qe^{-Bx} \quad (0 < x < a), \qquad (5)$$

there being no $\sqrt{(-1)}$ factor since B^2 is positive.

The constants in (3), (4), and (5) are not unrelated, since at the points $x = 0$ and $x = a$ the alternative values given by (3) and (5) and by (4) and (5) respectively, both for ψ and for $\partial\psi/\partial x$ must correspond: otherwise the solutions would be devoid of physical meaning.

For ψ at $x = 0$ and at $x = a$, we have

$$1 + M = P + Q,$$

$$Ne^{iAa} = Pe^{Ba} + Qe^{-Ba},$$

and for $\partial\psi/\partial x$ at $x = 0$ and at $x = a$,

$$iA(1-M) = B(P-Q),$$

$$iANe^{i.Aa} = B(Pe^{Ba}-Qe^{-Ba}).$$

These four equations may be solved for M, N, P, and Q. The important thing is that N need not be zero. Thus there is in fact a transmitted wave, and particles leak through the barrier. With the appropriate value of N, the expression for the ψ of the transmitted wave can be written down. $\psi\bar{\psi}$ then gives the density of particles passing. When B, that is $(U-E)^{\frac{1}{2}}$, or a is large, the dominant term in the expression is of the form e^{-2Ba}, which indicates how the probability of crossing the barrier falls off rapidly with its width and height.

The foregoing does not of course in any way constitute an explanation of how a particle in the ordinary sense of the word can penetrate into a region where its potential energy becomes greater than the kinetic energy which it possesses as it approaches. The application of the wave equation is simply an assertion that on the microscopic scale the rules according to which such a question arises are in any case inapplicable except as approximations. For most of the purposes we have in view, however, the approximations seem to be sufficiently good.

Velocity and equilibrium

Purely thermodynamic principles by themselves can have nothing to say about the absolute rate of phenomena, though, of course, they may impose conditions to which kinetic relations must conform. In a simple chemical equilibrium, the velocity constants of the two opposing reactions are related to the equilibrium constant by the equation $K = k_1/k_2$. For a system such as

$$CO+H_2O \rightleftharpoons CO_2+H_2$$

it might be supposed that since

$$\frac{[CO_2][H_2]}{[CO][H_2O]} = K,$$

the two velocities could be set proportional to $k_1[CO][H_2O]$ and $k_2[CO_2][H_2]$ respectively. But even this is not correct. Actually, for the system in question reacting in presence of solid carbon as a catalyst the two velocities are given by

$$\frac{k_1[CO][H_2O]^y}{[H_2]^{1-x}} \quad \text{and} \quad \frac{k_2[CO_2][H_2]^x}{[H_2O]^{1-y}},$$

where x and y are small. These expressions combine to give the correct form for K, but they are certainly not predictable from it. Still less are the numerical values of k_1 and k_2 determined. There are, of course, an infinite number of pairs of values for these two constants which combine to yield the required ratio for K.

An equilibrium constant depends upon the initial and final states only, a velocity constant upon the intermediate stages through which molecules must pass on the way from one to the other. In particular, there is, for a chemical reaction, a transition state in which reacting substances and products are indistinguishable. The kinetic theory tells us a good deal about the attainment of this transition state. In the formulation of its properties, thermodynamic analogies are also found helpful in a way which will appear at a later stage.

It may be noted at once, however, that since $k_1 = Ae^{-E_1/RT}$,

$$\frac{d \ln k_1}{dT} = \frac{E_1}{RT^2}, \quad \text{and similarly} \quad \frac{d \ln k_2}{dT} = \frac{E_2}{RT^2}.$$

Also $\quad \dfrac{d \ln K}{dT} = \dfrac{d \ln(k_1/k_2)}{dT} = \dfrac{\Delta U}{RT^2}, \quad$ so that $\Delta U = E_1 - E_2$.

Transition states

The key to much of chemical kinetics lies in the law of force which regulates atomic interaction. If two univalent atoms A and B unite, the molecule AB repels a third atom C, even though A or B might individually attract C more than they attract one another. Thus the exchanges

$$AB + C = AC + B$$

or $\qquad\qquad\qquad\qquad AB + C = BC + A$

can only come about by one of the following processes. (1) C is brought up to AB with enough kinetic energy to overcome the repulsion of AB. When it is forced up close enough it can expel B or A as the case may be. (2) AB is given enough energy to dissociate it into atoms, A or B then falling victim to C should it be in the vicinity. (3) AB is set in vibration with amplitude large enough to weaken the bond between A and B, C being brought up at the same time with sufficient kinetic energy to overcome any repulsion which the weakened combination A—B still exerts. There is a certain position where C can compete with A for B on equal terms. AB and C are then in what is called the transition state.

Initial state .	.	AB	C
Transition state ˙ .		A...B...C	
Final state .	. A	BC	

Practically all chemical changes involve variants or elaborations of one or other of these processes, and in general it may be said that before new structures are formed, energy must usually be supplied to disrupt or weaken existing ones. This energy is called *activation energy*. The probability that a given molecule or a specified small group of molecules possesses energy in excess of an amount E is proportional to $e^{-E/RT}$, and in general the velocity constant of a chemical reaction may be written

$$k = Ae^{-E/RT},$$

where A is a constant, or a function varying but little with temperature, and E is the activation energy. This equation expresses the well-known law of Arrhenius.

Since $\ln k = \ln A - E/RT$, the plotting of $\ln k$ against $1/T$ gives a line of slope E/R whence E can be determined.

Encounters between molecules are usually necessary for reaction. If the chemical change consists in the decomposition of a single molecule, an encounter may not be absolutely necessary, though even here the activation energy must be provided somehow and is usually brought in by collision with other molecules. Hence the rate of encounter is often a primary factor determining the reaction rate and can never be disregarded.

The meeting together of the requisite species and the provision of the activation energy are necessary but not sufficient conditions for reaction. Other factors, notably the orientations and the states of movement of the reacting molecules, must be favourable. If, for example, the transformation to be effected is AB+C = A+BC, the orientation A—B C is clearly favourable, while that of C A—B is not. Further, if at the moment when C approaches, the state of vibration of AB is such that the bond between A and B is extended and weakened, then reaction is more likely than if it is compressed.

Thus we should have

A——B	C	favourable
A—B	C	unfavourable.

Activation energy

The interplay of these three factors, provision of activation energy, encounter of the appropriate species, and existence of favourable orientations and conditions of internal motion, manifests itself in various ways according to circumstances.

It will first be convenient to consider the three factors separately.

In the majority of examples the activation energy plays a major role. E is very often ten or twenty times as great as RT, and in consequence the temperature dependence of the reaction velocity is very pronounced.

Throughout the range of chemical reactions whose velocities can be measured there is a clearly marked correlation between the value of E and the temperature at which the rate attains some specified standard value. In the equation

$$k = A e^{-E/RT},$$

if A were a universal constant, the ratio E/T would determine k. A is not a universal constant, but it often enough remains of the same order of magnitude through considerable series of reactions for the correlation in question to be clearly discernible.

In a series of reactions which are built on the same plan but differ in rate through the operation of such influences as varying substituent groups, as in the reactions of a series of substituted benzene derivatives, there is often a well-marked correlation from one member of the series to another between ΔE and $\Delta \ln k$.

For example, in the benzoylation of different substituted anilines, the rate changes by three or four powers of ten as the substituents in the benzene nucleus are varied. When E is plotted against $\ln k$ a straight line is found, in accordance with the equation

$$RT \ln k = \text{constant} - E.$$

The slope is $-RT$ as required. Incidentally, the influence of two substituents is rather accurately the sum of their individual effects. If the first changes E for the parent compound by ΔE_1 and the second by ΔE_2, the change produced by their simultaneous presence is $\Delta E_1 + \Delta E_2$, and the value of $\ln k$ corresponds.

A a

Observations of this kind, though not infrequently overlaid with other effects which will be considered in due course, are numerous enough to leave no doubt about the significance of the activation energy as one of the major factors determining the absolute rate of a chemical change.

Attempts have naturally been made to calculate activation energies from the theory of interatomic forces, and they have met with some success, though they are not really quantitative. The method of calculation depends upon a theorem which relates the potential energy of a system of several atoms to the energies of individual combinations of them taken two at a time. If, for example, there are four atoms A, B, C, and D, then the potential energy is given by the formula

$$E = Q + [\tfrac{1}{2}\{(\alpha_1 + \alpha_2 - \beta_1 - \beta_2)^2 + (\alpha_1 + \alpha_2 - \gamma_1 - \gamma_2)^2 +$$
$$+ (\beta_1 + \beta_2 - \gamma_1 - \gamma_2)^2\}]^{\tfrac{1}{2}},$$

where Q is the sum of the six Coulomb energies of the possible diatomic pairs, and α_1, α_2,... are the exchange energies of the six diatomic combinations. Information about α_1, α_2,... is obtainable from the spectra of the various diatomic molecules. A guess has to be made about the proportion of the whole contributed by Q, and E can then be calculated. It can be determined for all sorts of relative positions and distances of A, B, C, and D. In particular, the greatest interest attaches to configurations in which AB and CD are initially paired.

The results confirm what can be seen qualitatively from general considerations, namely that as AB approaches CD the energy increases, that is, there is repulsion, which rises to a maximum at a certain distance of approach. Lower energy states then become possible by regroupings to give AC and BD. Furthermore, the maximum itself is least pronounced for one particular mode of approach of AB to CD. This mode will represent the easiest reaction path, and the difference between the maximum energy on this path and the energy of the isolated molecules AB and CD is the activation energy.

The problem of three atoms is susceptible of a relatively simple graphical representation. If the reaction under consideration is $AB + C = A + BC$, then it is almost self-evident that the most favourable conditions of approach of C is along the line of AB. When this is so the energy can be conveniently expressed as a function of the two distances AB and BC, which may be employed as coordinates, and points of equal energy joined by lines. The result is a sort of contour map upon which the path of minimum energy from $AB + C$ to $BC + A$ can be followed. The path itself possesses a maximum, which, however, is a minimum with respect to any alternative path.

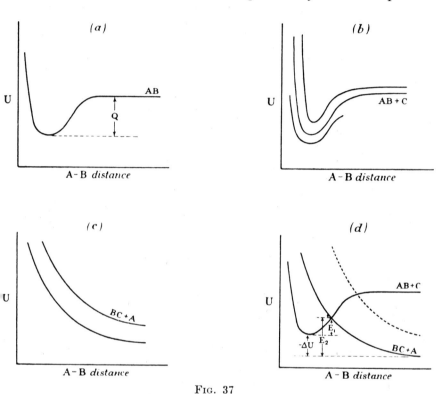

FIG. 37

Absolute calculations on this basis lead to values too crude to be of real use for quantitative purposes, but the comparison of series of related reactions gives illuminating results. In this sense the further consideration of the simple system $AB + C = A + BC$ will be useful. Let U, the energy, be plotted as a function of the distance AB. For the molecule AB the energy is represented by a curve with a minimum of the form shown in the Fig. 37 (a). The energy of dissociation is represented by Q. The presence of the atom C causes a general displacement of the curve, as shown in Fig. 37 (b). The molecule BC would repel A, so that the energy of $BC + A$ would be represented by the series of curves shown in (c), each curve corresponding to a given state of BC.

In the transition state of the reaction system (AB+C) becomes identical with (A+BC), and this condition is represented by the intersection of the two appropriate curves of the families already considered, as shown in (d). The activation energy would be given by E_1, and that of the reverse reaction by E_2. The heat of reaction would be approximately as marked on the diagram $(-\Delta U)$.

$$\Delta U = E_1 - E_2,$$

as required by the relations

$$\frac{d \ln K}{dT} = \frac{\Delta U}{RT^2}, \qquad \frac{d \ln k_1}{dT} = \frac{E_1}{RT^2}, \qquad \frac{d \ln k_2}{dT} = \frac{E_2}{RT^2},$$

and

$$K = k_1/k_2,$$

where K is the equilibrium constant, and k_1 and k_2 are the two velocity constants.

Fig. 37 (d) shows how the repulsion curve may cut the curve with the minimum in a variety of ways. If the point of intersection is far to the right, as shown by the dotted line, then E_1 becomes equal to Q, and the reaction resolves itself into the steps

$$AB = A+B,$$

$$B+C = BC.$$

In general, however, it appears likely that E_1 will be quite considerably less than the full energy of dissociation of AB. It is at once obvious that E_1 bears no sort of relation to $-\Delta U$. The activation energy always represents energy absorbed, whether the total energy change in the reaction is positive, negative, or zero. For this reason there can be no general relation between rate of reaction and equilibrium constant, and the early attempts to exploit the equation

$$\text{reaction rate} = \frac{\text{affinity}}{\text{chemical resistance}}$$

would be meaningless, even if a more precise definition could be given of chemical resistance.

On the other hand, if the general pattern of the reaction remains the same while alterations in the energy relations are brought about by variations in the nature of A, B, or C, then certain systematic correlations between changes in E and the corresponding changes in ΔU may be found.

The kinds of series here envisaged are exemplified on the one hand by reactions of an alkyl halide RX with various alkali metals, and on the other by the reactions with a given alkali metal of different halides, R or X being systematically varied. The sort of example where correlated changes in E and ΔU occur is illustrated in Fig. 38.

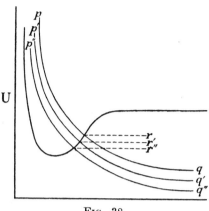

FIG. 38

Suppose a change in one of the reacting substances causes a lowering of the repulsion curve from pq to $p'q'$ or $p''q''$. The heat of reaction changes by an amount qq' or qq'' and the activation energy by rr' or rr''. The diagram makes it clear that an increase in the energy liberated in the reaction is, in this example, associated with a lowering of E, that is, an increase in rate of transformation. If the Morse curve in the region of the intersections is taken to be approximately linear, and pq, $p'q'$, $p''q''$ are of similar form, rr' and rr'' will be proportional to qq' and qq'' respectively, or in general

$$\frac{d(E)}{d(\Delta U)} = \alpha,$$

where α is constant.

Thus $\qquad\qquad E = \alpha\,\Delta U + \text{constant}.$

Since $\qquad\qquad E = \text{constant} - RT \ln k$

and $\qquad\qquad \Delta U = \text{constant} - RT \ln K$

$\text{constant} - RT \ln k = \alpha(\text{constant} - RT \ln K) + \text{constant}$

whence $\qquad\qquad \ln k = \alpha \ln K + \text{constant}.$

In other words, the logarithm of the velocity constant plotted against that of the equilibrium constant will give a straight line of slope α. From the geometry of the diagram α is seen to be less than unity.

Such relations are in fact not infrequently found. The best known of them is slightly different in character from that illustrated. It is the Brönsted relation between the velocity constants of acid-catalysed reactions and the dissociation constants of the acids which act as catalysts. Here the comparison is made virtually between the activation energy of one reaction and the equilibrium constant, not of the same but of a closely related reaction.

Influence of encounter rates

The range of possible activation energies allows every speed of reaction from the immeasurably fast to the almost infinitely slow. Conditions for collision between the appropriate kinds of molecule also permit a similar wide range, although the magnifying effect of the exponential factor is absent.

Rates of encounter in gases at atmospheric pressure are extraordinarily high. A bimolecular gas reaction occurring without the need for activation energy, and without any restrictive condition save the necessity that the molecules should meet, would be almost complete in an immeasurably short space of time. Only at extremely low pressures would its progress be observable. Under the conditions of very high rarefaction which may prevail in interstellar space, however, even free atoms could exist for long periods. It is indeed found that metastable excited species, which in the laboratory would be quenched by collisions, can in this undisturbed state in space take the time they require to emit spectra unknown on the earth. Very slow recombination reactions of atoms and ions are possible in the upper atmosphere.

If a reaction is bimolecular, the rate is directly proportional to the collision number, which for two molecules A and B in a gas is given by

$$Z = N_A N_B \sigma_{AB}^2 \left\{ 8\pi RT \left(\frac{1}{M_A} + \frac{1}{M_B} \right) \right\}^{\frac{1}{2}},$$

where N_A and N_B are the numbers of the two species in unit volume, σ_{AB} is the mean of the molecular diameters, and M_A and M_B are the molecular weights.

If the reaction is unimolecular, in the sense that the essential chemical transformation is an affair of one single isolated molecule, then the rate may or may not depend upon the encounter number. If the molecule receives its energy of activation, as it normally does, by collision, two cases arise. In the first the chemical reaction follows almost immediately upon the activation, so that its rate is determined by the speed at which the energized molecules are provided. In these conditions the reaction velocity is proportional to the collision number. The second case is that where the simple provision of activation energy is by no means the only condition to be fulfilled, and where this energy has to suffer internal redistribution in the molecule before the latter is disrupted or ready to reorganize its bonds. In these conditions the energized molecule is not unlikely, before the chemical transformation has supervened, to have made another collision in which it runs great risk of losing its high energy. A small proportion only of the energized molecules are, in such circumstances, bled off, as it were, by chemical reaction from the main supply, which remains in statistical equilibrium with the bulk of the population. The reaction velocity is now proportional to the number of energized molecules in unit volume, and this number in turn is proportional to the first power of the concentration, not, like the collision number, to its square.

The dependence of reaction rate upon encounters is reflected in what is termed the *order of reaction*. If the rate is directly proportional to the first power of a single concentration, the reaction is said to be of the first order. If it is proportional to the product of two concentrations or to the square of a single one, the reaction is of the second order. In a reaction of the third order the proportionality is of one of the forms: rate $\propto abc$, a^2b, or a^3.

A bimolecular reaction is normally of the second order, but, as has just beeen explained, a unimolecular reaction may be either of the first order or of the second order, and, in general, may show a transition from one class to the other.

Suppose there are n normal molecules in unit volume and a energized molecules. The rate of formation of the latter will be proportional to the rate of collision of normal molecules: the rate of removal will be the sum of two terms, one representing their deprivation in further collision, and the other their disappearance in actual chemical transformations. Thus the equation

$$\frac{da}{dt} = k_1 n^2 - k_2 na - k_3 a = 0$$

represents the steady state established in the system.

$$a = \frac{k_1 n^2}{k_2 n + k_3}$$

and   rate of reaction $= k_3 a = \dfrac{k_1 k_3 n^2}{k_2 n + k_3} = \dfrac{k_1 n^2}{1 + (k_2/k_3)n}.$

When n is small enough, the rate $\propto n^2$, and when n is large enough the rate $\propto n$. For intermediate values the order of reaction varies between one and two.

The real situation is somewhat more complicated than that suggested by the simple formula just derived. k_3 does not need to be constant. The transformation probability of an energized molecule may vary continuously with the amount of energy which it contains, or even discontinuously according to the mode of distribution of this energy, some modes of vibration, for example, being more likely to facilitate transformation than others. The variation of reaction rate with n in these circumstances can be quite complex.

By an argument already given (p. 92), the formula for the number of collisions in a gas may be applied in appropriate circumstances also to encounters in a solution. The condition that must be fulfilled is that repeated collisions of a given pair of molecules should count as effectively as an equal number of collisions between fresh pairs. When there is an appreciable activation energy, this is very likely to be true, since only one collision in a very large number actually leads to chemical transformation, and repeated chances of reaction offered to a given pair of molecules are as useful as many single chances offered to larger numbers. If, on the other hand, the chance of reaction at a given encounter is high, then the successive collisions which the pair might have made with one another are likely to be lost, since the molecules themselves are removed in chemical change, and the rate of the further transformation becomes dependent upon the diffusion of molecules through the liquid medium to find one another. This process is slow, and is a function of the viscosity of the medium in which the reaction occurs.

In most chemical reactions, however, the conditions are such that the rate of encounter between the relevant species of molecules is little influenced by the presence of other molecules. An important exception occurs with ionic reactions. Interionic forces are of long range and the mutual interference of ions is considerable. It leads to what is called the *salt effect* on reaction velocity. High concentrations of salts may exert some influence upon almost any reaction occurring in solution, but there is a specially well-marked effect upon bimolecular reactions between substances both of which are ionized.

Reactions between ions of like charge are accelerated by an increase in the total ionic strength of the solution: those between ions of unlike charge are retarded. Those in which either or both of the interacting species are uncharged suffer much less influence.

The simplest way of making calculations about the effect is to imagine a temporary complex formed by the collision of the two ions, to suppose that this is in equilibrium with its constituents, and to set the rate of reaction proportional to its concentration. Let C_A and C_B be the concentrations of the two ions, C_{AB} that of the collision complex. Let f_A, f_B, and f_{AB} be the corresponding activity coefficients.

Then
$$\frac{C_{AB}f_{AB}}{C_A f_A C_B f_B} = K$$

and
$$C_{AB} = \frac{f_A f_B}{f_{AB}} K C_A C_B.$$

Rate of reaction $= k'C_{AB} = k'\dfrac{K f_A f_B}{f_{AB}} C_A C_B.$

This is also $k C_A C_B$, where k is the conventional bimolecular constant.

Thus
$$k \propto \frac{f_A f_B}{f_{AB}}.$$

The influence of salts in the solution may now be referred to changes in f_{AB}, f_A, and f_B. The activity coefficient falls as the ionic strength rises, the fall being known both on theoretical and experimental grounds to be the more rapid the higher the valency of the ion. If A and B have like charges, AB is of high valency and f_{AB} is very sensitive to the salt concentration, its fall as the ionic strength rises being reflected in an increase of k. Conversely, if A and B are of unlike sign, AB is of lower valency and f_{AB} less sensitive than f_A and f_B to changes in the ionic strength. As the latter increases, the fall in $f_A f_B$ governs the decrease in reaction velocity.

Calculations can be made with the aid of the Debye–Hückel formulae (p. 279), though they are of quantitative significance only in regions of great dilutions.

The influence of ionic charges upon encounters may be great enough to dictate the whole mechanism of a reaction, and indeed it explains certain facts which at first sight seem a little strange. The well-known interaction of hydrogen bromide and bromic acid in aqueous solution proceeds according to the chemical equation

$$5HBr + HBrO_3 = 3Br_2 + 3H_2O.$$

It is found, by the variation of concentrations, to be kinetically of nearly the fourth order and in fact to follow approximately the differential equation

$$\frac{d[Br_2]}{dt} = k[H^+]^2[Br^-][BrO_3^-].$$

HBr and $HBrO_3$ are both highly ionized. Br^- and BrO_3^- are clearly the major participants from the purely chemical point of view, yet their approach is hindered by their like negative charges. If these charges are screened, as in the ion-pairs H^+Br^- and $H^+BrO_3^-$, the approach is much easier. We may then have the simple atomic exchange

$$HBr + HBrO_3 = HBrO + HBrO_2$$

followed by rapid secondary reactions of the unstable species formed. But, approximately, $[HBr] \propto [H^+][Br^-]$, since $[HBr]$ is a small fraction of the total, and $[HBrO_3] \propto [H^+][BrO_3^-]$, so that

$$[HBr][HBrO_3] \propto [H^+]^2[Br^-][BrO_3^-],$$

whence the overall order of the change. Here, incidentally, we have an example of the resolution of a reaction into a series of stages, each of maximum simplicity—a principle the importance of which will become increasingly evident.

A somewhat similar result is found with the reaction between nitrite and iodide ions in aqueous solution. Here, too, the NO_2^- and I^- ions react most efficiently when screened by hydrions and the rate is proportional to $[H^+][NO_2^-][H^+][I^-]$, that is to $[HNO_2][HI]$.

Another interesting example is that of the Sandmeyer reaction—the elimination of nitrogen from ArN_2Cl under the influence of CuCl. Here the dependence of rates upon concentrations shows that one reactant is the ion ArN_2^+ and that the other is the ion $CuCl_2^-$. These two oppositely charged ions are well adapted for mutual encounters. If $CuCl_2^-$ becomes $CuCl_4^\equiv$ the access of the ArN_2^+ to the copper atom is hindered and the reaction fails. The reaction rate $\propto 1/[Cl^-]^2$, and this is explained by the equilibrium $CuCl_2^- + 2Cl^- \rightleftharpoons CuCl_4^\equiv$.

Favourably related ionic charges of the reacting species on the one hand, and suitably coordinated central atoms on the other, are two, among others, of the factors which explain why so many of the reactions of inorganic chemistry involve subsidiary equilibria between simple and complex ions.

Transformation probabilities

As has been said, activation energy is necessary, and the requisite molecular species must come together, but other conditions must also be fulfilled before a chemical transformation is successfully completed.

This matter may be introduced by the consideration of certain striking contrasts between reactions of different orders. If we write

number of molecules reacting in unit time $= PZe^{-E/RT}$,

where Z is the encounter number and P a constant, then this latter factor may vary from one reaction to another over the range from 10^5 to 10^{-8}. In a fairly well-defined group of examples it has a value of the order of magnitude unity. These are all simple bimolecular reactions such as

$$CH_3Br + OH^- = CH_3OH + Br^-$$

and
$$2HI = H_2 + I_2,$$

where the subsidiary conditions to be satisfied at the moment of encounter of the activated molecules are relatively few and easy.

With other bimolecular reactions P ranges from 1 to 10^{-8}, but in no authenticated case of a single-stage transformation of this class does it exceed unity.

Some typical examples are the following:

$$Et_3N + EtI = Et_4NI \quad (P = 10^{-5}\text{--}10^{-8}: \text{various solvents})$$

$$C_6H_5COCl + C_6H_5NH_2 = C_6H_5CONHC_6H_5 + HCl$$
$$(P = 10^{-7}: \text{benzene solution}).$$

Reactions for which P is very small depend frequently upon the union of two molecules to form one, or at least upon the formation of more complex from less complex structures. In such examples correct orientation of the reacting molecules at the moment of encounter is clearly demanded, and also a favourable relation of the phases of their internal movements.

The necessity for special conditions of orientation and phase is perhaps more clearly realized if one considers the mechanical degrees of freedom of the whole system. When two molecules unite to form one, then three translational degrees of freedom and three rotational degrees disappear, and are replaced, since the total number remains constant in any mechanical system, by six vibrational degrees. These new degrees of freedom involve coordinated motions of atoms which, before the reaction, were executing uncoordinated motions, and which therefore must first chance to come into step before the new structure can be formed. It follows that the more elaborate the mechanical reorganization which the reaction involves, the lower will be the value of P. In a general way this expectation is fully confirmed.

It is at first sight paradoxical that in the simplest case of all, the union of two atoms, P falls again to very small values. This is not because the formation of the molecule demands other than the simplest conditions of encounter, but because its persistence once formed is impossible unless the released energy can be removed. For this purpose a collision with a third body is necessary, whereby the excess energy can be carried off. Atomic recombinations, which can be observed directly in streams of atomic hydrogen, and indirectly in various reactions of the halogens, and in the decay of active nitrogen, are in general ternary processes,

$$X+X+M = X_2+M.$$

The efficiency of M in removing the energy is very variable, and depends upon specific interactions of X_2 and M, which will be considered at a later stage.

If X and X are not atoms, their union to form X_2 does not demand to be clinched by the third-body collision. Evidence based upon the study of the photolysis of acetaldehyde, for example, shows that the process $2CH_3 = C_2H_6$ is generally bimolecular. The reason is clear. The energized molecule

$$
\begin{array}{ccc}
& H & H \\
& | & | \\
H- & C- & C-H \\
& | & | \\
& H & H
\end{array}
$$

would only be incapable of existence if the energy of formation remained in the C—C bond. This energy can, however, easily enough, become dissipated throughout the molecule in a way which, of course, is not possible for H—H. As long, however, as the excess energy remains in the molecule at all, there is always the possibility that it may collect in the C—C bond once more, and thus cause dissociation. This, in fact, would happen if the pressure were low enough, and the molecule left undisturbed by collision for a long enough time. It does not normally occur, the time required for the reversal of the combination being longer than the average time between the collisions of ethane with other molecules. In a sense, therefore, these collisions are necessary for the final and irrevocable completion of the reaction, but the rate of combination is not governed by their *number*, provided only that there are enough of them to make reversal improbable.

The quantitative formulation of this argument is worth giving. Combination of $2CH_3$ gives energized C_2H_6, which may be written $C_2H_6{}^*$. Then

$$2CH_3 = C_2H_6{}^*, \quad k_1,$$

$$C_2H_6{}^* = 2CH_3, \quad k_1',$$

$$C_2H_6{}^* + M = C_2H_6, \quad k_2,$$

$$d[C_2H_6{}^*]/dt = k_1[CH_3]^2 - k_1'[C_2H_6{}^*] - k_2[C_2H_6{}^*][M] = 0,$$

$$[C_2H_6{}^*] = \frac{k_1[CH_3]^2}{k_1' + [k_2][M]},$$

$$d[C_2H_6]/dt = k_2[C_2H_6{}^*][M]$$

$$= \frac{k_1 k_2[M][CH_3]^2}{k_1' + k_2[M]}.$$

Provided only that $k_2[M]$ is large compared with k_1', the rate reduces simply to $k_1[CH_3]^2$. At really low pressures quite different results would, of course, be found, the rate becoming proportional to $[CH_3]^2[M]$.

This matter has been discussed in some detail, because it leads directly to the consideration of unimolecular reactions, an example of which is in effect presented by the redissociation of the energized ethane. If the latter instead of retaining its energy from the process of formation, had received it in collisions, then the situation would have corresponded to an ordinary unimolecular decomposition.

In a unimolecular reaction, such as the decopomsition of a molecule like ether, P is normally much greater than unity. At first sight there may be a little difficulty in seeing how it can attain values of 10^3 or 10^5. The explanation is as follows. The reaction involves the series of steps represented in the scheme below:

Normal molecule $\overset{1}{\underset{1'}{\rightleftharpoons}}$ Energized molecule possessing activation energy E distributed at random

$\overset{2}{\longrightarrow}$ Transition state molecule $\overset{3}{\longrightarrow}$ Reaction product.
   with energy so distributed
   that the necessary links
   can be broken

The first process depends upon collisions, but the others are purely internal affairs. With a molecule of complex structure there are so many ways of receiving and losing energy, and so many degrees of freedom in which the energy can be stored, that the collection of the amount E is relatively easy. If a diatomic molecule is to dissociate, it must receive the activation energy in its one vibrational degree of freedom. For a polyatomic molecule the average energy in each of its numerous vibrational degrees is the same as that for the diatomic molecule in its one degree. Yet, given time for process 2 to occur, all this energy could conceivably collect into a single bond and so disrupt it. Thus, in extremely favourable circumstances, a polyatomic molecule with S vibrational degrees of freedom might rupture one of its bonds though the average energy taken over them all might be of the order of only $1/S$ of that which a diatomic molecule would require to rupture a bond of equal strength.

Calculation shows, as we shall see, that the chance of a total energy E in a molecule rises very steeply with the number of degrees of freedom in which it can be accommodated. For process 1, therefore, $PZe^{-E/RT}$ has a very large value. It is determined by all collisions putting into the molecule, in no particularly specified way, a total energy which for a single degree of freedom would be much greater than the average, but which for many degrees of freedom may be no more than a moderate excess. In the absence of a chemical reaction, process 1 and its reverse (the loss by further collisions of the energy gained) would come into equilibrium, so that the energized molecules would be a constant fraction of the total. This may still remain true even when processes 2 and 3 occur, provided that they are slow compared with 1 and 1'. The rate of reaction is then independent of the collision number, and can assume any value less than the maximum of $PZe^{-E/RT}$ (process 1) which, as we have seen, is very large. (If the rate approaches this maximum, then dependence on the collision number reappears.)

The improbability of the step 2, the mobilization of the energy from all parts of the molecule so that particular links can be ruptured, does not necessarily slow down the reaction very seriously, since on the scale of molecular happenings the time between collisions is relatively long, and allows the internal motions to run through very many cycles.

In a bimolecular reaction where both the colliding partners are necessary for the actual chemical change, they must meet with the energy of activation already more or less favourably distributed. For any mobilization of this energy they have not the relatively long time between collisions, but the extremely brief moment of the collision itself, after which they part, and further opportunity is lost. Thus it is that the rates of bimolecular reactions do not exceed $Ze^{-E/RT}$.

Unimolecular reactions, on the other hand, have the advantage of activation in stages. In collisions the molecules draw in energy in quantities which their many degrees of freedom may often render abundant: then in the period of relative quiet between collisions this energy is redistributed.

The ratio of the time between collisions to the duration of a collision, which is thus seen largely to determine the statistical differences between unimolecular and bimolecular reactions, can be roughly estimated. Two molecules might be deemed to be in collision while their separation is not more than about half their own diameter, that is for a time of the order of magnitude $\sigma/\bar{u}$. The time between collisions is of the order $l/\bar{u}$, where l is the mean free path. The ratio in question is then of the order l/σ. At atmospheric pressure in a gas l is of the order 10^{-5} and, σ being of the order 10^{-8}, the ratio is about 10^3.

At low enough pressures in a gas the time between collisions becomes large enough for an appreciable fraction of the energized molecules to decompose before losing their energy. The rate of reaction is now no longer independent of collisions, and the order changes from the first towards the second, according to the formula already discussed (p. 368).

Maximum rate of activation

It now remains to calculate the maximum possible rate of reaction in a unimolecular process.

The number of molecules N_j in a given energy state is represented by the formula
$$N_j/N = e^{-\epsilon_j/kT} / \sum e^{-\epsilon_j/kT}.$$

We will consider now a continuous range of momentum and space coordinates, p to $p+dp$ and q to $q+dq$, such that ϵ_j is of the general form $p^2/2m$, being the energy associated with the single coordinate p. We shall choose to regard N_j as the number of molecules in this range, and write it as dN. Then

$$dN/N = e^{-p^2/2mkT} / \sum e^{-p^2/2mkT}$$

$$= e^{-p^2/2mkT} dpdq / \sum e^{-p^2/2mkT} dpdq.$$

The denominator may with sufficient approximation be replaced by a definite integral, and we shall consider the case where the spatial distribution is uniform. Then

$$dN/N = e^{-p^2/2mkT} dp \left/ \int_{-\infty}^{\infty} e^{-p^2/2mkT} dp \right.$$

$$= \frac{e^{-p^2/2mkT} dp}{(2\pi mkT)^{\frac{1}{2}}}.$$

If now we require the fraction of the molecules with energies, corresponding to this one coordinate, between Q and $Q+dQ$ per gram molecule, where $Q = N\epsilon_j$, we must substitute for p and double the result, since a given energy corresponds to two numerically equal positive and negative values of p.

$$Q = Np^2/2m,$$

$$dQ = Np\,dp/m,$$

whence
$$dN/N = \frac{2 \times e^{-Q/RT} \times m^{\frac{1}{2}} Q^{-\frac{1}{2}} dQ}{(2\pi mkT)^{\frac{1}{2}} \times \sqrt{(2N)}}$$

$$= \frac{Q^{-\frac{1}{2}} e^{-Q/RT} dQ}{(\pi RT)^{\frac{1}{2}}}.$$

Now suppose we wish to know the probability that a molecule shall have energy between Q_1 and Q_1+dQ_1, corresponding to one coordinate, Q_2 and Q_2+dQ_2 corresponding to a second, and so on for n

coordinates, with the condition that $Q_1+Q_2+Q_3+... = E$. The required value will be the product

$$\frac{1}{(\pi RT)^{\frac{1}{2}n}} \int_0^E \int_0^E \cdots Q_1^{-\frac{1}{2}}e^{-Q_1/RT}dQ_1 \times Q_2^{-\frac{1}{2}}e^{-Q_2/RT}dQ_2 \cdots \times$$

$$\times \{E-(Q_1+Q_2+...)\}^{-\frac{1}{2}}e^{-[E-(Q_1+Q_2+...)]/RT}dE,$$

all the integrals being taken from 0 to E since, in principle, the whole of the energy might be associated with one coordinate. The above expression can be integrated by standard methods and the result is

$$\frac{e^{-E/RT}E^{(\frac{1}{2}n-1)}\,dE}{\Gamma(\frac{1}{2}n)(RT)^{\frac{1}{2}n}}.$$

The chance that a molecule possesses an energy greater than E distributed at random in the n coordinates is found by integrating with respect to E from E to ∞. The result is an infinite series of which the first term alone is of importance when E/RT is large, as it is in most problems of activation energy: it is

$$f(E) = \frac{e^{-E/RT}(E/RT)^{\frac{1}{2}n-1}}{(\frac{1}{2}n-1)!}.$$

As to the maximum possible rate of activation, we may proceed as follows. Suppose the activated molecules are those with energy greater than E in n square terms, as we have just considered. In statistical equilibrium, the number of molecules Z_1 entering the active state equals the number Z_2 leaving it. Now activated molecules are of exceptionally high energy: therefore nearly every collision of an energized molecule causes it to leave the active state. Thus

$$Z_2 = Zf(E),$$

where Z is the total number of collisions and $f(E)$ the fraction of active molecules. But $Z_1 = Z_2$: therefore rate of activation $= Zf(E)$.

From this last formula we see that the maximum possible rate of activation is

$$\frac{Ze^{-E/RT}(E/RT)^{\frac{1}{2}n-1}}{(\frac{1}{2}n-1)!}.$$

The factor $(E/RT)^{\frac{1}{2}n-1}/(\frac{1}{2}n-1)!$ may attain a very considerable magnitude with increase in n.

The experimental study of unimolecular reactions has been attended with not inconsiderable complications which arise from the existence of chain reactions. Nevertheless, it seems clear that in the decomposition of numerous organic compounds—ethers, ketones, alkyl halides, and so on—there is a truly unimolecular process, often

B b

occurring side by side with a chain reaction. The former does in fact show a transition from the first order to the second as the pressure falls; and the absolute rate can in general only be accounted for on the assumption that the energy of activation is received initially into not less than about 10 square terms (see p. 420).

Probability of internal energy redistribution

Suppose we have a molecule such as hexane, which is to suffer the decomposition represented by the equation

$$\overset{1}{C}H_3\overset{2}{C}H_2CH_2CH_2CH_2CH_3 = CH_4 + CH_2 : CHCH_2CH_2CH_3,$$

then it is obvious that a considerable amplitude of vibration in the link 1—2 is a necessary preliminary to the separation of the two carbon atoms. We wish to form some idea of the factors which determine the accumulation in this bond of energy entering the molecule in a random fashion.

The problem can be envisaged from several points of view. According to one, the molecule is regarded as a collection of s oscillators, possessing between them m quanta, and the question is raised: what is the chance that a particular oscillator should possess j of the m for itself? Here the quanta and the oscillators are likened to objects and boxes respectively and the solution is found by the usual statistical methods. The probability that the j quanta are localized increases of course with the excess of m over j, so that the transition rate of the energized molecules is a function of the total energy which they contain.

Now according to the formula derived on p. 368, the conventional first-order velocity constant is given by

$$kn = k_3 a = \frac{k_3 k_1 n^2}{k_2 n + k_3},$$

so that

$$k = \frac{k_3 k_1 n}{k_2 n + k_3}.$$

k_3 now becomes $f(m, j)$, so that for each value of m there is a different transition probability, and an integration has to be made over all energies. The formula derived is a rather complicated function of s, m, and j, the chief merit of which is that it allows a precise calculation of the variation of k with pressure. It still leaves the question of the absolute magnitude of k_3 unsolved, since it contains an arbitrary constant which is determined from the limiting value of k at high pressures.

The factors involved may be seen more clearly if we consider the simpler approximation that k_3 is a constant. From the above equation we have

$$\frac{1}{k} = \frac{1}{k_1}\left(\frac{1}{n}\right) + \frac{k_2}{k_1}\left(\frac{1}{k_3}\right).$$

If $1/k$ is plotted against $1/n$, the reciprocal of the initial concentration, there should be a straight line, making an intercept proportional

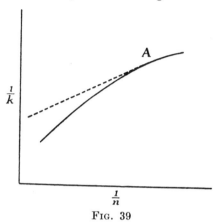

FIG. 39

to $1/k_3$. In fact, the general tendency for such plots is to show a strong curvature in the sense represented in Fig. 39. As the initial pressure drops ($1/n$ increases), the intercept made by the tangent to the curve becomes greater: that is $1/k_3$ increases, or k_3 falls. In fact at lower pressures there is an increasing contribution to the reaction from molecules with smaller transformation probabilities. These take longer, as it were, to make up their minds what they will do, and would at higher pressures lose their energy before reaching a decision. Thus the form of the curve provides information about the spectrum of k_3 values. At first it seemed that the formula depending upon the localization of j out of m quanta into one bond represented the experimental facts rather well—certainly better than the rough approximation with a constant k_3 (as it *should* do with an extra adjustable constant). And at any rate it became clear that k_3 was not constant.

But the earlier observations were largely complicated by unsuspected chain reactions, so that the numerical agreements were rather fortuitous. Further, a wider range of experimental material now suggests strongly that the values of k_3 fall into discrete groups: a given molecule seems to decompose by alternative unimolecular mechanisms to yield the same products. This raises the problem of the physical nature of k_3.

The statistical treatment of quanta in oscillators like objects in boxes leaves open the question of how they get there. To understand this we must drop the not very accurate idea of the vibrations of bonds, and of the energy in particular links, and realize that the fundamental quantities are the normal vibrations of a molecule as a whole. Consider the two linear modes of the three masses discussed on p. 259.

```
        1     2     3
      ← ○    ○    ○ →

      ← ○    ○ → ○ →
```

Any irregular linear vibrations of this system are superpositions of the two modes, which themselves are of unvarying amplitude in the absence of collisions. But since their frequencies are different, the amplitude of a particular bond, for example 1—2, waxes and wanes according as the separate modes reinforce or cancel one another. Now the maximum reinforcement lasts only for a passing instant and the bond 1—2 has its abnormal elongation for a minute fraction of the total period of the complex motion. In this sense the accumulation of energy in this bond is statistically very improbable, yet the brief instant may well be enough for the irrevocable chemical reaction.

Thus, given the requisite total energy in the various normal modes of a molecule, fleeting accumulations in particular bonds are inevitable provided that there is no disturbance by further collision. The time required for the process is of the order of magnitude of the period of the complex motion. If the amplitude reinforcement had to be very exact, and if the periods of the individual normal modes were incommensurable, the time could be very long indeed, but the first condition is not likely to be at all rigorous. Even so, the time clearly depends upon the arithmetical relations of the normal frequencies and is thus specific and not calculable from statistical considerations alone.

Although in statistical equilibrium all normal modes are excited to the same extent, the ease with which they individually gain and lose energy in collision may vary widely and specifically. (As long as easy acquisition of energy is associated with correspondingly easy loss, this specificity is not inconsistent with statistical principles.) Thus at any given moment various combinations of normal modes may exist in given molecules. For these combinations specific values of k_3 are quite conceivable.

Thermodynamic analogies

The non-exponential factor of the equation

$$k = Ae^{-E/RT}$$

can, for many purposes, be conveniently split into a collision number on the one hand and, on the other, a probability that various conditions are fulfilled in the encounter which provides the activation energy. For other purposes it is expedient to regard A in another way. Formally the equation may be written

$$k = e^{S/R}e^{-E/RT} = e^{-(E-TS)/RT},$$

whence
$$-RT \ln k = E - TS.$$

By analogy with the thermodynamic equation

$$-RT \ln K = \Delta U - T\Delta S,$$

$-RT \ln k$ may be called the *free energy of activation*, E the energy of activation, and S the *entropy of activation*. A small entropy of activation means a small reaction rate, or an improbable transformation, whether the improbability arises from rarity of encounter or from the difficulty of fulfilment of other necessary conditions.

The thermodynamic analogy can be carried farther if the molecules in their transition state, that is, in the condition where they are on the point of changing into reaction products, are regarded as constituting a definite and special chemical species. This species may be imagined to possess properties which can be formulated in the same way as those of normal molecules. There then arises the possibility of applying the statistical formula for the absolute value of an equilibrium constant:

$$K = \frac{\text{product of partition functions for resultant species}}{\text{product of partition functions for reacting species}} \times e^{-\Delta U/RT}$$

(see p. 150). If ΔU is replaced by E, K becomes

$$K^* = \frac{\text{concentration of transition molecules}}{\text{product of concentrations of reacting species}} = \frac{c'}{\Pi(c)}.$$

For example, if the reaction is $H_2 + I_2 \to 2HI$, $\Pi(c) = [H_2][I_2]$, while c' is the concentration of the hypothetical transition species

$$
\begin{array}{ccc}
H & \cdots & I \\
\vdots & & \vdots \\
H & \cdots & I
\end{array}
$$

It is supposed that the transition molecule possesses vibrational degrees of freedom, all save one of which resemble those of normal molecules. There is, however, one exceptional mode of vibration, namely that along a coordinate corresponding to the separation of the final products. For this the binding force is so weak that the molecule survives one period of vibration only. The rate of reaction is therefore $\nu c'$, where ν is the frequency of this vibration.

The rate of reaction being also given by $k_0 \Pi(c)$, where k_0 is the conventional velocity constant,

$$ k_0 \Pi(c) = \nu c' = \nu \Pi(c) K^* $$

or
$$ k_0 = \nu K^*. $$

Now, by the statistical formula,

$$ K^* = \frac{\text{product of partition functions for transition molecules}}{\text{product of partition functions for reacting species}} e^{-E/RT}. $$

The one special vibration of the transition molecule has a partition function which reduces to the form $kT/h\nu$ when the binding is weak (p. 133). Therefore we have

$$ k_0 = \nu \times \frac{\Pi'(f_A)\,(kT/h\nu)}{\Pi(f_{\text{initial}})} e^{-E/RT} $$

or
$$ k_0 = \frac{\Pi'(f_A)}{\Pi(f_{\text{initial}})} \frac{kT}{h} e^{-E/RT}, $$

where $\Pi'(f_A)$ represents the product of all the partition functions, except one, for the transition molecule.

To illustrate the meaning of these formulae we will consider briefly Eyring's treatment of the reaction $2NO + O_2 \to 2NO_2$. This had been shown by Bodenstein to be of the third order, with a rate proportional to $[NO]^2[O_2]$, and to be remarkable in that it goes the less rapidly the higher the temperature.

The system is composed of 6 atoms and thus possesses 18 degrees of freedom. In the initial state there are 9 translational degrees (3 for each molecule), 6 of rotation and 3 of vibration. For the transition state it is plausible to assume something of the form

which will possess 3 translational degrees, 3 rotational degrees, and a number of vibrations equal to $(18-6) = 12$ in all, of which one is the special one already discussed. The velocity constant will be of the form

$$k_0 = \frac{f_T^3 f_R^3 f_V^{11}}{f_T^9 f_R^6 f_V^3} \frac{kT}{h} e^{-E/RT},$$

where f_T, f_R, f_V signify partition functions for translation, rotation, and vibration respectively, and the powers are simply written as shorthand for products of the corresponding numbers of terms.

In general the vibrational partition functions are small compared with the rotational, and the latter in their turn with the translational. Consequently the product in the formula for k_0 is small, that is the concentration of transition complexes is low. The non-exponential factor in the Arrhenius equation is therefore small or, otherwise expressed, the entropy of activation is low. The reaction velocity will only be appreciable in these circumstances if E is small, which, for the oxidation of nitric oxide, it proves to be. If E is small enough, the influence of the exponential term is unimportant, and the temperature variation of k_0 may be determined by such terms in T as the partition functions themselves contain. In the present example the non-exponential term contains an inverse cube of the absolute temperature, which, since $E \to 0$, imposes the negative temperature dependence of the reaction velocity.

Absolute reaction rates

Attempts have been made in the foregoing example to calculate the absolute value of the reaction rate with the assumption that the frequencies of the transition complex are the same as those of the molecule N_2O_4, and with the further assumption of plausible dimensions for its structure. The various partition functions can then be worked out and these, with a value of E giving the correct temperature dependence, lead to a value for k_0. This is of the correct order of magnitude.

One of the great advantages of considering reaction velocity from the point of view of the transition state is that this method focuses attention upon the importance of changes in the degrees of freedom which accompany the chemical transformation. Whenever several molecules combine to form one, rotations and translations disappear and are replaced by vibrations. The magnitudes of the partition functions are such that the non-exponential factor is thereby diminished. When, on the other hand, a single molecule breaks up to give more than one, the replacement of the ordered vibrations by the less ordered translations and rotations of the fragments leads to a large non-exponential factor.

The general question of an absolute calculation of reaction rates is one of much interest. It might perhaps be said to be soluble in principle though not in practice. From the point of view of the equation $k = PZe^{-E/RT}$, on the one hand, or of the transition state equation on the other, the answer is much the same.

In the first place, the activation energy must be calculated from the theory of molecular forces. The principles according to which such a calculation is made are understood, but the execution is possible in a rough-and-ready manner only. E can, however, be derived from the temperature dependence of the reaction rate with some accuracy.

Z, the collision number, is calculable to within a power of ten. There is a little ambiguity in the definition of what constitutes the collision diameter, but this is not very serious. With regard to the factors of orientation and internal phase, unless the reaction is one of extremely simple molecules, then only rough guesses can be made as to the magnitude of P.

In about the same measure as these estimates are uncertain, knowledge of the configuration of the transition state is vague, and the assignment of values to the partition functions is arbitrary. Nevertheless, in certain cases the hypothesis that the properties of the transition complex resemble those of the reaction product enables one to assign values which are not far removed from the truth.

Collision numbers

An illuminating comparison of the two methods, and an analysis of the inner meaning of both, emerges from a simple calculation of the rate of encounter of two sets of masses which suffer no change other than the formation of what is virtually a diatomic molecule.

Let the masses be m_1 and m_2, and let them be deemed to be in the transition state when they are juxtaposed in a complex, the moment of inertia of the latter being I. In this state they possess only one vibrational degree of freedom, and this is the special one correspond · ing to the coordinate along which they will separate after collision.

According to the formula derived on p. 382, the 'reaction' of encounter and separation will proceed at the rate

$$k_0\, N_1 N_2 = N_1 N_2 \frac{\Pi'(f_A)}{(\Pi f_{\text{initial}})} \frac{kT}{h} e^{-E/RT},$$

N_1 and N_2 being the respective numbers of molecules in unit volume. $E = 0$. $\Pi'(f_A)$ consists of a three-dimensional translational function and a two-dimensional rotational function; $\Pi(f_{\text{initial}})$ of two separate three-dimensional translational functions. Thus

$$k_0\, N_1 N_2 = \frac{N_1 N_2 \dfrac{kT}{h} \dfrac{\{2\pi(m_1+m_2)kT\}^{\frac{3}{2}}}{h^3} \dfrac{8\pi^2\, IkT}{h^2}}{\dfrac{(2\pi m_1 kT)^{\frac{3}{2}}}{h^3} \dfrac{(2\pi m_2 kT)^{\frac{3}{2}}}{h^3}}$$

$$= N_1 N_2 (8\pi kT)^{\frac{1}{2}} \left(\frac{m_1+m_2}{m_1 m_2}\right)^{\frac{3}{2}} I.$$

To know I we must know the separation in the transition state, σ. Then

$$I = \frac{m_1 m_2}{m_1+m_2}\, \sigma^2$$

and the 'reaction' rate becomes

$$N_1 N_2 (8\pi kT)^{\frac{1}{2}} \sigma^2 \left(\frac{1}{m_1}+\frac{1}{m_2}\right)^{\frac{1}{2}}.$$

If we care to identify σ with the collision diameter, usually taken as the sum of the two separate radii, then this expression is none other than the normal formula for the rate of collision of unlike molecules.

Interchanges of energy by collision

As will have been seen, the interchange of energy between molecules in collision is an important factor in the establishment of equilibrium. It determines possible rates of activation, and also the efficiency with which a third body can stabilize a newly formed molecule by removing its excess energy.

The communication or removal of vibrational energy is specially important, and this proves to be a rather specific function of the forces which the molecules exert on one another when they approach. The way in which a molecule is set in vibration by an encounter with a second molecule is illustrated in Fig. 40. In (a) the atoms are at their normal equilibrium distance. In (b) under the influence of the forces exerted by a passing molecule, this equilibrium distance has assumed a new value. In (c) the perturbing molecule has passed leaving the atoms of the first one displaced from their natural distance. They therefore begin to vibrate.

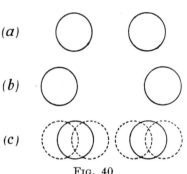

FIG. 40

According to this argument it would appear that the molecules which can most effectively communicate vibrational energy to another are those which exert the maximum perturbing action on its potential energy curve. This idea is in a general way borne out by experiment.

The most direct way of studying exchanges of vibrational energy is by the measurement of supersonic dispersion. At very high frequencies the successive rarefactions and compressions in sound waves follow one another so rapidly that the adiabatic temperature changes cannot affect all the degrees of freedom of the molecules. In particular, any vibrational degrees of freedom which are not easily excited will fail to take or relinquish their share of energy, and the molecule will appear to be of simpler structure than it is. The ratio, γ, of the specific heats will rise, and the velocity of sound, which depends upon it, will rise also. From the relation between the frequency and the sound velocity, therefore, calculations can be made of the ease with which the various vibrations are excited.

In general it may require very many collisions to effect the transfer of a single quantum of vibrational energy, and the actual number varies in a highly specific way. Correspondingly, the efficacy of different gases in stabilizing diatomic molecules formed by atomic recombination is very varied. The power of different gases to communicate the kind of activation energy required in unimolecular reactions is also specific.

XIX

ENERGY AND ENTROPY FACTORS IN REACTION VELOCITY

Resolution of reactions into stages

IT is evident that if complicated changes in the modes of motion of molecules have to accompany a chemical transformation, the non-exponential term in the expression for the reaction rate will be small. That the probability factor will be low, that the partition function of the transition complex will be unfavourable, and that the entropy of activation will be small are all equivalent statements of the same fact.

For the reasons so expressed, chemical reactions are frequently resolved into a *series of steps* for each one of which the entropy of activation is as large as possible. The overall transformation thus appears complex, especially if the observed rate is expressed in terms of the concentrations of the initial and final substances, but this apparent complexity is itself the result of the tendency to proceed by the simplest possible stages.

There are, of course, plenty of reactions which occur in a single chemical step. The unimolecular decompositions and some of the bimolecular reactions which have been discussed belong to this category, but there are even more examples of chemical changes which do not.

The reaction between stannous salts and ferric salts occurs formally according to the equation:

$$2Fe^{+++} + Sn^{++} = 2Fe^{++} + Sn^{++++}.$$

The probability that a reaction should really take place in this way is, however, extremely small. Not only does the equation demand the simultaneous collision of three molecules, but of molecules with multiple positive charges which would exert strong mutual repulsions. The observed relations between the rate and the concentrations of the various ions present are consistent with the idea that the principal reacting species are actually the ferric ion and the complex ion $SnCl_4^{--}$, which participates in the equilibrium

$$SnCl_2 + 2Cl^- \rightleftharpoons SnCl_4^{--}.$$

A simple series of one-electron transfers can then take place

$$SnCl_4^{--} + Fe^{+++} = Fe^{++} + SnCl_4^-,$$

$$SnCl_4^- + Fe^{+++} = Fe^{++} + SnCl_4.$$

The oxidation of oxalic acid by bromine shows rather complicated rate–concentration relations which can be formally reduced to a dependence of the rate-determining step upon the product

$$[HC_2O_4^-][HBrO].$$

A direct action of the acid oxalate ion and a molecule of hypobromous acid, although plausible enough as far as the probability of encounter is concerned, would involve a rather elaborate set of simultaneous atomic displacements to yield the reaction products, which are carbon dioxide, bromide ion, and water. The probable interpretation of what happens is much simpler. Halogens are to some extent ampho-teric and a small dissociation of bromine

$$Br_2 = Br^- + Br^+$$

is very likely, and involves no more than an electron redistribution. The cross equilibria which are immediately established in aqueous solution between Br^- and H^+ and between Br^+ and OH^- give at once, and in the most natural way, the bromine–bromide–hypobro-mite equilibrium. We may now consider the behaviour of the positive bromine ion when it encounters the oxalate ion $C_2O_4^{--}$.

If a positive bromine ion approaches the electron pair labelled (1) it can remove them and become a negative ion, $:\overset{..}{\underset{..}{Br}}:$, with a complete octet. Electron pair (3) now joins pair (2) with rupture of the bond between the two carbon atoms and formation of the double bond of CO_2. Then pair (5) joins pair (4) and the second molecule of CO_2 is formed, the whole process amounting to a simple flow of charge.

The rate may be set proportional to

$$[C_2O_4^=][Br^+];$$

$$[C_2O_4^=] = K_1 \frac{[HC_2O_4^-]}{[H^+]} = K_1 \frac{[HC_2O_4^-][OH^-]}{K_w}$$

since $$[H^+][OH^-] = K_w.$$

Moreover, since $$[Br^+][OH^-] = K_2[HBrO],$$

$$[Br^+] = K_2 \frac{[HBrO]}{[OH^-]}.$$

Therefore $$[C_2O_4^=][Br^+] = \frac{K_1 K_2}{K_w}[HC_2O_4^-][HBrO]$$

as required by experiment.

According to this interpretation, the key step in the reaction is of the utmost possible simplicity. It occurs between two univalent ions of opposite charge, and involves no more than an internal flow of electrons. The experimental complexity arises because the concentrations of the species which are able to undergo this simple change are themselves governed by a series of equilibria. In fact we normally seek to relate the rate of reaction not to the concentrations of the true participants but to other quantities.

Individual steps in chemical reactions might be classified in the following way:

1. Simple internal redistribution of electrons with the breaking of a bond in one place and the appearance of an ionic charge or a free bond in another place. This has just been illustrated.

2. Transfer of a charge from one atom or molecule to another. This is exemplified by the major steps in the oxidation of stannous salts with ferric salts.

3. Transfer of an atom from one molecule to another. This process is exemplified in the reaction (cited on p. 370) between HBr and $HBrO_3$.

4. Exchange of partners according to the scheme

$$\begin{array}{ccc} A—B & A & B \\ & | & | \\ X—Y & X & Y \end{array}$$

The reaction $2HI = H_2 + I_2$ belongs to this class.

The entropy of activation diminishes through the series 1 to 4, and it is rather seldom that any reaction involves a stage much more complex than one of those formulated.

On the other hand, it must be borne in mind that the energy demands usually become more exacting as the mechanism becomes more primitive. In the reaction of bromine and oxalic acid, great simplicity may be achieved by the co-operation of the positive bromine ion. But the amphoteric ionization of bromine will require a not inconsiderable amount of energy. With chlorine the corresponding dissociation will require even more, and there is evidence that the hydrolysis of chlorine takes place by the mechanism

$$Cl_2 + OH^- = HOCl + Cl^- \quad \text{rather than} \quad Cl^+ + OH^- = HOCl.$$

The former is one degree more complex but demands less activation energy than the latter.

Energy and entropy factors

The possible simplification of mechanism is limited, since the activation energy of the most primitive kinds of reaction steps may become extremely high. In one way nothing could be more simple from the point of view of entropy than the resolution of the reacting molecules into their atoms, and the re-addition of these, one by one, until the desired product is formed. There would, however, be a quite unnecessary expenditure of activation energy in the first stage of this process. The entropy and energy factors are always in opposition, and a compromise between them determines the reaction path actually followed. Thus the reaction $2HI = H_2 + I_2$ is more economical in respect of energy, and prevails over the alternative

$$HI = H + I$$

as the rate-determining step in the decomposition of hydrogen iodide, although in other ways the transition state is less probable.

Interesting light is thrown on this matter by the study of reactions in which conditions can be gradually varied by the introduction of substituents into the participating molecules, or by alteration of the solvent in which the interaction occurs. In some such series the differences in reaction rate are quantitatively accounted for by the variations in the activation energy alone, the value of the factor P (p. 371) remaining constant. The introduction of substituents into either benzene ring influences the benzoylation of aniline in this way, the correlation of ΔE and $\Delta \ln k$ being very close over a range of k

of about 10^5. The result appears to be true for the influence of substituents on the rate of reaction of benzene derivatives generally, applying also, for example, to the hydrolysis of various substituted benzoic esters.

In other series there is a *correlated variation of* $\ln PZ$ *and of* E, occurring in such a way that the change in one partly compensates the effect of the change in the other. A given increase in E, for example, does not cause, in a reaction of this type, so great a drop in the rate as it does in reactions of the first type, since PZ increases so as to tend to maintain it constant. Examples are found in the esterification of acids by alcohols, hydrolysis of certain alkyl halides, and many other series of reactions.

The reason for the distinction between the two classes seems to lie in the fact that changes in the reactants or in the solvent can influence reaction rates in various ways. The principal effect of a substituent in a benzene ring is to cause electron displacements which modify bond strengths on the one hand and affect the repulsion offered to approaching molecules on the other. There is little change made in the geometry of the transition state. In such cases the influence might be expected to appear almost entirely in E. In other systems not only the forces but the steric conditions in the neighbourhood of the reaction centres may be profoundly changed when the nature of one of the reactants or of the solvent is altered. Suppose, for example, that when A reacts with BC a rather exact alignment of the molecules permits the reaction to occur without a very high activation energy. E will be small, but so also, in view of the need for the precisely specified configuration, will be PZ. Suppose now that a change from BC to BC' renders this exact alignment impossible. The reaction will now occur only in so far as a greatly increased activation energy is provided (permitting, for example, the more drastic stretching of the bond B—C'). E will have risen, but so also, in view of the fact that the precise geometry is no longer important, will PZ. There will thus be a compensatory effect in evidence.

Such an effect can, of course, manifest itself in many different ways, but its general basis is that where plenty of energy is available (or must for independent reasons be provided) the need for very exactly defined configurations becomes less.

In some reactions a very precisely adjusted pattern of solvent molecules may help to lower the activation energy. If the reactants are changed so that, for steric or other reasons, this nicely balanced system is no longer possible, a greater E becomes necessary, but the entropy of activation rises, and the fall in rate is less than would have been imposed by the increase in E alone.

An interesting example is observed in the reactions of ester hydrolysis. In the alkaline hydrolysis of benzoic esters, changes in the substituent cause changes in rate wholly accounted for by changes in the activation energy. In the acid hydrolysis of esters and also in the acid-catalysed esterification reaction there is a marked compensation of the energy and the entropy terms. The alkaline and acid hydrolysis reactions may be formulated as follows:

Alkaline
$$
\underset{\text{OH}\quad\text{H}\cdot\text{OH}}{\overset{\displaystyle\overset{\text{O}}{\|}}{\text{R}\cdot\text{C}-\text{OR}'}}
$$

$$
\underset{\quad\overset{|}{\text{OH}}}{\overset{\displaystyle\overset{\text{O}}{\|}}{\text{R}\cdot\text{C}\quad\text{R}'\text{OH}}}
$$

$$
\overline{\text{OH}}
$$

Acid
$$
\underset{\text{H}\cdot\text{OH}\quad\text{H}^{+}}{\overset{\displaystyle\overset{\text{O}}{\|}}{\text{R}\cdot\text{C}-\text{OR}'}}
$$

$$
\underset{\quad\overset{|}{\text{OH}}}{\overset{\displaystyle\overset{\text{O}}{\|}}{\text{R}\cdot\text{C}\quad\text{R}'\text{OH}}}
$$

$$
\text{H}^{+}
$$

The chief resistance to reaction is represented by the energy required to bring the hydroxyl ion or the water molecule up to the carbonyl carbon. This energy is less with the hydroxyl ion, and one might suppose the reaction to approximate to the two-stage process:

$$(a)\quad \overset{\displaystyle\overset{\text{O}}{\|}}{\text{R}\cdot\text{C}}-\text{OR}'+\overline{\text{OH}} = \text{R}\cdot\text{COOH}+\overline{\text{OR}}',$$

$$(b)\quad \overline{\text{OR}}'+\text{H}_2\text{O} = \text{R}'\text{OH}+\overline{\text{OH}},$$

(b) being rapid compared with (a). If this is so, the orientation and distance of the water molecule become irrelevant, and the only influence of changes in R is on the energy term. In acid hydrolysis the water molecule is a much less active agent, the activation energy is greater, and the co-operation of the hydrogen ion is required. Furthermore, we might suppose the link between the carbonyl carbon and the alkoxyl group to weaken in different degrees according to the magnitude of the repulsion overcome by the approaching water. If this repulsion is great, the transition state may well be attained when the water is at a greater distance than when the repulsion is weaker; the entropy of the transition state is thus greater, and compensates to some extent the more adverse energy.

In these examples we are dealing with what in a subtle way really amounts to a change of mechanism. Much profounder changes of mechanism are encountered in the transition from ordinary molecular reactions to chain reactions.

Chain reactions

The progress towards equilibrium of most chemical systems depends upon statistical fluctuations whereby individual molecules or small groups of them escape from their relative minima of potential energy and pass into transition states whence in turn they proceed to other minima.

In a reversible reaction the transition state is common to the forward and to the reverse transformations, and the total energy absorbed in the change is related to the two activation energies by the equation $E_1 - E_2 = \Delta U$, E_1 being the activation energy of the forward reaction and E_2 that of the reverse.

When the change takes place in the forward direction, E_2 is given out by the products as they descend from the transition state, and if ΔU is negative, as in an exothermic reaction, E_2 is greater than E_1. Unless the reaction is actually endothermic, the amount of energy released by the products is therefore at least equal to the original activation energy. If it could be passed on efficiently from the products to fresh molecules of the reacting substances, it would suffice to activate them immediately. Often, however, it is dissipated by sharing among a number of molecules. Eventually, in so far as the temperature is maintained constant, any excess, equal to $-\Delta U$, is lost from the system. If the heat of an exothermic change does not escape as rapidly as it is generated, the temperature rises and the reaction rate steadily increases until an explosion occurs.

Without a general rise of temperature, however, there are more specific ways in which the effect of the original activation can persist. There may be specially effectual energy transfers from the activated products to fresh molecules of reactant, though any wide occurrence of such processes is perhaps doubtful. Much more significant is the circumstance that the activation energy of the first step may have been employed in splitting a molecule into free atoms or radicals.

C C

These store up the energy as chemical unsaturation, a form in which it is not wastefully dissipated, but remains available for further transformations whenever suitable opportunities arise. In this way originate what are called chain reactions.

The following are some well-known examples:

(1) $$Cl_2 = 2Cl,$$
$$Cl + H_2 = HCl + H,$$
$$H + Cl_2 = HCl + Cl;$$

(2) $$C_2H_6 = C_2H_5 + H,$$
$$H + C_2H_6 = C_2H_5 + H_2,$$
$$C_2H_5 = C_2H_4 + H;$$

(3) $$CH_3CHO = CH_3 + CHO,$$
$$CH_3 + CH_3CHO = CH_4 + CH_3 + CO;$$

(4) $$R + CH_2:CH_2 = RCH_2CH_2\text{---},$$
$$RCH_2CH_2\text{---} + CH_2:CH_2 = RCH_2CH_2CH_2CH_2\text{---};$$

(5) $$CH_4 + O_2 = CH_3 + H\text{---}O\text{---}O\text{---},$$
$$CH_3 + O_2 = CH_3\text{---}O\text{---}O\text{---},$$
$$CH_3\text{---}O\text{---}O\text{---} + CH_4 = CH_3\text{---}O\text{---}O\text{---}H + CH_3.$$

The initial step of a chain reaction is nearly always difficult, and requires the absorption of a large activation energy to produce the atoms or radicals which are the usual participants. The activation energy of subsequent stages is normally quite small, so that the propagation of the chain occurs with ease.

It not infrequently happens that a chain reaction and a molecular reaction take place concurrently and make contributions of comparable magnitude to the total observed chemical change. In the thermal decomposition of acetaldehyde vapour, for example, there are probably two major mechanisms, a direct molecular rearrangement : $CH_3CHO = CO + CH_4$, and a chain process similar to (3) above. The activation energy, E_1, for the formation of radicals is very much higher than that for the rearrangement, E, and in consequence the number of molecules which initiate chains is smaller in about the ratio $e^{-(E_1 - E)/RT}$ than the number which suffer simple decomposition. But for each primary act of decomposition into radicals there may be hundreds of secondary reactions. The net result is that the two mechanisms are of about equal importance in respect of the total reaction which they occasion. A highly improbable initiating process with a long sequence of consequences competes, and, as it proves, on about equal terms, with a much more probable process having no chain of consequences to multiply its effect.

Chains do not go on being propagated indefinitely. The free atoms or radicals sooner or later suffer fates which remove them from the cycle of operations. They may combine with one another, they may react with foreign substances, they may diffuse to the walls of the vessel and there suffer chemical reaction or adsorption, while radicals may undergo decomposition, or isomerization to inactive forms. The mode in which the chains are ended is one of the major factors determining the kinetics of these reactions, as will be evident from examples to be given later on.

The proofs that chain processes actually play an important part in the progress of chemical systems towards equilibrium are various. The most direct evidence comes from photochemical observations. A single quantum of light can bring about one primary process only, but it may be responsible for the ultimate chemical transformation of a very large number of molecules. The ratio of the molecules reacting to the quanta absorbed is called the *quantum efficiency* and may be identified with the chain length.

Another criterion is the susceptibility of the reaction to inhibition by small quantities of foreign substances capable of removing atoms or radicals. One part of nitric oxide in several hundred will very markedly slow down the decomposition of ethers, hydrocarbons, and other organic vapours, the effect being due to its combination with alkyl radicals. Large amounts of an inhibitor could, of course, act by the stoicheiometric removal of something normally participating in a non-chain reaction, but minute quantities could not. They must remove particles which would otherwise cause the transformation of molecules many times more numerous than themselves.

Chain reactions are sometimes, though by no means always, recognizable by the special forms of the equations relating rate and concentration. For example, the kinetic equation for the formation of hydrogen bromide from its elements would be very difficult to interpret except in terms of a cycle in which bromine atoms and hydrogen atoms are alternately generated (see p. 415).

Branching chains

One of the most striking phenomena shown by chemical reactions is the apparently abrupt transition from almost complete quiescence to inflammation or explosion which is sometimes brought about by a quite minute variation in conditions.

A mixture of phosphine and oxygen may be stored in a glass tube at the ordinary temperature and at a pressure of about 1 mm. for many hours without appreciable combination. Yet a quite small increase of pressure will cause the mixture to burst into vivid flame. No premonitory increase in reaction rate is detectable at pressures just below the inflammation point. In a somewhat analogous way, if to a 300 c.c. quartz vessel at 550° C. we add 200 mm. hydrogen followed by 100 mm. oxygen, the rate of combination observable is normally quite slow. It becomes slower still if the pressure is reduced and at about 100 mm. is almost imperceptible. Yet, if the pressure is reduced by another millimetre or so below this limit, the mixture explodes with a bright flash and a sharp sound.

The only explanation of these phenomena is that the reactions take place by way of what are called *branching chains*.

In accordance with the principle that there is a minimum disturbance of atoms and bonds at each individual step of a reaction, we might imagine the union of hydrogen and oxygen to occur in the following stages:

$$(1) \qquad H_2 = 2H \quad (\text{or } H_2 + O_2 = H_2O_2 = 2OH)$$

$$(2) \qquad H + O_2 = OH + O$$

$$(3) \quad OH + H_2 = H_2O + H$$

$$(4) \qquad O + H_2 = OH + H.$$

Every hydrogen atom introduced by any means into the system will after the cycle of events (2), (3), and (4) have generated three others. If there is no loss, the number will increase in geometrical progression with each cycle and the rate of reaction will tend to become immeasurably great. The individual atomic and radical reactions being rapid, the growth of the rate can occur in a space of time too minute for ordinary observation, with the result that any generation of hydrogen atoms in the mixture leads to practically instantaneous explosion.

But the condition that there should be no loss is an ideal one. In reality the atoms and radicals are removed in a variety of ways, and there will be a competition between the processes of chain-branching and the processes of removal. Except under certain sharply specified conditions where the two opposing rates balance, one or other must prevail. If branching prevails, so that there is in effect an increase in the number of active particles with each cycle of reaction, then there will be an explosion after the (usually imperceptible) interval necessary for the geometric multiplication. If, on the other hand, the removal mechanisms can keep the number emerging from each cycle no larger than that entering, then there will be a steady reaction rate, which in fact may be quite a slow one.

We shall have occasion at a later stage to study in detail the characteristics of a typical branching chain gas reaction, and all that need be said at this moment is that the expression for the rate usually assumes the form

$$\frac{F_1}{f_s+f_c-\phi},$$

where F_1 is a function of the concentrations characteristic of the step by which the chain is initiated, f_s is some function determining the breaking of chains by the walls of the vessel, f_c another function determining the breaking in the gas phase, and ϕ a function expressing the inherently branching nature of the chains.

When ϕ fails to be kept in balance by f_s+f_c the rate soars up towards infinity however small F_1 may be. Before it can actually reach an infinite value, of course, the evolution of heat in the system is so great that there is an explosion. In general f_s will fall as the pressure of the gas rises, since diffusion of active particles to the wall becomes more difficult. It is usually this effect which determines an abrupt onset of explosion as the pressure rises. On the other hand, f_c usually rises with increasing concentration of the reacting gases, so that its influence may be responsible for the quenching of an explosion on passage from a lower to a higher initial pressure. The two kinds of transition are exemplified in the experiments with phosphine–oxygen and hydrogen–oxygen mixtures which have just been quoted.

When the branching of a chain is held in check by the diffusion of atoms or radicals to the walls there is normally a marked dependence of the inflammation limit upon the size of the containing vessel. Rate of chain-branching depends upon the volume of reacting gas: removal by diffusion depends upon the surface area. Thus with increase in size there is a shift in favour of branching and an increase in explosive character. The critical pressure limit above which inflammation occurs moves downwards as the vessel becomes larger. There are well-established examples of all these effects.

The branching chain which leads to explosion is the extreme of a continuous series. Most chemical reactions begin with a minute and highly localized statistical fluctuation in which molecules pass to a transition state. Often the transformation of each molecule or group of two or three interacting molecules must await a fresh fluctuation. Sometimes, however, the original one can be propagated, either through a short or through a longer sequence of successive events which constitute a chain reaction. In the limit it gains momentum as it proceeds so that a branching chain results and leads to the catastrophic establishment of the final state of equilibrium.

Catalysis

We have already encountered various examples of the fact that in their progress to equilibrium chemical systems may follow multiple routes. Chain reactions and molecular reactions sometimes compete as alternatives, for example, in the decomposition of ethers, aldehydes, and hydrocarbons. Sometimes reactions which appear to be closely enough related to justify the expectation of similar mechanisms proceed in fact by different courses, as in the formation of the hydrogen halides. Sometimes again the divergence of route is more subtle, and reveals itself only in the differing energy–entropy relationships of the transition states of reactions belonging to related series. Examples of all these things might be multiplied indefinitely. Some alkyl halides in the gaseous state decompose by a chain reaction, others by a single-stage unimolecular mechanism. In some circumstances olefinic compounds take up halogens by a bimolecular reaction, in others by a reaction of higher order which may possibly involve molecules such as Br_4.

Whenever the addition of a new substance to the system offers the possibility of an alternative and more speedy reaction route, what occurs is called catalysis.

Examples are numberless. Nitrous oxide is decomposed by collisions with molecules of its own kind, provided that the activation energy to the extent of 50,000 to 60,000 cal. is available. In contact with platinum the activation energy of the reaction

$$N_2O + Pt = N_2 + Pt(O)$$

is only about half as great. The oxygen atom is more easily transferred to the platinum than liberated into space. Its subsequent escape after a sojourn on the surface of the solid occurs in conjunction with a second atom with which it unites to form a molecule.

Formic acid may suffer two alternative decompositions:

$$HCOOH = H_2 + CO_2 \quad \text{and} \quad HCOOH = H_2O + CO.$$

That yielding hydrogen and carbon dioxide is catalysed by various metals, which lower the activation energy in virtue of their affinity for hydrogen atoms. The alternative mode of reaction is favoured by oxides such as alumina, whose affinity for water lowers the activation energy for its extraction. The subsequent processes by which the products escape from the catalyst themselves require some energy, but a series of stages requiring lower activation energies can usually be run through more rapidly than a single stage with a much greater demand than any of the others.

Alternative routes of lower activation energy present themselves in homogeneous gas reactions. The decomposition of acetaldehyde is catalysed by iodine, which opens an energy by-pass in the following way:

$$(1) \quad CH_3CHO = CH_4 + CO,$$
$$(2a) \quad CH_3CHO + I_2 = CH_3I + HI + CO,$$
$$(2b) \quad HI + CH_3I = CH_4 + I_2.$$

E, whether for $(2a)$ or for $(2b)$, is much lower than the corresponding value for (1).

There is no sense or profit in talking about theories of catalytic reactions in general. The theory of catalysis is the theory of chemical reaction velocity, and the methods of operation of catalysts are as diverse as the modes of chemical change. Normally the catalyst adds a new path of reaction of lowered activation energy, but sometimes it is the non-exponential factor for the new mechanism which is more favourable, as for example in a chain reaction. Anything, such as an extraneous source of radicals, which initiates a chain reaction is of course a catalyst.

In a sense a solvent is one, though people with a taste for debate about terminology might question whether the word catalytic is appropriate to describe the influence of the entire environment. Environmental influences can certainly lower activation energies. Often they do this at the expense of compensating changes in non-exponential factors.

The following calculation, though crude, is significant, and illustrates a typical effect. Suppose that n solvent molecules suitably grouped around a transition complex lower the value of E by their united perturbing actions. Each makes a contribution e to the lowering so that $\Delta E = ne$. Let the chance that any one of them is correctly disposed for the job be p: then the overall chance of their co-operation is p^n, where p is less than unity. Compared with reaction in absence of solvent the rate now rises in the ratio $e^{ne/RT}$ and falls in the ratio p^n. In the equation $k = PZe^{-E/RT}$ we have $\Delta E = ne$, $P/P_0 = p^n$, whence it follows that $\Delta \ln P$ will be proportional to ΔE. In such a case the solvent may increase the reaction rate, but to a smaller extent than that indicated by the value of ΔE, since the non-exponential factor varies in a compensatory fashion.

It is conventional to classify certain types of reaction mechanism under the headings *homogeneous catalysis* and *heterogeneous catalysis* respectively.

Homogeneous catalysis does not really raise any special questions. Its problems are the general ones of deciding what chemical reactions are possible between molecules of different kinds; what the activation energies will be; and what general kinetic laws they will follow. But there is one piece of chemistry to which reference should here be made, and that is the widespread influence of acids and bases upon reactions which, as far as conventional chemical equations go, do not appear to demand them.

Acid-base catalysis

The formal equation for ester hydrolysis is

$$RCOOR' + HOH = RCOOH + R'OH,$$

and this is typical of a very large number of reactions in which the elements of water are added or removed. The hydrolysis is normally dependent upon the intervention of acid or alkali, when, according to good evidence, it proceeds by one of the mechanisms set forth on p. 392 and upon which some further comments may now be made.

Most molecules exhibit an internal electrical inhomogeneity, and this means that there will often be a point at which attack by a positive or negative ion is easier than attack by a neutral molecule. In the alkaline ester hydrolysis the key assault is made by the OH^- on a positive centre in the ester. The OH^- comes not from the water but from the catalyst. The water molecule contributes a complementary H^+ to round off a process already nearly complete, and leaves behind another OH^- to replace that consumed in the initial attack. The analogy of this whole set of operations with a chain reaction is to be observed. In a chain reaction a particle with the asymmetry of an unbalanced valency attacks a molecule from which it appropriates a piece to complete its own structure, leaving this molecule itself unbalanced, and so setting up a see-saw process of redistribution. Something similar occurs in the hydrolytic reaction, only that here the part of the free radicals is taken over by the ions.

The kind of initial disturbance which is most likely to set up the see-saw in hydrolytic reactions is the addition or removal of a proton or a hydroxyl ion, the removal of a proton in presence of water being equivalent to the addition of hydroxyl. Very many reactions are accordingly subject to what is called *general acid or basic catalysis*, any reagent, such as the anion of an acid, which can accept protons counting as a base and any reagent which can donate them counting as an acid. The H_3O^+ ion occurring in aqueous solutions of dissociated acids is in principle of no special importance in this connexion compared with other molecules such as undissociated carboxylic acids, which can also donate hydrogen ions. An aqueous solution of what is conventionally called acetic acid contains both HAc and H_3O^+ in equilibrium,

$$HAc + H_2O \rightleftharpoons H_3O^+ + Ac^-,$$

and both may exert catalytic effects. Often enough the rate of reaction in a solution containing acetic acid is proportional to

$$\{k_1[H_3O^+] + k_2[HAc]\}$$

and may depend upon other ionic species as well.

Although the reason for acid or basic catalysis is specially clear in reactions involving the addition or removal of water, the effect is not by any means confined to such reactions. It is very prominent in prototropic reactions such as the enolization of acetone. Here the first step appears to be the acceptance by the acetone of a proton from the acid to give an addition compound which readily isomerizes by a redistribution of charge. The result is a molecule from which any proton acceptor present, including water, will readily remove H^+ to leave the enol. The general principle is still the same.

In the acetone enolization reaction the rate-determining step is the first one, namely the transfer of the proton from the acid to the acetone. By a principle which has already been discussed (p. 365) the rate-constant k for the reaction in presence of an acid HA, shows a parallelism with the equilibrium constant of the reaction

$$HA + H_2O \rightleftharpoons A^- + H_3O^+,$$

which measures the acid strength of HA in water. This parallelism is expressed by the equation

$$\Delta \log k = \alpha \Delta \log K_a$$

for a series of acids.

The rate-determining step need not be the transfer of the proton from the acid catalyst to the molecule whose transformation is to be catalysed. We may write in general for the catalytic reaction of a substance X under the influence of an acid:

(1) $X + HA = XH^+ + A^-,$

(2) $XH^+ + A^- = X + HA,$

(3) $XH^+ = X'H^+,$

(4) $X'H^+ + B^- = X' + BH,$

X' being the reaction product from X. If (1) is rate-determining, we have the case already considered. The rate is $k_1[X][HA]$, and the reaction is said to exhibit general acid catalysis.

But (1) and its inverse (2) may both be rapid in comparison with (3). We shall then have

$$[XH^+] = K_1 \frac{[X][HA]}{[A^-]}, \quad \text{where } K_1 = k_1/k_2.$$

If the rate is determined by (3) it is

$$k_3[XH^+] = \frac{k_3 K_1[X][HA]}{[A^-]}.$$

But in *any* aqueous solution

$$\frac{[H_3O^+][A^-]}{[HA]} = K_a,$$

So that

$$\frac{[HA]}{[A^-]} = \frac{[H_3O^+]}{K_a}.$$

Therefore

$$k_3[XH^+] = \frac{k_3 K_1}{K_a}[X][H_3O^+],$$

and the reaction rate appears to be determined simply by the conventional hydrion concentration of the solution. The constant k_1 does not enter. If k_4 were rate-determining, other relations still would be found.

Evidently a wide variety of behaviour may be expected in catalytic reactions involving hydrolysis, enolization, and the like, and one may say that it is in fact found. A large amount of experimental work is concerned with the disentangling of the various relationships, especially in the field of what is sometimes called physical organic chemistry.

Heterogeneous catalysis

The problems of heterogeneous catalysis are of a somewhat different kind from the foregoing. Two of the most characteristic questions are, on the one hand, that of interpreting the various concentration–rate relationships which are found, and, on the other, that of understanding in what way the catalyst changes the activation energy so as to make a new reaction route possible.

As to the concentration–rate relations, these are at first sight sometimes a little surprising. They fall into line, however, when handled in the light of the principle that a heterogeneous reaction occurring on a solid surface is in many respects analogous to a *homogeneous reaction in two dimensions*.

In the first place we must know the surface concentrations of the reactants, a matter upon which the adsorption isotherm provides information, and for many purposes the simple Langmuir formula (p. 344) renders this service well enough. If the pressure of a constituent of the gas phase is p, the fraction σ of the solid surface which is covered is given by the equation

$$\sigma = \frac{p}{b+p}.$$

When p is small, σ is directly proportional to it, but when p is large, σ remains constant at a value of unity. Thus if we have a single reacting gas, undergoing for example a decomposition, the reaction can be of the first order at lower pressures and of order zero at higher pressures.

When ammonia suffers thermal decomposition at the surface of a heated tungsten wire, the rate is nearly independent of the ammonia pressure over quite a considerable range, the time taken for an assigned *fraction* to react *increasing* with the pressure. The decomposition of phosphine in contact with a silica surface is, on the other hand, of the first order, the time taken for a given fraction to react being independent of the pressure.

One gas may easily impede the reaction of another by preventing its access to the surface. The simplest case is where the inhibitory gas is rather strongly adsorbed, so that the reactant has available only the fraction of the surface which is left free. Since

$$\sigma_B = p_B/(b+p_B),$$

the free surface is given by

$$(1-\sigma_B) = b/(b+p_B).$$

When p_B is relatively large, or b is small, $(1-\sigma_B)$ becomes inversely proportional to p_B.

If p_B is the pressure of the inhibitory gas and p_A that of the reactant, then when the adsorption of the latter is not very strong, σ_A is proportional to p_A. The reaction rate will be proportional to $\sigma_A(1-\sigma_B)$ and thus to p_A/p_B.

The decomposition of ammonia on the surface of a glowing platinum filament follows approximately the equation

$$-d[NH_3]/dt = k[NH_3]/[H_2],$$

the interpretation of which is now obvious.

When the adsorptions are such that the limiting relations $\sigma_A \propto p_A$, or σ_A is independent of p_A, and $\sigma_B \propto 1/p_B$ do not apply, the kinetic equations are naturally more complicated.

If two gases, A and B, react together and both compete for the surface, the rate in general will be proportional to $\sigma_A \sigma_B$, since the probability of finding two molecules in juxtaposition is more or less proportional to this product. The reaction velocity may be proportional to p_A or to p_B at low values of either, and to $1/p_A$ or $1/p_B$ at high values, since excess of one reactant may displace the other from the surface. The rate as a function of p_A or p_B may then pass through a maximum at a given value of one or the other. The mechanism may not, however, require the simultaneous adsorption of A and B, but rather a collision from the gas phase of A with adsorbed B. The various combinations are, of course, quite numerous, but the most likely possibilities can usually be inferred from experimental results.

When the adsorption of one of the gases is neither very strong nor very weak, σ is proportional to $p/(b+p)$, that is, to a power of p between 0 and 1. Over limited ranges one may use the approximation that the rate depends upon some more or less constant fractional power of the pressure, positive for reactants, negative for inhibitors. In this way are to be explained the results quoted earlier (p. 358) for the water–gas reaction. The decomposition of nitrous oxide on a glowing platinum wire obeys the equation

$$-\frac{d[\mathrm{N_2O}]}{dt} = \frac{k[\mathrm{N_2O}]}{b+[\mathrm{O_2}]}$$

which could be represented with reasonable approximation by

$$-d[\mathrm{N_2O}]/dt = k[\mathrm{N_2O}][\mathrm{O_2}]^{-x},$$

where x is a positive fractional number.

The broad outlines of the kinetic interpretation of such reactions are clear enough, but there is material for deeper investigation in many details, such as: the extent to which one layer of molecules may be adsorbed on a layer of a different kind already present; the relative role of atoms and molecules of gases like hydrogen and oxygen adsorbed on metals; and the mobility of adsorbed atoms and molecules on the surface. It is beyond the scope of the present discussion to enter into these questions.

The formal kinetics of a heterogeneous reaction having been disentangled, the problem still presents itself why the route by way of the adsorbed condition should frequently prove more expeditious than that of a homogeneous reaction. There is no one single explanation, any more than there is one for the power of molecules to exert forces on one another in general. Numerous causes contribute.

In the first place, molecules adsorbed on a solid surface are in steady communication with a relatively unrestricted energy supply, so that limitations on the rate of communication of activation energy will not play the part which they may play in the reactions of the gas phase. Moreover, surface interactions have not the transiency of bimolecular collisons, and two molecules adsorbed on neighbouring sites have a better chance to attain the phase favourable to reaction than they have in the brief moment of a gas-phase encounter.

More important still is the active intervention of the surface atoms in the chemistry of the transformations, with the creation of fresh reaction intermediates, such as atoms and radicals which are held in a state known as that of *chemisorption*. Metals remove atoms of hydrogen or oxygen from substances containing them, and retain them as surface hydrides or oxides until they are ready to evaporate or to react with other species. Carbon surfaces, to quote another example, probably take up H_2 in the form of atoms, and H_2O as H and OH. These surface complexes resemble any ordinary compound in that they are held together by valencies, but differ from this in that the atoms of the surface are still held firmly as a part of the main solid lattice. The formation of these special surface compounds creates new reaction stages of lowered activation energy, since in a structure A—X, A will be removed more easily from X if it is simultaneously taken up with release of energy by M. Naturally M must not hold A too avidly, or the reaction will soon come to a halt—and susceptibility to inhibition by reaction products is indeed a not uncommon character of surface reactions.

The capacity to form the appropriate kind of covalent links— neither too strong nor too weak—is a matter as specific as any other chemical interaction, and general explanations can hardly be expected. Oxides are good catalysts for hydration and dehydration; certain metallic sulphides which form SH links intervene effectively in hydrogenations of organic compounds, and so on.

Sometimes the adsorption of a molecule A—X with resolution into the radicals A and X depends upon the correct interatomic spacings on the catalyst, and this opens the way to studies of the relation of catalytic power and crystal structure. The formation of covalencies with adsorbed atoms of one kind and another is a function of the electron orbitals of metallic catalysts, and a considerable field of investigation exists in the relation between the occupation of electron levels in metals and alloys and their catalytic properties. Electron distributions in solid carbon may also play a significant part in its catalytic reactions. Metallic impurities modify these distributions and so change activation energies directly, without opening qualitatively new reaction paths. These matters demand specialized study and we shall not enter further into them here.

Development of chemical kinetics

For the sake of showing a rather complex picture in better perspective we have given something like an analytical survey of the principles governing the progress of chemical reactions. The principles themselves may in the event seem almost self-evident, but at one time this was far from true. To correct any impression so created it will be useful briefly to outline the course of development of some of the main ideas. After that a more detailed examination of the actual behaviour of a few representative reaction systems may serve to correct the impression still further, and also to show how the relatively simple principles underlie a highly complex mass of facts.

The conception of a chemical system which evolves gradually in time was not so obvious to early chemists as it has since become. Preoccupation with the preparation of substances naturally leads to the rough-and-ready classification of reactions into those which go and those which do not, and encourages the search for conditions under which the desired transformations do actually occur. In the older literature there is a fairly widespread tacit assumption of a temperature where certain reactions first become possible—with the implication of a discontinuous transition into the realm of possibility. Although a prolonged action of substances is obviously required in many chemical operations, this fact was not the subject of much fruitful thought, the need being probably deemed to arise from some undefined kind of contact resistance.

The conditions in which slow reactions of relative simplicity become accessible to precise measurement are not normally obvious, and have to be discovered. Even when they have been found, the phenomena which become apparent would be, in the eyes of many, little more than curiosities. Nevertheless, the development of any phenomenon in time has a fascination of its own, and the laws which it follows have an attraction to those interested in the quantitative aspect of things. The application of the so-called law of mass action led to the idea of reaction order, and provided a basis for a rational classification of slow chemical changes. Examples of reactions of different orders were sought and found, and indeed the existence of this convenient system of grouping not infrequently led to the over-simplification of the real relations. But the obvious molecular explanation of the order in terms of collision probability did not fail to arouse interest in the statistical theory of reaction rates. Even so, an unconscious tendency to compare chemical changes with phenomena of viscous flow or movement under friction persisted, terms such as chemical resistance were endowed with a fictitious significance, and catalysts were likened to lubricants.

One of the most potent stimuli to thought about the actual

happenings in slow chemical transformations was the striking law of temperature-dependence. This, of course, has the same form as the thermodynamic equation for the variation of equilibrium constant, and the first interpretation assumed an equilibrium between normal and hypothetical active molecules. The latter were supposed to be formed endothermically from the former, to increase in number as the temperature rises, and to be the actual participants in the chemical reaction. Increasing knowledge of kinetic theory and of statistical molecular theory in general made it clear that the active molecules need not be special chemical forms, but are simply those with excess of energy.

The notion of how this energy facilitates the transformation became more precise over a series of years in the light of concurrently evolving ideas on spectroscopy, quantum mechanics, and molecular forces in general. The idea of activation has passed from the status of a slightly fanciful hypothesis to that of something very nearly self-evident. The transition has been in part due to the inherent reasonableness of the idea, but largely also to various experimental discoveries—that of reactions where the absolute rate could be calculated from the number of collisions between suitably energized molecules, and that of the quite definite correlations existing between changes in the activation energy and changes in the velocity throughout series of related chemical reactions. At this stage, pictures of the intimate mechanism of chemical transformations in terms of molecular happenings began to acquire vividness and colour.

The problem of unimolecular reactions came to the fore with the question of how the molecules receive their activation energy. A hypothetical reaction in which rate and concentration are connected by the equation $-dc/dt = kc$ would go half-way to completion in a time independent of the initial value of c. In a gas, therefore, this time should be the same at infinite dilution as at atmospheric pressure. The implication at one moment seemed to be that the supply of activation energy could not be dependent upon collisions, and the only alternative agency was absorbed radiation. But did any gaseous reaction follow this law? At the time when this discussion arose, obvious candidates for the role, such as the decomposition of phosphine and arsine, were disqualified by their heterogeneity, so that no answer was forthcoming.

The discovery of unimolecular reactions in the decomposition of

organic vapours, such as that of acetone, provided the missing experimental material, and it soon became clear that they did not
follow a uniform first-order law, but the transitional type of relation
which has already been explained. Collisions were established as the
major mode by which activation energy is in fact communicated.

But a new difficulty arose from the apparent insufficiency of the
collisions to provide energy at the required absolute rate. The way
out was provided by the now very natural idea that multiple internal
degrees of freedom can be drawn upon to contribute to the activation
process. The theory of reaction rates now becomes correlated with
the study of normal modes of vibration of complex molecules.
Fresh questions about the dependence of transformation probability
on energy excess or energy distribution arise and the subject
enters its specialized phase—where there are still some unsolved
problems.

In the meantime the theory of chain reactions was gradually
coming into its own. Beginning with the need to explain how a single
quantum of light could provoke the combination of thousands of
molecules of hydrogen and chlorine, the theory served to account
for abnormally high activation rates in general, and to interpret the
mysterious phenomenon of negative catalysis by minute traces of
inhibitory substances. Presently it proved to give the only possible
explanation of the complex and varied phenomena revealed by the
experimental study of gaseous combustion reactions. The natural
extension of the idea to include branching chains was thoroughly
justified by its application to the various kinds of explosion limit,
at first sight so puzzling, shown by systems such as that of hydrogen
and oxygen.

The simplest participants in chain reactions are atoms and radicals.
These are now quite familiar entities. Hydrogen atoms may be
generated in discharges, pumped along tubes, and allowed to raise
wires to incandescence: methyl radicals can be produced in furnaces
and watched as they eat away mirrors of tellurium from the cooler
walls of the exit channel. But at one time it was a very bold hypothesis to assume the intervention in ordinary chemical reactions of
such unfamiliar species.

The discovery of the unimolecular reactions which depend upon
collisions blurred the classification in terms of orders, and the complex kinetics of chain reactions still further lessened its utility as a

D d

practical system. Elementary stages in reaction mechanisms certainly have definite orders: the steps

$$C_2H_5 = C_2H_4 + H,$$
$$H + O_2 = OH + O,$$
$$H + H + M = H_2 + M$$

being of the first, second, and third orders respectively. But this statement does not relate the rates to the concentrations of the substances which are introduced into the system as major reactants, and the individual steps can only be formulated when the mechanism has been analysed. From the point of view of concentration relationships, chemical kinetics often presents a complexity which looks somewhat discouraging. But the complexity is only the outcome of combinatory processes in which essentially simple stages follow one another in many different ways.

The immediately accessible experimental material is not infrequently a somewhat tangled skein, but when unravelled reveals an underlying unity and continuity. The pattern of the whole subject becomes clearer and more symmetrical as time goes on.

Some of the manifold modes in which elementary mechanisms are combined are best illustrated by examples, a selection of which are set forth in the next chapter.

XX

SOME TYPICAL REACTION MECHANISMS

Reactions of different orders

As has become evident, the chemical changes which are directly measured by analytical methods are relatively seldom of a single definite integral order. Nevertheless, examples exist which do conform to the simple classification, and they include some important reactions. It will be convenient to start this brief survey of typical reactions with the consideration of some of these.

First-order reactions

These are not necessarily or even usually unimolecular. Some examples are the inversion of sucrose under the influence of a constant concentration of hydrion, the decomposition of nitrous oxide on the surface of an incandescent gold wire, the decomposition of phosphine in contact with the walls of a silica reaction vessel, the homogeneous decomposition of nitrogen pentoxide over considerable ranges of pressure. An interesting contrast occurs in the hydrolytic reactions of the alkyl halides. The lower halides, and the primary compounds generally, react with alkali according to a second-order law. Tertiary halides, such as t-butyl chloride, are hydrolysed in aqueous solution according to a first-order law, the rate being independent of the concentration of acid or alkali present. The rate-determining step is either the ionization of the halide or a direct attack by the solvent:

$$RCl = R^+ + Cl^- \quad \text{(slow)}$$
$$R^+ + H_2O = ROH + H^+ \quad \text{(rapid)}$$

or
$$RCl + H_2O = ROH + H^+ + Cl^- \quad \text{(slow)}.$$

The formal representation of a first-order change is

$$A \rightarrow B.$$

When $t = 0$, $[A] = a$; at time t, $[A] = (a-x)$,

$$dx/dt = k(a-x).$$

Hence
$$\int \frac{dx}{a-x} = kt + C$$

and
$$-\ln(a-x) = kt + C.$$

When $t = 0$, $x = 0$, so that $C = -\ln a$.

Therefore
$$kt = \ln \frac{a}{a-x}.$$

The time of half-change, $t_\frac{1}{2}$, is given by $x = \frac{1}{2}a$, so that
$$t_\frac{1}{2} = \ln 2/k = 0{\cdot}693/k.$$

The time of half-change is thus independent of the initial concentration. This is the best practical criterion of a first-order reaction.

It should be noted that the initial rate, dx/dt, is proportional to a, the rate being expressed correctly as change of concentration in unit time. If 'rate' is expressed as the change in the *fraction* of the original substance, then it is $(1/a)(dx/dt)$, and independent of a. This convention, although sometimes used, is incorrect.

The equation for a reversible first-order reaction is not without interest. The formal scheme is

$$A \rightleftharpoons B.$$

When $t = 0$, $[A] = a$, $[B] = 0$; at time t, $[A] = (a-x)$, $[B] = x$.

Hence
$$dx/dt = k_1(a-x) - k_2 x,$$

or
$$\frac{dx}{k_1 a - (k_1 + k_2)x} = dt,$$

giving
$$\frac{-\ln\{k_1 a - (k_1 + k_2)x\}}{k_1 + k_2} = t + C.$$

Since when $t = 0$, $x = 0$, $C = -\dfrac{\ln k_1 a}{k_1 + k_2}$.

Hence
$$(k_1 + k_2)t = \ln \frac{k_1 a}{k_1 a - (k_1 + k_2)x}.$$

At equilibrium, $dx/dt = 0$, so that
$$k_1(a - x_{eq}) = k_2 x_{eq}, \qquad k_1 a = (k_1 + k_2)x_{eq}.$$

Therefore
$$(k_1 + k_2)t = \ln \frac{(k_1 + k_2)x_{eq}}{(k_1 + k_2)(x_{eq} - x)},$$

or
$$kt = \ln \frac{x_{eq}}{x_{eq} - x},$$

where $k = k_1 + k_2$.

If the initial concentration is replaced by the drop in concentration which occurs by the time equilibrium is reached, the equation for an irreversible reaction may thus be used in the ordinary form.

Second-order reactions

Excellent examples are found in the hydrolytic reactions of esters with alkalis, the interaction of alkyl halides with hydroxyl ions, the benzoylation of amines, and the union of tertiary amines with alkyl halides to give quaternary ammonium salts. Among gas-phase reactions the decomposition of hydrogen iodide, on the one hand, and the union of hydrogen with iodine on the other provide the classical examples. The absolute rates in this last case are rather closely given by: *collision number* $\times e^{-E/RT}$.

There is little doubt that a reaction such as $H + O_2 = OH + O$ follows the second-order law, but this can only be inferred from the fact that the assumption leads to correct results when introduced as part of the theory for a more complex mechanism in the hydrogen–oxygen reaction.

For a second-order reaction the formal equations are as follows:

$$A + B \rightarrow C.$$

When $t = 0$, $[A] = a$, $[B] = b$; at time t, $[A] = (a-x)$, $[B] = (b-x)$.

Therefore
$$dx/dt = k(a-x)(b-x),$$

or
$$\frac{1}{(b-a)}\left\{\frac{dx}{(a-x)} - \frac{dx}{(b-x)}\right\} = k\,dt,$$

and
$$\frac{1}{b-a}\ln\frac{b-x}{a-x} = kt + \text{const.}$$

When $t = 0$, $x = 0$; whence

$$\frac{1}{b-a}\ln\frac{a(b-x)}{b(a-x)} = kt.$$

If $a = b$, this expression is indeterminate, and we proceed otherwise.
$$dx/dt = k(a-x)^2,$$

giving
$$\frac{1}{a-x} = kt + \text{const.}$$

When $t = 0$, $x = 0$; whence

$$\left(\frac{1}{a-x} - \frac{1}{a}\right) = kt.$$

The time of half-change for the case where $a = b$ is given by $t_{\frac{1}{2}} = 1/ka$, and is thus proportional to the inverse of the initial concentration. When a is not equal to b, $t_{\frac{1}{2}}$ is a less simple quantity and is given by $x = \frac{1}{2}a$ or by $x = \frac{1}{2}b$ as the case may be.

If a and b are nearly but not quite equal, both the formulae just derived for the relation of x and t become inaccurate. To find a satisfactory equation we now proceed as below. We write

$$b = a + \Delta.$$

Then

$$\frac{dx}{(a-x)(a-x+\Delta)} = k\,dt.$$

Division yields the series

$$\frac{dx}{a-x}\left\{\frac{1}{a-x} - \frac{\Delta}{(a-x)^2}\cdots\right\} = k\,dt,$$

whence

$$\frac{1}{a-x} - \frac{\Delta}{2(a-x)^2}\cdots = kt + C.$$

When $t = 0$, $x = 0$, so that

$$kt = \left\{\frac{1}{a-x} - \frac{1}{a}\right\} - \frac{\Delta}{2}\left\{\frac{1}{(a-x)^2} - \frac{1}{a^2}\right\}\cdots,$$

the first term in Δ sufficing when Δ is small.

Reactions with fractional orders: (a) Ortho-para hydrogen conversion

A good example of a change initiated by free atoms is the spontaneous interconversion of ortho- and para-hydrogen which occurs in the gas phase at a red heat. The mechanism depends upon a dissociation followed by an exchange of atomic partners thus:

$$H_2^P \rightleftharpoons 2H$$

$$H + H_2^P \rightleftharpoons H_2^O + H.$$

If we start with pure para-hydrogen

$$[H] = \sqrt{K}[H_2^P]^{\frac{1}{2}},$$

and the initial rate of interconversion is given by

$$-\left(\frac{d[H_2^P]}{dt}\right)_{\text{initial}} = k_0\sqrt{K}[H_2^P]^{\frac{1}{2}}[H_2^P] = k[H_2^P]^{\frac{3}{2}}.$$

The initial rate then varies as the $\frac{3}{2}$ power of the initial pressure. For a given value of the latter, however, which does not change as the conversion proceeds, $[H]$ remains constant and the reaction follows the first-order law

$$-\frac{d[H_2^P]}{dt} = \{k_1[H_2^P] - k_2[H_2^O]\} \times \sqrt{K\{[H_2^P] + [H_2^O]\}}^{\frac{1}{2}},$$

where

$$[H_2^P] + [H_2^O] = \text{constant}.$$

Reactions with fractional orders: (b) Hydrogen–halogen reactions

Another good example of a reaction initiated by free atoms is found in the combination of hydrogen and bromine. The rate is expressed by the equation

$$\frac{d[\mathrm{HBr}]}{dt} = \frac{C_1[\mathrm{H_2}][\mathrm{Br_2}]^{\frac{1}{2}}}{1 + C_2([\mathrm{HBr}]/[\mathrm{Br_2}])},$$

qualitative inspection of which suggests the following ideas.

Since the rate is proportional to the square root of the bromine concentration, the reaction is probably started by the few bromine atoms in thermal equilibrium with the molecules

$$\mathrm{Br_2} \rightleftharpoons 2\mathrm{Br}, \tag{1}$$

so that $\quad \dfrac{[\mathrm{Br}]^2}{[\mathrm{Br_2}]} = K \quad$ and $\quad [\mathrm{Br}] = \sqrt{(K[\mathrm{Br_2}])}.$

The degree of dissociation being small, $[\mathrm{Br_2}]$ is very nearly equal to the total bromine concentration. The most likely fate of atomic bromine, apart from recombination, is reaction with hydrogen:

$$\mathrm{Br} + \mathrm{H_2} = \mathrm{HBr} + \mathrm{H}. \tag{2}$$

Atomic hydrogen will attack bromine molecules

$$\mathrm{H} + \mathrm{Br_2} = \mathrm{HBr} + \mathrm{Br}. \tag{3}$$

The empirical equation expressing the experimental results shows that the reaction is inhibited by hydrogen bromide, but in a way which becomes relatively less serious the higher the concentration of bromine. Evidently hydrogen bromide and bromine are in competition for something which is necessary for the continuation of the chain, the only probable competitor to reaction (3) being

$$\mathrm{H} + \mathrm{HBr} = \mathrm{H_2} + \mathrm{Br}. \tag{4}$$

The steps (1)–(4) may therefore be tentatively assumed. Hydrogen atoms will not accumulate in the system, but will rapidly reach a small steady concentration such that their respective rates of formation and removal are equal. We have, therefore,

(a) $d[\mathrm{H}]/dt = k_2[\mathrm{Br}][\mathrm{H_2}] - k_3[\mathrm{H}][\mathrm{Br_2}] - k_4[\mathrm{H}][\mathrm{HBr}] = 0.$

We have also

(b) $d[\mathrm{HBr}]/dt = k_2[\mathrm{Br}][\mathrm{H_2}] + k_3[\mathrm{H}][\mathrm{Br_2}] - k_4[\mathrm{H}][\mathrm{HBr}].$

This, of course, is not equal to zero.

Substitution of $[Br] = \sqrt{(K[Br_2])}$ and elimination of $[H]$ gives

$$d[HBr]/dt = \frac{2k_2\sqrt{K}[H_2][Br_2]^{\frac{1}{2}}}{1+(k_4/k_3)([HBr]/[Br_2])}$$

in agreement with experiment.

Difficulty is sometimes experienced in understanding the validity of a steady-state condition, such as $d[H]/dt = 0$, for a system in which a reaction is proceeding. $[H]$ does of course change in the long run, but only gradually and in so far as $[H_2]$ and $[Br_2]$ change. As long as these major concentrations suffer no appreciable modification, $[H]$ is constant, and given by (a). As the changes described by (b) proceed, $[H]$ shows secular variations from one steady value to another progressively. The establishment of the stationary state described by (a) occurs according to a time scale much smaller than that governing the total reaction.

The photochemical combination of hydrogen and bromine occurs according to the same plan as the thermal reaction except that the steady concentration of bromine atoms is very much increased by the illumination.

$$Br_2+h\nu \rightleftharpoons 2Br.$$

If I_{abs} is the intensity of the absorbed light, the equating of the rates of dissociation and recombination gives

$$kI_{abs} = \ddot{}[Br]^2,$$

whence $\qquad\qquad$ $[Br] = (kI_{abs}/k')^{\frac{1}{2}},$

which replaces $\qquad$ $[Br] = (K[Br_2])^{\frac{1}{2}}$

in the thermal reaction.

In the corresponding photochemical reaction between chlorine and hydrogen the relations are at first sight rather different, yet entirely explicable by one simple circumstance, namely that most of the chlorine atoms do not recombine as in the bromine system, but suffer other fates. It is no longer permissible to write $[Cl]^2 = K[Cl_2]$, but the various reactions of the atoms must be specifically taken into account.

We may write generally

$$Cl_2+h\nu = 2Cl, \tag{1}$$

$$Cl+H_2 = HCl+H, \tag{2}$$

$$H+Cl_2 = HCl+Cl, \tag{3}$$

$$Cl \rightarrow \text{removed from system by other agencies.} \tag{4}$$

Then

$$d[\text{Cl}]/dt = k_1 I_{abs} - k_2[\text{Cl}][\text{H}_2] + k_3[\text{H}][\text{Cl}_2] - f([\text{X}])[\text{Cl}] = 0,$$

where $f([\text{X}])$ is written to represent the appropriate function of the concentration of substances involved in the removal of the chlorine atoms. Also

$$d[\text{H}]/dt = k_2[\text{Cl}][\text{H}_2] - k_3[\text{H}][\text{Cl}_2] = 0,$$

$$d[\text{HCl}]/dt = k_2[\text{Cl}][\text{H}_2] + k_3[\text{H}][\text{Cl}_2]$$

$$= \frac{2k_1 k_2 I_{abs}[\text{H}_2]}{f([\text{X}])}.$$

Here I_{abs} represents the absorbed light. If the rate is expressed in terms of the incident light, we must write

$$I_{abs} = I_0 \phi([\text{Cl}_2]),$$

where ϕ is proportional to $[\text{Cl}_2]$ at very low concentrations and independent of it at higher ones.

In some circumstances chlorine atoms are largely removed by reaction with inhibitors, in which case $f([\text{X}])$ is simply $k_4[\text{X}]$, where $[\text{X}]$ is the inhibitor concentration. Oxygen may play such a role if present in the system. In narrow capillary tubes the atoms are removed to a considerable extent by diffusion to the walls. The rate then becomes a function of the radius of the tube and of the diffusion coefficient of the atoms through the reaction mixture. This depends in a rather complicated way on the composition. In very specially purified gases and not too narrow tubes recombination of chlorine atoms to molecules does become important, and a dependence on $\sqrt{I_{abs}}$ rather than I_{abs} can be demonstrated.

It will be seen that very varied relations are to be expected according to the conditions of working, which affect the completeness of light absorption, the relative roles of reaction with inhibitors, recombination in the gas, diffusion to the walls, and so on. It is scarcely to be wondered at that before the problem was as well understood as it has now become in the light of the general study of chain reactions, many conflicting views were held, not only about the interpretation, but about the facts themselves.

Third-order reactions

The simplest of the third-order reactions is the recombination of atoms in presence of a third body: for example $2\text{H} + \text{M} = \text{H}_2 + \text{M}$.

It plays a part in the decay of active nitrogen, the glowing gas produced by the passage of an electric discharge through ordinary nitrogen under the correct conditions. The intensity of the glow diminishes with time according to a second-order law, but the decay constant itself is proportional to the total pressure of the molecular nitrogen present. These facts are strongly suggestive of the process $N+N+N_2 = N_2+N_2$, and this almost certainly does occur, though the full story of active nitrogen is much more complex.

The combination of nitric oxide with oxygen follows the kinetic equation

$$-\frac{d[NO]}{dt} = k[NO]^2[O_2].$$

Since the only known homogeneous third-order gaseous reactions, apart from atomic recombinations, involve two molecules of nitric oxide, it is possible that there is an equilibrium

$$2NO \rightleftharpoons N_2O_2$$

and that N_2O_2 reacts bimolecularly with the third partner in the scheme. At small concentrations $[N_2O_2]$ would be proportional to $[NO]^2$, so that the kinetic relations would correspond to a third-order reaction.

In any event there arises the question of what constitutes a ternary encounter. We must first define a distance within which two molecules, A and B, are deemed to be in collision. They will remain in this range for a time, τ, which may be regarded as the duration of the collision. We must next specify a distance to within which the third molecule, C, must approach during the period τ. With these conventions the number of ternary encounters can be calculated in the usual way. The formula expressing this number is

$$Z_{ABC} = N^3 \tau \sigma_{AB}^2 \sigma_{ABC}^2 \, 8\pi RT \left(\frac{1}{M_A}+\frac{1}{M_B}\right)^{\frac{1}{2}} \left(\frac{1}{M_{AB}}+\frac{1}{M_C}\right)^{\frac{1}{2}} c_A c_B c_C,$$

where N is Avogadro's number, c_A, c_B, and c_C are the concentrations in gram-mols. per c.c., M_A, M_B, M_C are the molecular weights of A, B, and C, and M_{AB} is that of A and B taken together. σ_{AB} is $\frac{1}{2}(\sigma_A+\sigma_B)$ and σ_{ABC} is $\frac{1}{2}(\sigma_A+\sigma_B+\sigma_C)$, σ_A, σ_B, and σ_C being the collision diameters of the respective molecules. The time τ may well depend upon the nature of the pair of molecules concerned, the collisions being of varying elasticity. The assumption that two molecules of nitric oxide make somewhat inelastic collisions, characterized by large values of τ, is rather more general than that of an actual formation of the molecule N_2O_2, though in the end it amounts to much the same thing.

The reaction of nitric oxide with hydrogen follows approximately the kinetic equation

$$-\frac{d[NO]}{dt} = k[NO]^2[H_2],$$

and more exactly the equation

$$-\frac{d[NO]}{dt} = k_1[NO]^2[H_2] + \frac{k_2[NO]^2[H_2]}{1+a[NO]} + \frac{k_3[NO]^2[H_2]}{1+b[H_2]},$$

where a and b are constants.

A likely interpretation of this relation is that the binary collision-pairs $NO.NO$ and $NO.H_2$ both have finite but different lives, and that the probability of encounter of the former with H_2 or of the latter with NO during the relevant time-interval tends towards unity when the appropriate concentration is high enough (cf. the discussion on p. 373).

An alternative method of treating termolecular reactions which avoids the formal difficulty of defining the conditions for ternary collisions is that of estimating the partition functions for the transition state. The procedure has already been illustrated (p. 382). The formal superiority of the theory is, however, counterbalanced by the arbitrariness of the molecular constants assigned to the transition complex.

As to the concentration–time relationship in a termolecular reaction, the equations assume one of the forms

$$\frac{dx}{dt} = k(a-x)^3,$$

$$\frac{dx}{dt} = k(a-x)^2(b-x),$$

$$\frac{dx}{dt} = k(a-x)(b-x)(c-x).$$

As an example of the integrated forms we may take that of the second which is

$$kt = \frac{1}{(a-b)^2}\ln\frac{b(a-x)}{a(b-x)} + \frac{1}{(a-b)}\left\{\frac{1}{a} - \frac{1}{a-x}\right\}.$$

In general, activation energies of termolecular reactions are low, since otherwise the rates would be negligible. The activation energy for an atomic recombination is zero, that for the combination of two radicals small but not necessarily vanishing. For the formation of C_2H_6 from $2CH_3$ a rearrangement of valencies from a planar to a tetrahedral disposition must occur and this probably requires one or two thousand calories.

Unimolecular reactions: thermal decompositions of diethyl ether

The study of this reaction, which takes place with measurable speed in the region of 500° C., serves to illustrate a number of different matters. The main chemical change is represented by the equations

$$C_2H_5OC_2H_5 = CH_3CHO + C_2H_6,$$
$$CH_3CHO = CH_4 + CO,$$

the second stage being rather rapid compared with the first. There are some by-products.

The existence of a chain mechanism is revealed by the inhibitory action of nitric oxide, a few millimetres of which will reduce the rate of reaction of several hundred times as much ether to a steady limiting value, about a quarter of the original. Larger quantities of propylene reduce the rate to precisely the same limit, which must be that of the molecular decomposition without chains. This is shown diagrammatically in Fig. 41.

The chain reaction is of the first order with respect to the ether at higher pressures, and tends towards the second order at lower pressures. A further important clue to the nature of the chain process is the fact that the amount of nitric oxide required to lower the rate to a given fraction of the original is independent of the ether pressure. This suggests that the nitric oxide acts by removing a radical which, although necessary for the continuance of the reaction, does not itself attack ether. The following series of steps is consistent both with the facts just quoted and with the principle that the mechanism should involve stages of maximum simplicity.

$$C_2H_5OC_2H_5 = CH_2OC_2H_5 + CH_3, \tag{1}$$
$$CH_3 + C_2H_5OC_2H_5 = C_2H_6 + CH_2OC_2H_5, \tag{2}$$
$$CH_2OC_2H_5 = CH_3 + CH_3CHO, \tag{3}$$
$$CH_3 + CH_2OC_2H_5 = C_2H_5OC_2H_5. \tag{4}$$

The subsequent decomposition of the acetaldehyde is relatively rapid, though in fact a certain small amount does accumulate in the system. (3) is demanded by the constancy of the nitric oxide inhibition at different ether pressures and (4) by the overall order of reaction.

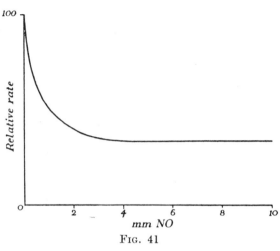

FIG. 41

Let
$$[C_2H_5OC_2H_5] = X,$$
$$[CH_3] = M,$$
$$[CH_2OC_2H_5] = R.$$

Then for a steady condition

$$\frac{dM}{dt} = f(X) - k_2 MX + k_3 R - k_4 MR = 0,$$

$$\frac{dR}{dt} = f(X) + k_2 MX - k_3 R - k_4 MR = 0,$$

where $f(X)$ is the rate of process (1).

If the chains are of some length most of the ether is decomposed in process (2), so that

$$-\frac{d[C_2H_5OC_2H_5]}{dt} = k_2 MX$$

$$= k_2 X (k_3/k_2 k_4)^{\frac{1}{2}} \left(\frac{f(X)}{X}\right)^{\frac{1}{2}}.$$

Now $f(X)$ is the rate of the primary decomposition of the ether, and if this is of the first order,

$$f(X) = k_1 X,$$

so that

$$\frac{d[C_2H_5OC_2H_5]}{dt} = k_2(k_1 k_3/k_2 k_4)^{\frac{1}{2}}[C_2H_5OC_2H_5].$$

The result is consistent with the experimental findings except at low pressures. Here the overall order rises, which means that $f(X)/X$ changes more rapidly than X. That is to say, the primary process itself is showing a transition to a higher order, in accordance with the general theory of unimolecular reactions which has already been explained.

If we had assumed the recombination process (4) to involve two methyl radicals, the order of reaction, even for the higher pressures, would have been greater than unity. Such a result is found experimentally in the case of the decomposition of ethane.

In presence of nitric oxide there is added to the above sequence the step

$$CH_2OC_2H_5 + NO \rightarrow \text{inactive products.} \tag{5}$$

Solution of the stationary state equations now gives an expression for the rate of decomposition as a function of the nitric oxide concentration. The relative degree of inhibition proves to be the same at all ether pressures. If the nitric oxide had been assumed to react with methyl in competition with the ether in process (2), the predicted result would have been that for higher ether pressures more nitric oxide would be required to cause the same fractional reduction in rate. Such a result is in fact found in the decomposition of ethane. Thus the action of nitric oxide not only reveals the presence of chains but in various examples throws some light upon their detailed nature.

The residual molecular reaction, measurable in presence of enough nitric oxide to suppress the chains and reduce the rate to its steady limit, still tends to the first order at higher pressures and to the second at lower pressures, in accordance with the behaviour to be expected of a unimolecular transformation with collisional activation. The activation energy is 67,000 cal. for a gram molecule of ether. The transition from the first order to a higher order is in progress at pressures in the region of 200 mm. If one makes the approximate assumption that at this pressure the rate of activation is just sufficient, then about 18 square terms are necessary to account for the rate, according to the formula which has already been discussed (p. 376).

An interesting property of the reaction is that in the region where the rate begins to fall below that corresponding to the steady first-order constant of higher pressures the addition of hydrogen to the system restores it to its normal value. It seems that collisions with hydrogen molecules are specifically effective in the communication of activation energy.

The ether decomposition is, as has been seen, a matter of some complexity, yet it falls clearly enough under the heading of unimolecular reactions. The mechanism as a whole involves no less than three such changes.

First, there is the primary step of the chain reaction, which in certain ranges of pressure impresses its own first order on the overall process. The activation energy of this primary decomposition into radicals must be high, but does not appear directly in the observed value of E, which is a function of the separate values for each step in the total series. The rate of the initial reaction is, of course, very low, but is multiplied by the chain propagation.

Secondly, the decomposition of the heavy radical first formed from the ether is itself a unimolecular reaction. The activation energy will be very low and therefore its provision by collision will present no difficulty, so that the reaction can easily maintain a first-order behaviour.

The third unimolecular reaction is the direct molecular decomposition of the ether molecule into C_2H_6 and CH_3CHO. It has an intermediate activation energy, communicable by collision at a rate sufficient to maintain an approximately first-order reaction rate at moderate pressures. Observations at very high pressures show that here new types of collision mechanism appear to make a contribution to the activation mechanism.

Thermal decomposition of nitrous oxide

This reaction illustrates very well the failure of the simple classification into orders. It might have been expected to follow a second-order law, and indeed to be obligatorily bimolecular, since

$$2N_2O = 2N_2 + O_2$$

seems at first sight a more likely chemical process than

$$N_2O = N_2 + O.$$

A reaction which is influenced by binary collisions only and which is truly bimolecular in the chemical sense cannot become of the first order at higher pressures. This, however, is what the nitrous oxide

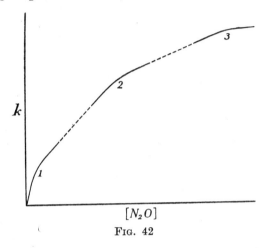

$[N_2O]$

Fig. 42

decomposition does. It would seem, therefore, that the more favourable entropy of activation associated with the unimolecular splitting off of the atom counts for more than the less favourable activation energy which this process must involve.

The conventional first-order constant, k, shows, however, a rather surprising variation with pressure. In the lowest regions it varies in proportion to $[N_2O]$ (that is, second-order behaviour). It then shows a series of changes indicated (though not to scale) in Fig. 42. The transitions marked 1, 2, and 3 are in the regions 50 mm., 5 atmospheres, and 30 atmospheres respectively. It would seem that there is a superposition of several unimolecular reactions, in the manner suggested by Fig. 43.

In a unimolecular reaction there is, as has been explained, a delay between collision and transformation. With nitrous oxide this delay may be partly due to the fact that the separation of N_2O into $N_2 + O$ involves an actual change in the spectroscopic multiplicity of the system.

The average activation energy varies with the pressure. It seems not improbable that various combinations of normal modes of vibrations are associated with different activation energies and different transformation possibilities (cf. p. 380).

Behaviour analogous in this respect is shown by various aldehydes in their thermal decompositions, and something of the same general type appears in the pyrolysis of various paraffins.

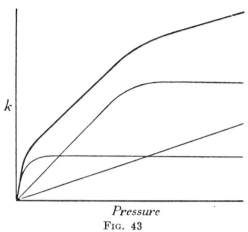

Pressure

FIG. 43

The reaction of hydrogen with oxygen

Below about 450° C. the union of hydrogen with oxygen occurs exceedingly slowly except in contact with the surface of a solid catalyst. The kinetic relations shown by the heterogeneous reaction are very varied and depend upon the mode of adsorption of the individual gases. In the region 450–650° C., however, a gas-phase reaction of great interest makes its appearance, and exhibits in classical form all the characteristics which have led to the recognition of chain propagation and chain-branching.

To fix our ideas we will consider the phenomena which occur in a quartz vessel of about 300 c.c. capacity at 550° C., with a mixture $2H_2 + O_2$. If the pressure is below about 1 mm. the reaction is very slow indeed and largely confined to the vessel wall: but if it is raised above this limit immediate inflammation takes place. At all pressures up to 100 mm. this explosive process prevails. Just above 100 mm. the rate becomes very slow once more. The transition from the region of slow reaction to that of explosion is abrupt. For example, 200 mm. H_2 may be introduced into the vessel and 100 mm. O_2 added, the total pressure then being reduced by pumping out gas until it falls to, say, 105 mm. The mixture may be observed for

E e

several minutes during which the reaction will be barely detectable. If, however, the pressure is reduced further, a sudden burst of flame occurs as the limit at 100 mm. is passed. Above 100 mm. there is a steady reaction of measurable rate which increases continuously and rapidly with increasing pressure until at about 600 mm. a fresh transition to explosion occurs.

The relations described may be summarized thus:

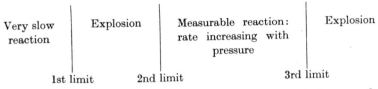

| Very slow reaction | Explosion | Measurable reaction: rate increasing with pressure | Explosion |
| 1st limit | 2nd limit | | 3rd limit |

It is evident that in its essence the reaction is an explosive one, but that in certain restricted regions the explosion is quenched by the agency of factors to be determined.

If atoms or radicals of the types H, O, and OH should by any means gain access to the system there is the possibility of the branching chain $$H + O_2 = OH + O.$$

Since O and OH each regenerate radicals, the reaction rate will rapidly grow to the point of explosion. Free atoms and radicals must be formed in small concentrations from the dissociations $H_2 \rightleftharpoons 2H$ and $O_2 \rightleftharpoons 2O$ and from reactions such as $H_2 + O_2 = 2OH$, so that there is good reason for accepting the branching-chain hypothesis.

Below the first limit the diffusion of atoms and radicals to the wall is fast enough to balance the rate of production by branching, and there is no net increase with time. A steady state is possible in which all the species are maintained at definite concentrations. The reaction rate to which this state corresponds is, as it happens, very low. At the first limit the pressure is just great enough to reduce the diffusion below the point where it can balance the formation. The steady state ceases to be possible, the reaction rate rises autocatalytically until, in an imperceptible space of time, inflammation occurs.

This interpretation of the first limit is confirmed by two experimental facts:

(a) that the explosion occurs at lower pressures in a larger vessel. where the diffusion path is longer, than in smaller vessels where it is shorter;

(b) that the critical pressures of hydrogen and oxygen are lowered by the presence of inert gases which impede diffusion, and more by heavier gases such as argon than by lighter gases such as helium.

A complete quantitative theory of the diffusion of all the radicals and atoms present is complicated, but the important properties of the system are illustrated qualitatively by a calculation based upon a simplified model. We will assume that the reaction

$$H + O_2 = OH + O$$

is the only one in which branching occurs, that one gas, H_2, O_2, or an inert gas M, is in large excess, and further that the control of branching depends predominantly upon the removal of H-atoms at the wall. The concentration of that gas which is in excess and so determines the diffusion is $[X]$.

Then
$$\frac{d[H]}{dt} = \phi + k_1[H][O_2] - K[H].$$

ϕ is the rate of original formation of atoms. $k_1[H][O_2]$ gives the rate of multiplication, since OH and O in their turn generate fresh H-atoms. K is the rate of removal to the wall at unit concentration: it will be inversely proportional to $[X]$, directly proportional to the diffusion coefficient, D, of H through X and an inverse function of the vessel size. For a long cylindrical vessel, it is approximately proportional to $1/r^2$. Then $K = K_0 D/[X]r^2$. The condition for a steady state is that

$$\frac{d[H]}{dt} = 0, \quad \text{or that} \quad [H] = \frac{\phi}{K_0 D/[X]r^2 - k_1[O_2]}.$$

If one gas is not in excess, $[X]/D$ is replaced by a rather complex function of all the concentrations and all the diffusion coefficients.

As $[O_2]$ rises, the denominator of the fraction decreases and $[H]$ rises. When $k_1[O_2]$ approaches $K_0 D/[X]r^2$, $[H]$ tends to infinity. Before it reaches this value, however, the explosion occurs. Increase in D raises the critical pressure: increase in $[X]$ lowers the value of $[O_2]$ which is possible without inflammation. The expression seems to permit negative values of $[H]$ when $k_1[O_2] > K_0 D/[X]r^2$. This is not so, since the equation is only valid up to the point where a stationary state just ceases to be possible: its derivation is, of course, based upon the assumption of such a state.

In the conditions which we have chosen for the description of events the first limit occurs at about 1 mm.: above this the diffusion to the wall of the relevant chain-propagating particles ceases to play much part. We neglect it in the discussion of the second limit, which occurs at a pressure roughly a hundredfold greater.

The special characteristics of the second limit throw a good deal of light upon the mechanism of the whole reaction. The critical pressure is independent of the size of the vessel. The control of chain-branching which now sets in and leads to a slow reaction operates through events in the gaseous phase. Moreover, addition of inert gases helps to quench the explosion, and lighter gases, which have greater molecular velocities, are more effective than heavier ones with smaller velocities. There is thus a very strong suggestion that the control process is a recombination reaction in which a third body is required to remove the energy released.

Now a very definite quantitative relation exists between the partial pressures at the second limit of the various gases present, namely the strictly linear one

$$a[H_2] + b[O_2] + c[M] = \text{constant}.$$

This highly characteristic form cannot be accounted for by the assumption of such a process as $H + H + M = H_2 + M$, but requires one of the type $$H + O_2 + M = HO_2 + M,$$

which leads to it in the following way:

$$\text{rate of branching} = K_1[H][O_2],$$
$$\text{rate of quenching} = \sum K_2[H][O_2][M],$$

the summation applying to all gases present. For the steady state which just becomes possible at the limit

$$K_1[H][O_2] = \sum K_2[H][O_2][M],$$
$$\sum K_2[M] = \text{constant},$$

or $$a[H_2] + b[O_2] + c[M] = \text{constant}.$$

The relative values of the constants a, b, and c can be calculated with some measure of success from the kinetic theory on the assumption that they correspond to the frequencies of ternary collisions.

Above the second limit there is a steady reaction. The rate increases rapidly with rising pressure: it is catastrophically reduced by the presence of iodine, which presumably removes hydrogen atoms.

It is a function of the vessel size, being very much greater in larger vessels than in smaller ones.

No elaborate assumptions are needed to account for these facts. If HO_2 is formed in the quenching process just described it has two possible fates: diffusion to the wall or reaction with hydrogen:

$$HO_2 + H_2 = H + H_2O_2 \quad \text{(or } H_2O + OH).$$

The balance of the two processes accounts for the characteristics of the steady reaction. Moreover, calculation shows that as the pressure increases further the diffusion of the HO_2 itself will be so much impeded that a third explosion limit is reached.

The events occurring at all pressures reasonably far above the first limit are expressed by the following set of equations, which may not represent quite the whole truth, but certainly contain a good proportion of it.

Initiating reaction yielding H or OH, rate $= f_1$

$$OH + H_2 = H_2O + H, \tag{1}$$

$$H + O_2 = OH + O, \tag{2}$$

$$O + H_2 = OH + H, \tag{3}$$

$$H + O_2 + M = HO_2 + M, \tag{4}$$

$$HO_2 \rightarrow \tfrac{1}{2}H_2O \quad \text{(walls)} \tag{5}$$

$$HO_2 + H_2 = H_2O + OH \quad \text{or} \quad H_2O_2 + H. \tag{6}$$

These lead, by the methods already illustrated, to the following expression for the rate of formation of water in the steady state:

$$\frac{d[H_2O]}{dt} = \frac{f_1\{(1 \cdot 5k_5 + 2k_6[H_2])/(k_5 + k_6[H_2])\}}{1 - 2k_2/\sum k_4[M] - k_6[H_2]/(k_5 + k_6[H_2])}$$

$\sum k_4[M]$ includes separate terms for $M = H_2$, O_2, etc. k_5 involves the vessel size and the diffusion coefficient of HO_2 through the gas mixture.

In the series of chemical equations from which the final rate expression is derived, certain omissions have been made for simplicity. First, the diffusion to the wall of all chain-carrying particles except HO_2 is neglected. This is justified by the fact that the second and third limits occur at pressures so much higher than the first. It must be realized, however, that the equations therefore make no pretension to include the latter, which has been treated quite separately.

The condition for explosion is that the denominator in the rate expression should equal zero. For given proportions of H_2, O_2, and

M this condition is satisfied in general by two values of the pressure, one corresponding to the second limit and the other to the third. As pressure rises the second term in the denominator falls: this makes for quiescence. But as the pressure rises still farther k_5, which measures diffusion of HO_2, falls and the third term therefore rises. This tends to reduce the denominator to zero again and raises the rate of reaction towards an infinite value.

The general predictions of the theoretical formula are satisfactorily in agreement with experiments on the third limit. The conditions of explosion derived from it are quite independent of the form of the function f_1, which describes the mode of initiation of the chains. For this reason the latter has proved somewhat difficult to determine. The initiating reaction is very probably one of the following:

$$H_2+O_2 = 2OH \quad \text{or} \quad H_2+M = 2H+M.$$

Either assumption gives an expression for the reaction rate which corresponds qualitatively with experiment, but some difference of opinion exists as to which is the more satisfactory. In any case the very steep increase in rate with $[H_2]$, $[O_2]$ or inert gas pressure depends mainly upon the rapid variations in the denominator.

In the variety of phenomena which it displays, the hydrogen–oxygen reaction is of not inconsiderable complexity. Yet this complexity is an embroidery on an essentially simple theme. The chemistry of the system is largely a repetition of a very primitive process

$$H+O_2 = HO_2, \quad HO_2+H_2 = H+H_2O_2,$$

but on this is superposed the possibility that unless the HO_2 is stabilized it breaks up in a more spectacular way, so that

$$H+O_2 = OH+O.$$

All the complications now arise from the competition between these two modes of reaction, and from the balance of chain propagation and diffusion. It is, as it were, from the physics rather than from the chemistry of the system that the intricate pattern is derived.

Oxidation of hydrocarbons

The basic theme of the hydrogen–oxygen reaction is the repetition of the cycle

$$H+O_2 = HO_2,$$
$$HO_2+H_2 = H_2O_2+H.$$

Oxygen is potentially a biradical, $-O-O-$, which could itself attack the molecule H_2, after which process the normal chain cycle would follow (though it may ordinarily be initiated in other ways). As we have seen, it is the alternative $H+—O—O— = OH+O$ which gives the branching chains and leads to most of the highly characteristic properties of the system.

The occurrence of this latter reaction is in some degree associated with the fact that the single link in $—O—O—$ is considerably less than half as strong as the double link in $O=O$, so that once the molecule has been excited to the condition of the biradical the separation of the two atoms is a less drastic sequel than might have appeared.

At first sight the oxidation of hydrocarbons exhibits characteristics which are very different from those of the hydrogen–oxygen reaction. Yet the differences are rather in the embroidery than in the essential design.

The simplest cycle of operations by which the oxidative breakdown of a paraffin could be initiated is:

$$RH+—O—O— = R+HO_2,$$
$$R+—O—O— = R—O—O—,$$
$$R—O—O—+RH = R—O—O—H+R \quad \text{or} \quad R—O—O—R'+R''.$$

Once again, however, there are superposed complexities due to various competing modes of chain termination and especially to the existence of a mechanism for the branching of chains, namely:

$$R—O—O—R' = RO—+R'—O—,$$

which is basically similar to that which can occur with oxygen and hydrogen, except that the resolution of the hydrocarbon peroxide into radicals does not occur very readily. The kinetics of hydrocarbon oxidation are best understood in terms of the assumption that the process of splitting of $R—O—O—R'$ is slow and only attains a significant rate when finite quantities of the peroxide have accumulated. It appears further that the peroxide has other possible fates and may suffer alternative decompositions which do not give the two radicals necessary for the chain-branching.

Some of the most characteristic facts about the oxidation of paraffins will now be briefly summarized, though we shall not enter into any detailed discussion of the matter.

In the first place, there are two modes of reaction corresponding to what are called the high-temperature mechanism and the low-temperature mechanism respectively. In certain examples, such as that of normal propane, the rate shows an anomalous temperature-dependence. In a certain range of temperature increase the rate actually falls away, as though some active intermediate were suffering a decomposition which is not further linked with the main chain reaction. This is believed to be the alternative peroxide decomposition just referred to.

The high-temperature mechanism is more in evidence with the lower paraffins and the low-temperature mechanism with those from pentane upwards. In the former there is probably a repetition of a relatively simple cycle of radical chain reactions, but in the latter the branching chains derived from the peroxide fission are believed to be the dominant feature. This splitting, in contrast with the branching reaction of the H_2/O_2 system, is a *slow* reaction, so that the maximum rate of oxidation is attained *gradually*. The radical R—O— can often be written $R'CH_2O$— which by a simple internal rearrangement of electrons gives R' and $HCHO$, and in fact there is a very copious production of formaldehyde from the beginning of the oxidation of the higher paraffins.

The rate of oxidation is very sensitive to the nature of the hydrocarbon, and in the series of normal paraffins increases with extraordinary rapidity as the length of the molecule becomes greater. These effects are probably associated with the dependence upon its structure of the stability of the peroxide which controls the branching.

Kinetic schemes based upon these ideas give a good general account of the observed facts. They will not be considered in detail, but it may be remarked that they provide one more example of how relatively simple motifs interplay to produce a pattern of no little complexity.

XXI

PROPAGATION OF CHEMICAL CHANGE

Propagation of reactions in space

THE spatial coordinates in a chemical reaction system have obtruded themselves so far only in a rather limited way. In a gaseous reaction which is catalysed by the surface of the containing vessel the rate is proportional to the ratio area/volume, and in chain reactions where active particles may be lost by diffusion to the wall of the container the geometry of the latter assumes considerable importance. Even so, in the examples so far encountered the macroscopic chemical change is uniform throughout an extended region of space. In other examples, however, there is an actual propagation of the reaction. The possible types of system are very varied and include, on the one hand, those where one reacting substance must diffuse into another and, on the other hand, those where successive elements of substance are raised to the temperature of reaction by the heat liberated in preceding elements. Here the complete description of events may require partial differential equations in at least one spatial coordinate as well as the time coordinate.

In homogeneous reactions no new structures are formed except, of course, the molecules of the product themselves. If, however, new phases are produced, especially new solid phases, their establishment demands a spatial propagation of the reaction.

Various interesting properties of systems where reactions progress both in space and time will now be considered.

Attack by a gas on a solid

When a corrosive gas attacks a solid such as a metal it often yields a coherent film of product through which it must itself diffuse. The diffusion path increases as the reaction progresses, so that the rate becomes less and less. In certain simple cases the amount of chemical change is proportional to the square root of the time. In general, however, secondary complications, such as the recrystallization of the product (whereby gaps in the film are opened), mask the simple law.

Kinetics of crystal growth

Crystal growth is not only important in itself but it may be the determining factor in the progress of a chemical change. When a solid such as calcium carbonate undergoes a decomposition, the product, in this example calcium oxide, often, indeed usually, forms a new lattice, and the establishment of this may govern the rate at which the whole process occurs.

Crystal growth from supersaturated solutions or vapours occurs normally by the deposition of fresh molecules on existing faces, the rate being governed by the degree of supersaturation, by the diffusion coefficient of the dissolved (or gaseous) substance, and by the ease of removal of the latent heat which is set free. Molecules deposited on a plane surface appear to be capable in some cases of translational motion across it, and in suitable circumstances can seek out, after deposition, positions of lower potential energy.

If there is no pre-existent crystal face, a nucleus must first be formed. This process depends upon the chance encounter of the appropriate molecules or ions, and may be very difficult. The necessity for it leads to the phenomenon of delayed crystallization, to supersaturation, and to supercooling.

Even when there is already a large crystal to act as a base, a kind of two-dimensional nucleation is necessary. If one layer of the lattice grows to completion, a new one can only start when a certain minimum number of molecules form a fresh centre. A single molecule on the top of a completed layer is subjected to forces on one side only. One which can be accommodated on a ledge or in an angle is much more firmly held. Sometimes crystals suddenly stop growing, and this may possibly occur when by accident a complete and perfect face has been achieved. If cracks and dislocations occur in the crystal, they may provide ledges on which deposition is easier, and it is indeed true that most crystals grow as mosaics of small blocks not quite in perfect alignment with one another.

The imperfections can arise from various causes, such as inhomogeneity of temperature and the presence of minute impurities, and, once established, will tend to be perpetuated. The imperfection of most crystals has more influence than any other factor upon their mechanical strength, which unfortunately gives little information about the actual lattice constants.

Nucleation and growth rate are separately and specifically

influenced by factors such as temperature and the presence of foreign substances, and the relative growth rate of individual faces may be changed. For this reason the size and habit of crystals are subject to very complex variations. Although these are usually difficult to interpret in detail, they may be empirically controlled to produce materials with physical properties adapted to various practical ends.

Nucleation is much influenced by solid particles such as dust, possibly because these act as bases for oriented layers of adsorbed molecules which simulate larger nuclei of the crystalline substance itself.

As has been said, certain special characteristics may appear in reactions where the initial substances and the products constitute separate phases. If a solid has to be deposited, then the rate of reaction may be determined by the growth of the new lattice. The decomposition of arsine is an example where the reaction takes place in contact with the layer of solid arsenic which forms on the walls of the vessel.

Reactions where a new lattice has to be formed are usually dependent upon the formation of nuclei. In the calcium carbonate decomposition, for example, the chemical change normally progresses at the boundary of the calcium carbonate and of the oxide. Calcium oxide molecules are more stable in a lattice of other calcium oxide molecules than they would be in the midst of calcium carbonate molecules. This is known from the fact that the oxide and the carbonate do not form solid solutions. The rate of decomposition therefore depends upon two factors, the rate of nucleus formation and the rate of growth of such nuclei as are already formed.

Nucleus formation can, in principle, go on occurring throughout the whole reaction, so that the number of nuclei increases with time. Rate of growth depends upon the area of contact between the old and the new phase, and this for a given nucleus first increases as the nucleus grows and then decreases as the old phase is consumed. In general, therefore, the curve representing the amount of reaction as a function of time is sigmoid in shape (Fig. 44). The precise form of such curves and the place where the maximum slope occurs depend upon the geometry of the nuclear growth and upon the relative rate of production of fresh nuclei as the reaction goes on.

Perhaps the most important ideas emerging from the study of reactions of this kind are two: (a) how the energy released by the placing of a newly formed molecule in a favourable lattice position may contribute to the lowering of the activation energy for its formation; (*b*) how, in general, an existing pattern of molecules possessing some element of stability tends to reproduce itself by the acquisition of fresh molecules. This is the first intimation of the possibilities of organic growth.

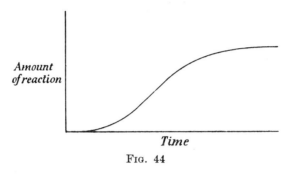

FIG. 44

Polycondensation reactions

There is another adumbration of organic growth in the formation of high polymers which separate out as insoluble masses of material capable of yielding fibres and sheets. The extended structures are traversed by covalencies, so that in a sense chemical change and crystal growth are indistinguishable processes. Although the kinetic principles governing the actual reactions apply equally well in cases where the total molecular weight is small, the most characteristic and important products are the macromolecular ones. For this reason reference to the subject has been reserved till now, though it could have been included in the last chapter.

The kinetic relationships of polycondensation reactions are determined, in a way not unfamiliar, by the varying modes of combination of relatively simple elements to give a rather complex scheme.

In a reaction such as the esterification of a glycol by a dibasic acid the progress of events can be described with quite good approximation by consideration of the rate of change in the concentrations of the actual functional groups themselves (in this example, hydroxyl or carboxyl) without reference to the size of the molecule in which they for the time being exist. The assumptions underlying this procedure are (*a*) that the volume of the system does not appreciably change as the condensation reaction goes on, and (*b*) that the rate of reaction of these functional groups does not vary much with the length of the rest of the molecule. Both these conditions are reasonably well satisfied in important practical cases. Thus we have what amounts to a bimolecular reaction between a certain group A and another group B.

A separate problem arises, however, in calculating what is of fundamental importance, namely the distribution of molecular weights among the polycondensation products present in the system at any given stage of the reaction. Dimer is formed from two monomer molecules, trimer from monomer and dimer, and in general a molecule composed of n monomer units from one of s units and one of $(n-s)$ units. Suppose we have a simple type of reaction

$$M_x + M_y = M_{x+y},$$

then the general equation for the production of M_n will be of the form

$$\frac{dM_n}{dt} = \tfrac{1}{2}k \sum_{s=1}^{s=n-1} M_s M_{n-s} - kM_n \sum_{s=1}^{s=\infty} M_s.$$

In this equation the rate constant, k, of the reaction between M_x and M_y is assumed independent of x and y. The first term on the right-hand side represents the gross rate of formation of M_n from smaller molecules: the factor $\tfrac{1}{2}$ must be introduced since otherwise each molecule would be counted twice over. The second term represents the removal of M_n by further reaction which may occur between M_n itself and other molecules of any size at all. The mathematical problem of calculating the relative numbers of molecules of each molecular weight present when a given fraction of the functional groups have reacted is now soluble. The details of this special theory will, however, not be pursued here.

Another important type of polymerization is illustrated by the formation of polyethylene. This reaction needs to be initiated by a free radical, which may be generated in various ways such as photolysis of an aldehyde or the oxidation of some of the ethylene itself,

$$R + C_2H_4 = RCH_2CH_2-$$
$$RCH_2CH_2- + C_2H_4 = RCH_2CH_2CH_2CH_2-$$

and so on. Such a reaction proceeds until one of two things happens: either termination of the chains, or what is called transfer.

There are various mechanisms of termination: combination of two growing radicals, combination of a growing radical with some extraneous radical, isomerization of the active radical to a non-rea‹ form (for example with its free valency in a sterically less acces‹ position), this isomer presently recombining with something else‹ rate which does not affect the kinetics of the main reaction.

Chain transfer is a process by which the growing radical split a part of itself which can initiate a new chain, for example

$$R(CH_2)_nCH_2CH_2CH_2— = R(CH_2)_nCH:CH_2+CH_3.$$

The evidence that this relaying process occurs is that in some ɪ tions the kinetic chain length is demonstrably considerable, while average molecular weight of the polymer formed is relatively n smaller than would correspond to it.

The kinetic treatment of these polymerization reactions dep‹ upon the establishment of stationary state equations for the ɪ of formation and disappearance of all the transitory intermedi‹ The form of the expressions derived for the rate of the main reac depends largely upon the mode of chain ending, and the const entering into the formulae are those characterizing initiation, pr gation, and termination respectively. Special means may be ployed for the study of some of these constants in isolation, whe‹ rather complicated relations can be unravelled. For example, reaction may be excited photochemically, in which case the rat initiation is calculable from the number of quanta of light which absorbed. This method can be applied with ease to those ɪ merization reactions which are started by radicals formed, for ample, in the photolysis of aldehyde:

$$CH_3CHO+h\nu = CH_3+CHO.$$

In certain examples of reactions stimulated by light absorp the rate varies as the square root of the intensity. The propaga processes can then be studied by a method which yields directly mean life of the growing radical. Some chains will continue f‹ finite time after the exciting light has been cut off, and if their is long enough, a rapidly alternating illumination is equivalen‹ a steady illumination of proportionally reduced intensity. W] however, the period of alternation is comparable with the life of active particles this will no longer be true, and from the deviat‹ from equivalence the life can be calculated.

When information about initiation and propagation is inde‹

dently available, conclusions about the mode of chain ending can be derived with some certainty from the overall kinetic relations between rate and concentration of the reacting substances.

Macromolecular products will normally be incompatible with their monomeric components and will separate out as new phases. Polymerization and what amounts to crystal growth then may continue together. As soon as part of the system becomes more or less rigidly localized the possibility that diffusion effects take control of the rate enters.

Periodic precipitation phenomena

Variety is introduced into the structures which may be formed by chemical reaction and by crystal growth through a special circumstance which leads to a spatial periodicity. It is best illustrated in the formation of what are called Liesegang rings. Although these are perhaps not much more in themselves than a physicochemical curiosity, they illustrate a principle which probably lies at the basis of important biological phenomena and is one of the origins of organic form.

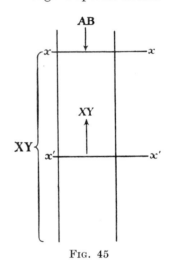

FIG. 45

If a solution containing a salt AB diffuses into another containing the salt XY so that an insoluble compound AY is precipitated, the following sequence of events is possible. In the plane xx (Fig. 45) the concentration of the ion A is initially zero and gradually rises. Presently the product [A][Y] reaches a value where precipitation of AY should occur according to the conditions of equilibrium. But in the absence of nuclei this fails to happen. The ionic product continues to rise until it is large enough to allow a spontaneous formation of nuclei, at which point a rapid precipitation of the insoluble salt occurs. The concentration of Y in the neighbourhood of xx now falls to a low value, and a gradient is created along which XY diffuses backwards towards xx and contributes to further precipitation. The region below xx now becomes denuded of XY, so that AB which has already reached there and continues to arrive has little to react with and diffuses on towards $x'x'$ where again the product $[A][Y]$ can rise to the point of precipitation. A series of bands of precipitate separated by clear intervals can thus arise.

Such a phenomenon can be observed when two salts interdiffuse in a narrow capillary, or, more easily, in a tube containing gelatine, which prevents convection and the settling of the precipitate. The gelatine itself may exert a profound influence on the course of the band formation, since it greatly modifies the production, growth, and coagulation of the nuclei.

The essential conditions for the spatial periodicity have, however, nothing to do with the gelatine. They are: precipitation, back diffusion with impoverishment of the zone on the remoter side, penetration of the diffusing salt through the reaction zone and the zone of impoverishment to regions where the ionic product can once again attain a value permitting precipitation.

The Liesegang rings are in all probability the prototypes of many of the periodic structures observed both in inanimate and in animate nature.

Flames and explosions

The propagation of flame and explosion is one of the most spectacular manifestations of chemical change. It differs from the examples hitherto considered in that the temperature of the system is not uniform.

There are two kinds of flame, one in which the combustible gases interdiffuse as in an ordinary gas jet, and the other in which they are pre-mixed. In the first the speed of burning is determined by the diffusion rate. In the second it is determined by a more complex combination of factors which requires detailed examination.

When a flame traverses a pre-formed combustible mixture which is at rest in a horizontal tube, a zone of intense reaction moves along the tube with a definite velocity. If the gas mixture is streamed through the tube at an appropriate rate, the flame front itself may be maintained stationary at the mouth. In either case the relative velocity of flame front and gas mixture is the same. If the speed of the stream is less than the rate of travel of the combustion zone, the flame performs the operation known as striking back. If, on the other hand, the gas stream emerges from the tube faster than the combustion is propagated, the flame spreads forth from the mouth and assumes a conical form (distorted to some extent by various secondary influences).

The size of the cone depends upon the speed of flow and the rate of flame propagation. In Fig. 46, the front AB is maintained stationary

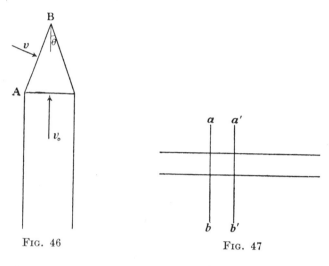

FIG. 46   FIG. 47

by the flow of gas. The propagation rate v normal to AB balances the component in this direction of v_0, the streaming rate. Thus

$$v = v_0 \sin \theta.$$

As to the normal propagation rate itself, it may be treated in the following way. Suppose the flame travels from left to right along the axis of a tube of unit cross-section as shown in Fig. 47. For simplicity the heat lost from the side walls is neglected in comparison with that passed on by conduction. Let the temperature at the point x on the axis corresponding to the section ab be T, that at $x+dx$ corresponding to $a'b'$ being $T+(\partial T/\partial x)\,dx$. By the law of thermal conductivity the amount of heat entering the element between the two cross-sections is $-K(\partial T/\partial x)$ in unit time, and that leaving it is

$$-K\frac{\partial}{\partial x}\left(T+\frac{\partial T}{\partial x}\right)dx.$$

The balance, $K(\partial^2 T/\partial x^2)\,dx$, is that which is retained by the element. If an amount of heat Q is generated in unit time in each unit of volume by chemical change, then $Q\,dx$ is produced in the element

F f

whose volume is $1 \times dx$. A total of

$$\left(Q + K \frac{\partial^2 T}{\partial x^2}\right) dx$$

accumulates in it in each second. The rate of rise of temperatu[re]
being $\partial T / \partial t$, it follows that

$$C_p \rho \frac{\partial T}{\partial t} = Q + K \frac{\partial^2 T}{\partial x^2}, \qquad (1$$

where C_p is the specific heat and ρ is the density.

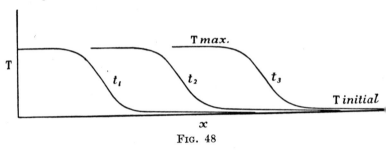

FIG. 48

While the flame front is well to the left of ab, $\partial T/\partial x$ is negativ[e]
T is low, and Q is negligible. As a result of conduction from th[e]
approaching flame front, T at the point x gradually rises: the ra[te]
of chemical change in the element assumes an appreciable value [so]
that Q increases and finally becomes very great. The element itse[lf]
now becomes the flame front and the temperature rises to a val[ue]
so high that all the heat generated can be passed on by conducti[on]
through $a'b'$. The maximum temperature of the flame front is n[ow]
reached.

Except during the first instants after the ignition of the mixtu[re]
the curve of temperature distribution will be of uniform shape a[nd]
will simply displace itself to the right as the flame travels. Th[e]
steady state is illustrated in Fig. 48, where the various curves indica[te]
the temperature distributions prevailing at times which increa[se]
from left to right.

T is clearly of the form

$$T = f(x - vt),$$

where v is the velocity of propagation and f is a function whose for[m]
remains to be determined. It must be a function of $(x - vt)$ since[,]
one shifts one's point of observation to the right at a rate given [by]
$x/t = v$, T must maintain a constant value.

Differentiation gives

$$\frac{\partial T}{\partial t} = -vf'(x-vt),$$

$$\frac{\partial T}{\partial x} = f'(x-vt),$$

so that

$$\frac{\partial T}{\partial t} = -v\frac{\partial T}{\partial x}$$

and (1) becomes

$$-vC_p\rho\frac{\partial T}{\partial x} = Q + K\frac{\partial^2 T}{\partial x^2}. \qquad (2)$$

By the Arrhenius equation the rate of heat liberation, which is proportional to the reaction rate, is of the form

$$Q = Ae^{-E/RT},$$

which may be introduced into (2), giving

$$-vC_p\rho\frac{\partial T}{\partial x} = Ae^{-E/RT} + K\frac{\partial^2 T}{\partial x^2}. \qquad (3)$$

ρ, C_p, and K are measurable properties of the substances concerned and the reaction rate constants A and E are determinable from experiments made with isothermal systems at various temperatures.

The problem of calculating v would thus in principle be solved if the equation (3) were integrable, which unfortunately it is not.

Various approximate methods of treatment have, however, been introduced. One approximation which leads immediately to a considerable simplification is neglect of the heat employed in warming up the mixture compared with that released by reaction and passed on by conduction. Another is the assumption that the reaction rate becomes negligible at a temperature $T_{max} - \theta$, where for mathematical reasons θ is regarded as sharply defined.

In some of the older theories it was assumed that no reaction at all occurs below a definite 'temperature of ignition' above which there is a constant velocity of reaction up to the maximum temperature of the flame. This conception is, of course, wrong in principle, but serves for a qualitative treatment of some aspects of the problem. In any case a quantitative theory is extremely difficult to establish, since, apart from the purely mathematical complications, there are other factors which obscure the situation. The reaction velocity is not constant during the passage of the flame front, but varies as the combustible material is consumed. It does this, moreover, according to a law the complexity of which is revealed by isothermal studies of such systems as the hydrogen–oxygen one. The assumption that heat does not escape from the sides of the tube is obviously inexact and, furthermore, neither thermal conductivity nor specific heat are independent of temperature.

Nevertheless, equation (3) is valuable in that it expresses the physical nature of flame propagation correctly enough in general terms.

One rather important modification of the theory ascribes a major role in the propagation of the flame to the actual diffusion of atoms and radicals rather than to the conduction of heat. Since most of the chemical reactions of high-temperature combustion are chain reactions, the contribution of active particles must be significant. The order of magnitude of the propagation rate will not, however, differ much whether the governing factor is diffusion of heat or diffusion of particles.

There is a very different story to tell when normal flame propagation gives place to *detonation*. In this phenomenon the expansion caused by the rise in temperature compresses the adjacent layers and thereby heats them sufficiently to bring them to the point of reaction. Something like a wave of adiabatic compression traverses the system with a velocity of the order of magnitude of that of sound. The detonation wave differs from a sound wave in that a fresh evolution of heat occurs in each volume element, whereby the temperature maintained and the compression intensified. The speed of travel about three powers of ten greater than that of normal flame, and for a given explosive mixture has a characteristic and constant value.

XXII

THE ORGANIC WORLD

Living matter

In some of the foregoing pages we have dealt with structure, in others with function. We pass now to a brief consideration of certain matters where structures and function are more closely interlocked than in any of those which have so far been encountered.

The survey of physical chemistry has revealed the existence of a whole hierarchy of structure and patterns, those of the nuclear components, those of the electrons in the atom, of the atoms in molecules, and of atoms, molecules, and electrons in all the varied gaseous and condensed forms of matter as we ordinarily know it. But this is not the end. Rocks and mountains, lakes and rivers, winds and snow-storms are large-scale versions of things which might exist in test-tubes, but the world of living organisms is of a different kind. It is ordered, it is differentiated, it grows and reproduces itself, it is purposive: it adapts itself and it evolves. Finally it becomes the seat of consciousness.

Yet neither the structures nor the phenomena of living things are necessarily discontinuous with those of the inanimate creation, and it is a question for impartial investigation whether or not they are.

This problem in its general outlines belongs strictly and necessarily to physical chemistry. If the growth and functioning of living matter is governed by laws of a special kind, while part of what goes on—for example, oxidations and reductions—is clearly an affair of chemistry, then it is important to know where the bounds may lie. If these bounds do not exist, then a story which has been traced from nuclear particles and electrons to macromolecules and giant lattices, and from crystal growth to branching-chain reactions, would seem peculiarly unfinished if it stopped short and ignored the general principles which regulate the more intricate forms abounding in nature.

It will be a necessary development, therefore, of what has gone before to inquire into some of the properties of living cells, though this will be done only in quite general terms. We are not concerned with the details of any of the biological sciences, but only with the physico-chemical mechanisms which render these sciences possible— if indeed they do fulfil this function. The question of consciousness

will be deferred until the end, since the study can be carried a lo
way without reference to it. From the start it is, of course, qui
obvious that the laws of physics and chemistry can never accou
for conscious experience—they do not even use a language in whi
any single aspect of it is describable at all, though they themselv
are in some way the products of conscious thought.

As has been said, scientific explanations continually refer the u
known to the known. Molecules are likened to sensible objects f
as long as this comparison is fruitful: then their behaviour is describ
in terms of differential equations, a process which depends upon t
fact that the construction of differential equations is a functioni
of the human intelligence which provides various kinds of satisfa
tion. Thus scientific laws are interpreted, or indeed constructed, l
the combination of elements derived from sensible experience
rational thought, and it might be something of a vicious circle
reverse the procedure. However this may be, we know by trial th
much of biology is discussable without any reference to consciou
ness, and this for the time being is enough.

The creation of order

The first problem, on the physical plane, to consider is the creati
of order by living things. Unstable and reactive substances are bu
up in reactions which go with a not inconsiderable increase of fr
energy, and the question has from time to time been raised wheth
in the course of these happenings something has directed them alo
paths other than those prescribed by the second law of therm
dynamics. This, however, is no more so than it is in the growth
a crystal, where a regular geometrical lattice emerges spontaneou
from a chaotic solution.

In crystallization the creation of order is compensated. Wh
molecules from a solution join a lattice, energy is released and m
be conducted away. It raises the temperature and increases t
chaotic motion of whatever body receives it. All through physi
chemistry there are examples of such compensation, with the deg
of order increasing in one respect and decreasing in another resp
to an extent which balances or exceeds the first.

The balance in vital processes .depends upon the coupling
chemical reactions. In all living cells there occur reactions acco
panied by decrease of free energy, and among these the oxidat

of substances such as glucose plays a prominent (though by no means unique) part. At the expense of this decrease there happen the various transformations leading to the formation of compounds of low entropy.

The coupling loses most of the mystery which it may once have possessed when it is now regarded in the light of the more general understanding of reaction mechanisms. Since these usually involve a series of stages, a linking through active intermediates is quite easily accounted for. If the reaction

$$A_2 + B_2 = 2AB$$

takes place with decrease in free energy, and the reaction

$$XY = X + Y$$

with an increase, there might at first sight be some difficulty in seeing how the first could pay for the second. But if the first is resolved into the steps

$$A_2 = A + A,$$
$$A + B_2 = AB + B,$$

the active intermediates A and B can intervene in the dissociation of XY according to the equations

$$A + XY = AX + Y,$$
$$AX + B = AB + X.$$

This interlinking of diverse reactions is the key to all vital mechanisms. As will appear they are linked in many kinds of way.

It has been mentioned that the oxidation of glucose is a common source of energy for the synthesis of unstable compounds, but many other processes, oxidations of very varied organic substances, anaerobic dismutations, and even the oxidation of sulphur to sulphuric acid are on occasion brought into action, especially by bacteria, whose versatility and virtuosity in this respect are astonishing.

Given that this coupling of reactions occurs it would be surprising if it did not play its part in the determination of many cell phenomena.

General types of substance built up in living cells

The actual process of growth involves the building up of substances such as proteins, polysaccharides, and nucleic acids, all of which are macromolecular compounds formed by reactions of polymerization and polycondensation. Reactions of this type are not unfamiliar in the inanimate world. They usually involve radical chains, and sometimes they are heterogeneous. In the formation of ethylene polymer a free radical adds on successively an indefinite number of ethylene molecules. In what is known as the Fischer–Tropsch reaction, hydrocarbons of considerable molecular weight are synthesized from carbon monoxide and hydrogen on the surface of a catalyst consisting essentially of cobalt; and they probably grow by the repeated accretion of CH_2 units formed in the hydrogenation of cobalt carbides. In some polymerization reactions provoked by light, a half-formed polymer survives for long periods in the dark and continues to grow on re-illumination. This is reminiscent of the way in which living cells may continue in a resting phase until provided with suitable raw materials, when they begin to increase and multiply once more.

The heterogeneous element is usually present in cell reactions. From various living tissues enzymes may be isolated. These are substances of high molecular weight, in general of a protein character, and sometimes susceptible of crystallization. They possess highly specific catalytic properties in respect of such reactions as hydrogenations and dehydrogenations, hydrolysis, and the like. They are heterogeneous catalysts for biochemical reactions, and in the process of cell growth they are themselves synthesized. Being largely of a protein nature, they contain repeating patterns of

$$-CH-NH-CO-$$
$$|$$
$$R$$

groups, quite possibly with free radical ends by which the structure can be extended at need. They contain free carboxyl and amino groups which make their functioning extremely sensitive to the hydrogen-ion concentration of the medium. Like other protein substances they suffer on subjection to heat (and some other agencies) a process known as denaturation.

The denaturation of proteins is a process in which the whole structure becomes less highly ordered. The rate at which it occurs has an extraordinarily high temperature coefficient which corresponds to an enormous activation energy. This fact is important and shows various things. In the first place, the high value of E points to a not inconsiderable stability of the ordered structure itself. Secondly, the fact that the rate of reaction is not thereby reduced to a low value necessitates the conclusion that the non-exponential factor of the denaturation process is very high. In other words, the entropy of activation is great, so that the transition state is much less ordered than the initial state. Thus the high non-exponential factor is direct evidence of the considerable degree of order which the protein must have had before denaturation.

So far, then, we have the picture of growth dependent upon the production of ordered macromolecular patterns, largely through the agency of heterogeneous reactions on other ordered patterns which themselves become reproduced at some stage of the total process.

From another point of view the self-synthesis that occurs in the formation of living matter bears some analogy with crystal growth, where also an existing pattern guides the new molecular units into suitably ordered positions. The entropy of activation for the synthetic process is increased by the existence of the persistent structure of the continuously maintained ordered pattern itself. We are always concerned in living processes with the maintenance and expansion of ordered structures which already exist. To understand the process of growth it is not necessary to solve the problem of the primary origins of these prototypes themselves.

The first formation of living matter may well have depended upon certain fluctuations from normality of a transcendently improbable kind, but, unlike the fluctuations upon which ordinary chemical activation depends, these are preserved for all time by the reproduction processes themselves. The latter utilize the free energy of degradative chemical changes to maintain a permanently improbable state.

In ordinary oxidation reactions, such as those of gaseous hydrocarbons, the chain processes continuously produce free radicals, but these are as continuously lost by recombination. In living matter the active centres, which could, for example, quite well be the free radical ends of incomplete macromolecules, are not subject to rapid dissipation processes, since they are more or less rigidly incorporated in large and ordered structures.

One might in very general terms regard a mass of living matter as a macromolecular, polyfunctional free radical system, of low entropy in virtue of its order, with low activation energy for various reactions in virtue of its active centres, and possessing a degree of permanence in virtue of a relatively rigid structure.

Some degree of rigidity and even of spatial coordination can arise from the polyfunctionality of the macromolecular systems. Among the latter the nucleic acids have a special importance. They are substances which occur with great regularity in the nuclear region of cells, that is to say in the denser central core discernible in many, and in which various processes preliminary to division often occur. Nucleic acids are polymers of nucleotides which contain a pentose sugar linked on the one hand to a cyclic nitrogen base and on the other to phosphoric acid.

In the nucleic acids themselves, according to X-ray analysis, the flat nucleotide plates are piled into columnar structures of indefinite extension. The spacings between successive plates of the column correspond rather closely to the longitudinal spacings of proteins. It is not at all unlikely that the piles of nucleotides guide the formation and fix the position of the protein chains in somewhat the same fashion as a trellis supports a vine. Protein chains themselves, which consist in some way in repetitions of peptide units, possess side chains which may contain functional groups, so that cross-linkages from chain to chain of the same or of different kinds can occur at suitable points. Thus enormous networks which possess continuity and structure are easily conceivable. From the frequency of occurrence of the nucleic acids, and from the regions in which they occur, the view has developed that they themselves constitute what is probably the main element of structural continuity and play a major part in guiding the deposition of fresh matter during growth.

Cells

The structure of most living matter is cellular, and the simplest organisms which can reproduce themselves unaided are the bacteria consisting of single cells. Viruses in general may well be non-cellular and some at least can be obtained in the form of crystals. They can multiply, but only in so far as they penetrate other cells and make use of some of the internal machinery which these contain.

Growth and reproduction involve obviously the coordination of a spatially rather more complex set of reaction systems than is contained in something which can form a homogeneous crystal.

Cells are of small volume, varying over considerable ranges. With many bacteria, for example, the linear dimensions run from $0\cdot1$ to $10\,\mu$. The shape may be spherical, roughly cylindrical, or more complicated. The internal structure varies: some contain a well-defined central core or nucleus, while in others the nucleus, if it exists, is only faintly differentiated and requires special methods to be rendered evident. Some cells are contained by well-defined walls of cellulose or similar material, while others are bounded by a layer in which it is difficult to detect real chemical discontinuity but which is certainly the seat of orientation and adsorption phenomena with the attendant electrical effects.

Without inquiring into the origin of the first cells, we can see that given their existence, their structure is in certain ways physico-chemically well designed for a preservation of type.

When a cell grows, nutrient materials must diffuse in from the surrounding medium and waste products must diffuse out. As synthetic processes go on, the volume increases, and this brings into play a general mechanism known as the *scale effect*. Nearly all physico-chemical phenomena involve some relation of areas and volumes, and when the scale of anything is increased these change in a different ratio, areas being proportional to the square of the linear scale and volumes to the cube. We have already seen that the generation of radicals in a gas reaction is proportional to the volume of the vessel, and their destruction to the surface area, the consequence being that a steady state which exists in a system of a given size becomes impossible if the scale is magnified.

As a cell grows, the total amount of reaction occurring in it tends to increase in proportion to the volume, while the supply of raw material and the removal of the products increases only as the area of the surface. The chemical conditions must therefore change. Some concentrations must fall: others must increase. As a result there become possible happenings of various types: precipitation of substances which act as independent growth centres; surface-tension changes which may cause the breaking down of larger structures into smaller, as a jet of liquid breaks into droplets; and other events which might initiate the process of division of the cell.

The details of what occurs are not known, though there is much interesting experimental material, including the fact that division can be accelerated or delayed by chemical actions, and the shapes and sizes of cells modified accordingly.

In some cells there are produced localized structures known as chromosomes which split and rearrange themselves in an elaborate way just before division: in others, especially bacteria, such bodies, if present, are not visible, and their evolutions, if they occur, are not apparent.

In more complex plants and in animals, although the cells of individual tissues, of course, multiply, the reproduction of the entire organism is, in general, an affair of certain special cells, and in these the hereditary characters are located in the chromosomes. One chromosome is usually the seat of a whole set of characters and is said to contain a number of genes.

There seems to be little in the last resort that a gene can be but a fragment of a specific macromolecular pattern, capable of being copied in growth by the laying down of fresh molecules in conformity with the same design. When the gene appears in a chromosome it occurs in a phase which is mechanically distinct, or partly so, from the rest of the cell. In bacteria, which possess no obvious chromosomes, the genes would be simply fragments of the general macromolecular architecture with which the various chemical functions of the cell happen to be linked.

From the cases where the regions of molecular texture associated with particular properties belong to the undifferentiated cell structure to the cases where they are coagulated or crystallized into separate phases, there may well be a continuous transition.

When characters are located in genes which in turn are contained in discernible chromosomes, and where reproduction involves the union of two cells, male and female, a large part of the problem of heredity relates to the permutations and combinations of the genes. The effects of their changing combinations are far more evident, far more frequent, and as it happens, more important in biology generally than changes in the genes themselves. Hence the idea, valid over wide regions of genetic studies, as a first approximation, that genes are universal and immutable. The whole vast subject of Mendelian inheritance, about which few doubts can exist, stands in this sense apart from chemistry.

But in unicellular organisms the situation is different. Isolated cells grow and divide. All their contents are reproduced without any recombination process of genes from separate parent cells—and even if claims that occasional conjugations of bacterial cells occur proved to be well founded, it would not alter the fact that individuals can actually be observed to divide in isolation under the microscope. The situation with unicellular organisms is different in another important respect also. In a complex animal or plant most of the cells which multiply occupy fixed locations and receive their nutrient

materials in a controlled fashion by defined routes. They are thus
largely protected against environmental changes. Single cells such
as bacteria, on the other hand, are exposed directly to the effects
of all the physical and chemical changes in their surroundings. It
might therefore be expected that with bacteria these factors would
have relatively much more influence in determining the variation of
properties from generation to generation than they could have with
complex organisms where genic recombinations dominate the picture.

The place of chemistry in the study of cell phenomena

From what has been said it appears that in a systematic inquiry
into the chemical basis of living processes the logical order is the
following: first, the investigation of the growth, division, heredity,
adaptation, and functioning of unicellular organisms directly exposed
to the action of their environment; secondly, the study of the rise
of multicellular forms and of the differentiated functions which lead
to the development of special organs; thirdly, consideration of the
reasons for the separation of genic material into mechanically distinct
phases, which, after the differentiation of sexual cells, permits all
the Mendelian combinatory processes to occur, and so removes a large
part of the phenomena of heredity from the domain of chemistry to
that of mathematics and statistics.

It must be said at once that this programme of inquiry can hardly
be implemented at the present time and will certainly not be pursued
very far in the present account. Nevertheless, the form of it is to be
observed, since it helps to place in perspective a question which arises
at quite an early stage in the study of single cells, namely that of
the inheritance of acquired characters.

It is widely held that, with debatable exceptions, properties acquired by a complex plant or animal as the result of nurture, exercise,
or mutilation are not transmitted to the progeny. This experimental
finding, which is at any rate very largely unquestionable, has led to
the doctrine that genes are subject to modification only by rare and
discontinuous mutations called forth by agencies having nothing to
do with the property which the genes control. For example, a cat
might (theoretically) produce Manx kittens because a gene had been
changed by gamma-rays, but never because its own tail and the tails
of its forebears had been cut off. This doctrine might be transferred
to single cells, which are subject to very powerful influences from

the medium in which they grow, and it might be maintained that no such influences could produce a transmissible effect. If heritable changes in, for example, bacteria—and there are many—must be ascribed to mutations unrelated to the conditions of growth, then a large slice of territory which might seem to belong by right to chemistry must be transferred elsewhere.

But from what has been said there seems to be no good reason for this conclusion. The non-inheritance of acquired characters could be very naturally explained by the screening of the genes of complex animals from environmental influences rather than by their complete immutability, and a chemical theory of changes in bacterial cells would then cease to appear in any way heterodox. At any rate we shall state briefly some of the aspects of such a theory.

Bacteria as examples of unicellular organisms

From now on we shall confine our attention principally to bacteria, since they are single cells, without obvious chromosomes, and multiply by growth and simple division into two. Special methods of staining or of microscopic observations are thought to reveal concentrations of nuclear matter in parts of the cell, and division of this material may precede that of the cell as a whole. But any complex picture of the marshalling and division of chromosomes as observed in some cells is absent. The chemistry has at least the appearance of being more important than the mechanics.

Bacteria are found in the air, in the soil, and in association with various animals and plants, both in health and disease. They may be isolated, cultivated in pure strains, and preserved in stock cultures.

When placed at a suitable temperature, usually 20–45°, in a nutrient medium, bacteria grow and multiply. Some of them need only ammonium salts as sources of nitrogen, a simple compound such as acetic acid as a source of carbon, some phosphate, sulphate, and a few metallic ions such as magnesium and potassium. Others require more complex organic substances, but the important fact is that many do not.

The chemical reactions which they bring about are numerous and diverse. With many species a few cells introduced into a liquid medium multiply to a uniform turbid suspension in which the growth can be studied quantitatively by microscopic observation in minute counting chambers, by turbidimetric methods and other means.

The law of growth

In favourable conditions the mass of bacteria in a culture increases with time according to the law

$$m = m_0 e^{kt},$$

where m_0 is the mass at the start and k is a constant.

Each element of mass adds to itself a constant fraction in each unit of time, as appears in the differential form of the above equation

$$dm/dt = km.$$

Constant conditions of supply could not possibly be maintained in the interior of a single cell if it increased in size without limit. They are, however, maintained by the division process, so that, in so far as the mean size of the cells remains nearly constant, the growth law may also be expressed in the form

$$n = n_0 e^{kt},$$

where n_0 and n are the numbers of cells at time zero and time t respectively.

Changing conditions sometimes influence the relative rates of growth and division so that the proportionality of m and n is not strictly preserved, a matter which, however, need not be considered further in the present connexion.

As long as growth follows the above law it is said to be logarithmic. In a vessel where fresh medium is continually supplied and old medium removed bacteria may be maintained in the logarithmic phase indefinitely, but in a static system one of two things happens: either the supply of material becomes exhausted, or the concentration of inhibitory products formed by the bacterial reactions becomes too high. Growth then ceases and the cells enter what is usually called the stationary phase.

When a small number of cells are transferred to a new medium after remaining in the stationary phase for some time, or, in general, when they are transferred to a growth medium of markedly different composition, there is usually a considerable delay before logarithmic growth is re-established. This period is known as the lag phase. During the lag there is either an apparently complete arrest or else growth at a rate far short of the maximum.

From the physico-chemical point of view, there seems little doubt that the lag represents the time required for the establishment of a steady state in a complex series of consecutive reactions. We may envisage the cell as a macromolecular structure with different chemical functions in different places. The protein-like catalysts called enzymes are dispersed in space. In order that the complex organic compounds of which the cell (including the enzymes themselves) is built up may be formed from the very simple starting materials which are often employed, an elaborate production line is necessary. The products of one enzyme must diffuse to the next enzyme and there undergo a further stage in processing. Pervading the cell there must be a whole series of active intermediates, and in the balanced state of logarithmic growth all these must attain steady concentrations. When the logarithmic phase is interrupted, the intermediates are dispersed in various ways, and before growth can be resumed at an optimum rate they must accumulate once more.

Now the essential nature of a living cell consists in the intimate interlinking of its various reactions, and it probably happens that there are pairs of enzyme systems in which neither can function properly without substrate derived as a product from the other. It is easy to show that in such circumstances the time required to re-establish a disturbed steady state may be very considerable.

It has also to be borne in mind that the cell accomplishes two things at the same time. On the one hand, its enzymes bring about catalytic reactions in which simple molecules undergo relatively simple changes, such as the oxidation of pyruvic acid, deamination of glycine, and so on. On the other hand, the enzyme substance itself, and the nucleoproteins and the polysaccharides and so on are all identically reproduced. It is hardly conceivable that the auto-synthetic reactions are not intimately coupled with the simpler catalytic reactions of the enzymes. Such reactions can, of course, still be brought about by the enzymes after they have been isolated from the cell, and in these circumstances they are not linked with growth. But growth never occurs without the operation of the enzymes, and this suggests that in effect the rate of increase of enzymatic substance, and indeed of the cell as a whole, is governed by an equation of the form:

enzymatic material+substrate (active intermediate)

= increased enzymatic material+products utilizable in

further cell reactions.

Enzyme expansion during growth certainly demands the laying down of ordered patterns of molecules, and if this occurs by the continuation of unfinished structures with free radical ends, fresh free radicals can be released.

$$\begin{array}{l} \text{A—A—} \\ \text{A—A—A—A—A— A—} \end{array} + \text{A:B} \rightarrow \begin{array}{l} \text{A—A—A—} \\ \text{A—A—A—A—A—A—} \end{array} + \text{B}$$

But the molecule A:B of this scheme will not be the normal substrate, since growth does not accompany the functioning of the enzyme in a test-tube. A:B will be derived from some other enzyme. A cyclical linking of processes is highly probable. In an interlocking system the rate of growth of each part, though dependent upon that of another, can follow the simple autocatalytic law.

A few elementary calculations on a simple model of such a system will now be considered.

Linked enzyme systems

Suppose we have an enzyme, to be referred to as enzyme 1, which expands its substance by reaction with an intermediate derived from another enzyme, j, the concentration of this substance being c_j. The rate of increase of 1 can be expressed by the equation

$$dx_1/dt = \alpha_1 k_1 c_j,$$

where α_1 and k_1 are constants.

The intermediate itself is formed by the reaction of the enzyme j with other constituents of the medium. c_j reaches a steady value governed by its rate of formation and its rate of consumption, if we neglect losses from the cell by diffusion. We write therefore

$$dc_j/dt = k_j' x_j - k_1 c_j = 0.$$

Now a similar set of conditions applies to enzyme j and we have

$$dx_j/dt = \alpha_j k_j c_k, \qquad dc_k/dt = k_k' x_k - k_j c_k = 0,$$

where c_k is the concentration of an intermediate derived from another. enzyme k. (α_1 and α_j are stoicheiometric factors relating consumption of intermediate to formation of enzyme substance.)

There can be similar cross-linking of various other enzymes and intermediates, but we shall idealize the problem by considering two

G g

enzymes only, 1 and 2. Thus we take x_j to refer to enzyme 2, and enzyme k which supplies it to be enzyme 1. Then

$$dx_1/dt = \alpha_1 k_1 c_2, \qquad dc_1/dt = k_1' x_1 - k_2 c_1 = 0,$$
$$dx_2/dt = \alpha_2 k_2 c_1, \qquad dc_2/dt = k_2' x_2 - k_1 c_2 = 0.$$

From these it follows that

$$dx_1/dt = Ax_2 \quad \text{and} \quad dx_2/dt = Bx_1,$$

where A and B are constants.

The solution of these equations may be verified by substitution to be

$$x_1 = \tfrac{1}{2}\{(x_1)_0 + (A/C)(x_2)_0\}e^{Ct} + \tfrac{1}{2}\{(x_1)_0 - (A/C)(x_2)_0\}e^{-Ct},$$

$$x_2 = \tfrac{1}{2}(C/A)\{(x_1)_0 + (A/C)(x_2)_0\}e^{Ct} - \tfrac{1}{2}(C/A)\{(x_1)_0 - (A/C)(x_2)_0\}e^{-Ct},$$

where $C^2 = AB$. When t becomes large the ratio x_1/x_2 tends to the constant value $A/C = C/B$, the terms in e^{-Ct} becoming negligible. Now

$$(1/x_1)dx_1/dt = Ax_2/x_1 \quad \text{and} \quad (1/x_2)dx_2/dt = Bx_1/x_2.$$

When t is large, both these reach the constant value C. x_1 and x_2 both refer to the total mass in all the bacteria, and if the cells have been grown for a considerable time in the same conditions, each enzyme will increase according to the simple exponential law

$$(1/x)\,dx/dt = \text{constant}.$$

This occurs in spite of the fact that neither of the primitive equations for the individual enzymes has this autocatalytic form. Although much over-simplified, this calculation strongly suggests that the linking of the various cell processes may be such as to render the functioning of the enzymes effectively autosynthetic.

The interesting thing about this conclusion is not that it gives us any sort of detailed picture of autosynthesis (which it does not aim to do) but that it will show the possibility of adaptive changes in the living cell.

Adaptation

One of the most remarkable properties of bacteria—which we are still taking as representative of living cells in general for the purpose of relating physical chemistry to biological behaviour—is their adaptive capacity. This manifests itself in various ways, of which the most important are adaptation to utilize new carbon or nitrogen compounds, and adaptation to resist the action of toxic substances.

If a strain of bacteria cultured over a long period in a medium containing glucose as a source of carbon is transferred, for example, to one in which the glucose is replaced by another sugar, they may evince at first a considerable reluctance to use this. They grow with a long lag, or at a rate well below the optimum. After they have grown in the new medium for some time, however, the lag accompanying further transfers disappears, and the rate rises to a steady maximum. The bacteria are said to have become trained.

In an analogous manner, training to resist the action of inhibitory substances is possible. Certain drugs in smaller quantities retard growth and in larger quantities suppress it altogether. If the cells are allowed to multiply for some time in the presence of gradually increasing amounts of the inhibitor, they may become adapted to grow at the normal rate at drug concentrations exceeding perhaps a hundredfold those which originally would have stopped any growth at all. Bacteria may also be trained to dispense with various organic substances which originally they demanded for their multiplication.

The major question is whether these matters have a chemical or a purely biological explanation. And here a word must be said about what constitutes this distinction. There is, of course, no doubt that the effect of a drug depends upon a physical or chemical action upon the living tissue, and in this sense one part of the explanation is unquestionably physico-chemical, but this is not the whole story. According to one possible theory of adaptation, certain cells are inherently resistant to a given drug and others are sensitive. In a mixed population of sensitive and resistant cells, the growth of the former would be retarded relatively to the latter by the inhibitor, so that selection would occur and the composition of the strain would be displaced more and more in favour of the resistant type. If normal bacterial strains were heterogeneous in this respect, such a process of selection could account for some of the phenomena of adaptation. This explanation would be essentially non-chemical. If, on the other hand, the inhibitor changed the conditions of growth in such a way as to favour the synthesis of a somewhat different type of cell material, then a more obviously physico-chemical theory of the action would be possible. However, the distinction between the two types of theory is not absolute.

There are two variants of the more strictly biological theory. The first is that adaptable strains are heterogeneous and that, to take drug adaptation as an example, a selection of the inherently resistant members of the population occurs. This view proves inadequate for many experimental reasons, of which the most direct and conclusive is that strains of bacteria carefully cultured from isolated single cells still show adaptive properties as marked as those of any other strains. The second variant of the theory is that during the multiplication of the bacteria of an initially homogeneous strain occasional *mutants* are thrown off, and that these possess special properties which they transmit to all their progeny. What causes the mutation is not specified, but whatever it is, it is not, according to the theory, any direct intervention of that substance or condition to which the cells become adapted. The adaptation is apparent only, and consists in the selection of the mutant strain under the appropriate conditions of growth.

Effectively the mutation is due to chance, and in this sense the theory is not a physico-chemical one. Evidently something in the macromolecular texture of the cell must have suffered a change such that in succeeding generations a permanently different pattern is laid down. But a change in pattern which is associated, for example, with non-inhibition by a given drug, is assumed to occur independently of the presence of the drug. In contrast with the theory of spontaneous mutations stands that of an induced change which potentially affects all the cells of the population.

The mutation theory may be said without injustice to have acquired its dominant position partly because any rival seemed to be disqualified under the rule that acquired characters are not transmissible. But, as we have seen, the applicability of the rule to unicellular organisms has a very doubtful justification.

It may be said further that the potentialities which would have to be attributed to accidental mutation verge on the improbable, since the same strain of cells may become adapted successively to resist several toxic substances and to utilize several carbon sources with optimum efficiency—the superposition of each new form of training leaving the results of previous training unimpaired.

These reflections do not, however, disprove the hypothesis of accidental mutations, for which if necessary in the last resort a physico-chemical hypothesis could be devised. Part of the macromolecular substance could possibly, as a result of some extremely rare kind of activation—by thermal energy, light quanta, or cosmic rays—undergo a local change of structure, as a result of which it would guide the deposition of all subsequent material into a permanently altered pattern.

As to an experimental decision between the two hypotheses of induced and spontaneous mutation, this has proved an extremely interesting and involved technical question which is beyond the scope of the present discussion. The evidence seems in fact to be in favour of the natural view that adaptations very often arise in response to the action of the environment of the cells, that is that they are induced: but it would be wrong not to state that this conclusion would be challenged by some. However this may be, it is obvious that we should in any case at least examine how an adaptive response of the cell might in principle depend upon a simple kinetic mechanism.

Possible adaptive mechanisms

The possibility of adaptation seems to follow clearly enough from the conclusion that the different enzyme systems obey the law of autocatalytic growth and that when the bacteria are cultured under constant conditions the amounts of the different enzymes settle down to steady ratios. The proportions depend upon the various reaction velocity constants. If something changes the constants, then the proportions should gradually change also.

Let us first consider adaptation to resist a toxic substance. Such a substance may well inhibit a particular set of enzymes. At first the synthesis of certain special parts of the cell will be retarded, and division may be impossible until some standard amount of the enzymes whose growth is retarded has in fact been built up. The drug thus delays multiplication. By the time division does occur, those parts of the cell which were not inhibited have attained more than their normal proportions, and yield a correspondingly enhanced concentration of their active intermediates. These in turn will finally be able to neutralize the action of the inhibitor itself.

A simple calculation shows that the enzyme proportions will change on growth until the multiplication rate is restored to normal. Here we have an automatic development of a drug resistance. The treatment of a very rough model of the system is as follows.

Suppose there are consecutive processes in which enzymes 1 and 2 are reproduced, the first of the sequence providing the substrate for the second. The first enzyme grows according to the equation

$$dx_1/dt = k_1 x_1, \qquad (1)$$

where x_1 is the total amount of enzyme 1, not in a single cell but in the whole mass of bacterial substance.

The second grows according to the equation

$$dx_2/dt = k_2 c_1 x_2, \qquad (2)$$

where c_1 is the concentration of the intermediate formed by the first. It is determined by the equation

$$n \, dc_1/dt = \alpha_1 k_1 x_1 - Kc_1 n - \alpha_2 k_2 c_1 x_2 = 0. \qquad (3)$$

This last equation expresses the balance between formation and loss of the intermediate. The first term on the right represents formation by enzyme 1, the third consumption by enzyme 2, and the second loss by diffusion, this process being proportional to the total area of the cell wall and therefore to the total number, n, of the cells among which the bacterial mass is distributed. α_1 and α_2 are factors giving the yields of intermediate from enzyme and of enzyme from intermediate respectively.

If the division of the cell has to wait until some critical amount of enzyme 2 has been formed,

$$n = \beta x_2, \qquad (4)$$

where β is a constant.

The overall growth-rate constant is given by

$$k = (1/n)\, dn/dt = (1/x_2)\, dx_2/dt. \qquad (5)$$

From equations (1) to (4),

$$\frac{x_1 - (x_1)_0}{x_2 - (x_2)_0} = \frac{\beta K + \alpha_2 k_2}{\alpha_1 k_2} = \rho, \qquad (6)$$

where $(x_1)_0$ and $(x_2)_0$ are the amounts at the time zero. It also follows that

$$k = (1/x_2)\, dx_2/dt = k_2 c_1 = (k_1/\rho)(x_1/x_2). \qquad (7)$$

When the culture has been growing for a considerable time in a constant medium, x_1 and x_2 are very large compared with $(x_1)_0$ and $(x_2)_0$, so that

$$(x_1/x_2)_{\text{equil}} = \rho$$

and therefore

$$k_{\text{equil}} = (k_1/\rho)\rho .= k_1.$$

Now let a small quantity of the culture be transferred to a medium containing a drug which inhibits the synthesis of enzyme 2. ρ rises to ρ' and the initial rate of cell multiplication is determined by the rate of growth of enzyme 2. It is expressed by

$$\frac{1}{(x_2)_0} \frac{dx_2}{dt}.$$

From equation (6) $dx_1/dx_2 = \rho'$, in presence of the drug, so that $dx_2/dt = (1/\rho') dx_1/dt$. But the original material was taken from a system where the old value of ρ prevailed, so that

$$(x_1)_0/(x_2)_0 = \rho.$$

Therefore $\quad \dfrac{1}{(x_2)_0} \dfrac{dx_2}{dt} = \dfrac{\rho}{(x_1)_0} \dfrac{dx_2}{dt} = \dfrac{\rho}{\rho'} \dfrac{1}{(x_1)_0} \dfrac{dx_1}{dt} = \dfrac{\rho}{\rho'} k_1.$

The initial growth rate is thus reduced in the ratio ρ/ρ'.

On continued growth the ratio x_1/x_2 attains the new value ρ', so that new transfers of cells to fresh medium are made subject to the condition that $(x_1)_0/(x_2)_0 = \rho'$.

$$\frac{1}{(x_2)_0} \frac{dx_2}{dt} \quad \text{is now} \quad \frac{\rho'}{\rho'} k_1 = k_1.$$

Thus the multiplication rate would have returned to normal and adaptation would appear to have taken place.

The question of adaptation to new sources of material, such as fresh sugars or other carbon compounds, presents some interesting aspects. The simplest mode of approach to the problem is to make the natural supposition that the multitudinous enzymatic reactions of the cell depend upon varying combinations of quite simple unit processes, a good deal of their specificity residing in the mode of combination, that is in the order of the unit steps, and in the extent to which each is needed for the particular synthetic sequence to be followed. Suppose cells are transferred to a new medium where substantially the same enzymes are used in a different way, for example a reducing enzyme which played a minor role in the old scheme may be involved in a key step in the new. The parts played by enzymes 1 and 2 in the old sequence are now taken over by j and k, i.e. these latter become 1 and 2 of the new sequence.

Thus, in the sense of the foregoing equations,

$$(x_1/x_2)_{\substack{\text{initial} \\ \text{new}}} = (x_j/x_k)_{\substack{\text{equil}, \\ \text{old}}}$$

$$k'_{\text{initial}} = (x_j/x_k)_{\substack{\text{equil} \\ \text{old}}} (k'_1/\rho'),$$

where the letters with dashes refer to the new growth sequence. Now it may well happen that $(x_j/x_k)_{\text{equil}}$ of the old sequence is quite small, in which case growth in the new medium will initially be very slow. But as it proceeds, $(x_j'/x_k)_{\text{equil}}$ gradually tends to the value $(x_1/x_2)_{\text{equil}} = \rho'$, so that $k'_{\text{equil}} = k'_1$, i.e. the growth-rate constant starting from a very low value, rises eventually to the optimum value k'_1 which the mechanism allows.

Adjustments of this kind will occur at rates comparable with the growth rate itself and will be completed only in so far as the bacterial substance formed under the new conditions outweighs that originally present.

Considerable elaboration of these simple schemes is possible, and would indeed be necessary for their applicability to real systems in more than a descriptive way.

Interesting and complex questions arise in connexion with the stability of adaptive changes, which sometimes survive long periods of growth in the absence of the conditions provoking them, and sometimes suffer reversal. These questions will, however, not be dealt with further here.

Nor will it be expedient to enter further into the question of the relative importance of such kinetic mechanisms and of the mutations which are postulated by many biologists. Two remarks may, however, be made. First, the kinetic theory of the adaptive process explains naturally why the training of cells to resist a drug at a given concentration produces a strain whose resistance is precisely graded to that particular concentration but not to higher ones: discontinuous gene-mutation would be thought to give resistance bearing no special relation to the concentration at which the cell was trained. Secondly, if adaptive mechanisms such as the above are never in fact employed by real cells, it is rather difficult to understand why they are not.

Another thing should also be said at the present juncture. It is this: the range of adaptive possibilities open to a given strain of bacteria, remarkable as it is in many ways, is bounded. The cells will become acclimatized to many new sources of carbon, but not to all. One particular bacterium, for example, can be trained to utilize a whole series of sugars and many simple organic acids, but cannot be induced to grow with erythritol. Many types of bacteria related to *Bact. coli* utilize lactose, with or without training, but inability to do so remains characteristic of the typhoid sub-group of that family. In terms of the views which have just been discussed this limitation in the amplitude of the possible changes is quite understandable. The shifts in enzyme balance which have been envisaged as the basis of adaptation do not involve the creation of fundamentally new enzymatic functions. On the other hand, profound mutation caused by very rare processes of high activation energy could be envisaged, and might in the course of evolutionary history have been the origin of fresh species. Such events, however, are not observable in normal experimentation.

Patterns of chemical reactions

That aspect of the living cell in which it most clearly appears as a physico-chemical system is the one which reveals its functioning as a complex pattern of relatively simple chemical reactions.

It is the mode of combination of these reactions which in many respects determines the characteristic behaviour.

There must be sequences of *consecutive* reactions, and from the way in which these are probably linked there follows the possibility of adaptive changes. Variations in the relative velocity constants impose adjustments of the proportions of enzymatic material; and these in their turn are responsible for changed biochemical properties, and for an automatic attainment, in appropriate circumstances, of an optimum growth rate.

The individual simple steps of complex reaction mechanisms may be combined in other ways. If they are linked in a *cyclical* manner, there arises the possibility that a temporary interruption of the cycle may be very difficult to rectify. If each of two enzyme systems provides an intermediate needed by the other, and if the intermediates are lost by diffusion during a suspension of activity, then restoration of the stationary state may be very tardy, and long lag phases may become evident.

Many interesting cell phenomena depend upon the existence in the reaction network of *parallel* or *competing* branches. These can be responsible for effects which have the appearance of being purposive.

Certain bacteria utilize nitrate as their source of nitrogen but not so well as they utilize ammonium salts. If to a culture actively growing in nitrate an ammonium salt is added, the reduction of the nitrate stops immediately and completely, as though the cells chose the preferred source.

Again the cells grow in presence of oxygen with the oxidation of their carbon source: in the absence of oxygen they depend upon a dismutative fermentation of the carbon compound, one portion of which is oxidized at the expense of the rest, which is reduced. If oxygen is passed into the fermenting culture, not only does the oxidative breakdown supervene, but the alternative process is actually inhibited. This *Pasteur effect* operates as though the cells knew how to select the more economical growth process.

In neither of the two examples quoted is it a question of the mere competition between a slower and a much faster process, nitrate and ammonia consumption on the one hand and aerobic and anaerobic growth on the other differing in overall rate by a factor which is, in the cases mentioned, less than two.

The explanation in broad outline is as follows. The oxidation of the carbon substrate involves a series of reactions whereby hydrogen is removed by other carrier molecules, which may be typified by X, X passing to XH_2 in the process. Continued growth involves the steady re-oxidation of XH_2. In the stationary state there will be a definite ratio XH_2/X in the system. Optimum growth in ammonium salts with a carbon source such as glucose occurs when this ratio is rather low. When cells have become adjusted to grow in nitrate, which they must reduce, the ratio has become higher. Addition of ammonium salts which permit the alternative mechanism leads to a lowering of XH_2 to the point where the nitrate can no longer be reduced.

Aerobic and anaerobic growth are distinguished by the circumstance that in the former the re-oxidation of the compounds such as XH_2 is performed by molecular oxygen, whereas in the latter it is performed by one of the carbon compounds which is fermented. A relatively high concentration of XH_2 prevails during the anaerobic growth: if oxygen is passed, XH_2 is oxidized and it is no longer able to attack the fermentable carbon source.

The details of these mechanisms are a little more complex, and partly bound up with adaptive changes which cells undergo when the growth process changes, but the essential principle is clear enough; that the phenomena depend upon the branching in the reaction network involving the oxidation-reduction systems.

Growth and form

From here on only the roughest outlines of the remaining extent of the subject can be given, the merest sketch which indicates the areas to be filled in one day with colour and detail.

From the single cell we must pass to the multicellular structure and thence to the differentiated organism. We have seen in a rough way a series of analogies by which the cell can be brought into the physico-chemical picture. Polycondensation reactions lead to growing macromolecular structures, and, given that these are part of a cell, the scale effect ensures a gradual disturbance of the chemical environment which can divert the course of events whenever the size exceeds a critical value. The coming into being of the cell necessitated an initial coordination, both of structures and of processes, into which there is little hope of probing at present, but given its existence, some idea of the principles governing the mechanism for its perpetuation can be formed. One way in which division could be provoked depends upon the operation of surface forces. If on growth the lengthening of the diffusion paths caused an accumulation of a substance which strongly affected the surface tension of the boundary layers, then the cell might split as a larger drop splits into smaller ones. Again, with a two-way flow of materials into and out of the cell, periodic precipitation phenomena are possible, and these may influence the formation of nuclei or of wall-building substance. The details of these matters are not known, but just as the kinetic linking of reactions contains the general principle of adaptive functioning, so the scale effect and the diffusion laws contain the first requirements for the evolution of organic form.

It is, however, a long way from here to the shapes and structures of living nature. The direction of the path is somewhat as follows. When a crystal of a simple substance grows, the geometry of its solid state is essentially rectilinear. With macromolecular substances new possibilities arise. On the one hand, some of the structural properties of the large molecules themselves tend to impose symmetries of the same kind as the crystallographic symmetries. There are evidences of these in such matters as the regular ranking of leaves on stems, and in the approximate bilateral symmetry of most animal forms. On the other hand, in systems with large size and flexibility, formed of sheets or fibres, or indeed of sheets enclosing actual fluid, the imposition of rounded forms by the surface forces becomes more and more marked. Plants do not look much like crystals, yet they grow along well-defined axes, and, conversely, the fern-like forms of ice crystals on window-panes are highly suggestive of some vegetable structures.

Buddings and branchings may well be controlled by what might roughly be called crystallographic factors: shapes in general by hydrostatic, hydrodynamic, and surface energy factors.

But the very characteristic property of most organic forms is their high degree of differentiation. About the origin of this only very general statements can be made, but these, although lacking in detail, seem not unreasonable. We accept the fact of cell division, and note that in many cases the separation of two cells formed in this process may be incomplete. Anthrax bacilli tend to remain joined in long chains: staphylococci cluster into grape-like bunches. Under the influence of certain inhibitory drugs bacteria in division may fail to complete the formation of the normal cell-wall. Suppose now that the two cells of a joined pair (under the influence, say, of ultra-violet radiation) had suffered mutation in such a way that each lost a separate specific synthetic function. They could now grow and multiply as a pair, but not singly. This would mean that the combination constituted a very primitive multicellular organism. In the course of ages further differentiations could be added.

Once anything approaching a continuous mass of tissue has evolved fresh factors come into play. Concentration gradients between one part and another are created, the scale effect enters into operation in new ways, periodic precipitation phenomena along the diffusion paths become possible, and these in their turn may cause re-direction of the axes of growth. The more complex the paths of inward and outward diffusion, the greater are the possibilities for the spatial separation of the various steps in the sequences of chemical reactions. Permeability effects and osmotic separations come into play. The importance of all these physico-chemical factors is strikingly attested by the fact that the material in certain embryos has been shown not to be predetermined in function, but to have its ultimate organization determined by the influence of other cells with which it is brought into relation.

In some such way as that outlined the stage is set for all the complex interplay of events which govern biological form and function. The drama which then unfolds is not for physical chemistry to record.

Concluding remarks

The attempt to explain the functioning of a living cell in terms of physico-chemical laws presupposes that there is no effective intervention of consciousness into the part of the phenomenon under investigation. This clearly is a limitation, at least at one end of the scale of organic being. Everyone is directly aware of the fact that his actions are in many respects indissolubly related to his sensations and his thoughts. However these may be analysed by philosophers, there is no question of describing them in the language of physics and chemistry. The sensation of 'green' is *not* the same as, or anything like, the equations for the propagation of light in such-and-such a spectral region, nor does it resemble the chemistry of retinal substances or the physics of brain cells. It is *sui generis*. Nor can my belief that I am about to will myself to open the door be described in terms which could be intelligibly used of a physical phenomenon. The suggestion was once debated that the uncertainty principle in physics is related to free will. This is surely fallacious. The principle in question might, roughly speaking, justify the statement that an observer does not know what an electron will do next. But belief in free will rests in no way upon the fact that other observers do not know what my next move will be: it rests upon my own conviction that I myself do know.

Apart from this mistaken attempt, practically nothing constructive has been said about the interrelation of the two worlds of thoughts and sensations on the one side and of physical and bodily phenomena on the other. They are parallel and they react upon one another. But they seem separated by an unfathomable abyss. According to some philosophers this idea is false, and what for brevity may be called the mental and the physical are two inseparable aspects of a single unanalysable whole. If this is so, it is hard to understand why the technique of description required for the two is of such a pronounced duality. To maintain that there is no problem is to belittle one of two things: either the world of human experience, or else the vast coherent system of nature which scientific description constructs. Nor will men of science be much attracted by the way out of idealist philosophers according to whom there is no external reality and to whom the mental world alone exists. To suppose that the universe is a private dream (which includes the illusion of other people dreaming the same dream as oneself) is too much.† The compromise according to which real things exist but the spatio-temporal mode of their existence is a creation of the mind is now generally regarded with coolness, and seems to refer the question back rather than to solve it.

What must, however, be recognized is that scientific laws do largely depend for their formulation upon the selection of what we consider significant and of what we consider simple. The wave equation can only be said to provide explanations of things to minds which attach significance to mathematics. In this sense the scientific description of the world does contain a subjective element. It lies, however, simply in what we think worth saying about reality, rather than in our idea of the status of this reality itself.

The question of the physical and mental aspects of experience remains. All that can be said is that they are concomitant. If we ask naïvely how the concomitance works, all that can really be said is that we do not know (or with more dignity and less honesty that it is a meaningless question). In this connexion it is interesting to note how many concomitances there are in physics about which no more can be said. Electrons pass from one energy level to another and light quanta appear; mass dissolves and energy traverses space; particles follow statistical laws and are said to be like waves; they are found on the wrong side of barriers too high for them to surmount; space-time is curved in the neighbourhood of gravitating bodies. All that is known is that one set of observations will in such cases be relatable to another set of observations of a different kind. To ask for more is according to one view to invent an illusory difficulty, and according to another view to set human intelligence a task which it is not built to carry out. According to a third possible one, it is something which may ultimately be solved by patient progress.

There is no pressing need for the man of science to make up his mind on this subject. For practical purposes we can fortunately neglect the conscious world (or the conscious aspect of the world) in considering simple cell systems, primitive organisms, and even, it

† As fallacious as the connexions between the uncertainty principle and free will are those between the theory of relativity and a subjective theory of the world. Because observers in relative motion have their individual time scales, it does *not* follow that there is anything subjective about their measurements. In relativity, space and time are functionally interdependent (space-time), but this is an objective fact about the universe. In the world of Euclid and Newton two observers can have their own x-coordinates at any moment without the implication that their measurements are subjective, and it is no different with any of the coordinates of space-time.

appears, large parts of human physiology. A considerable number of bodily activities are automatic for a good deal of the time (though subject to sudden interventions of the conscious element). It is important, however, that when we do say anything about the problem we should avoid such errors as confusion of happenings in the brain with sensations, or quantitative matters like wave-lengths with qualitative matters like colour.

There things must be left. As has been said at various stages of this account, scientific interpretations express the unknown in terms of the known, and the known into which the translation is made becomes progressively more sophisticated. There is no particular reason for supposing that this process is in any way completed or that the last word has been said on any of the fundamental questions. Nor can scientific inquiry predict its own future: that is perhaps the greatest fascination of its adventure.

INDEX

PRINTED IN GREAT BRITAIN
AT THE UNIVERSITY PRESS, OXFORD
BY VIVIAN RIDLER
PRINTER TO THE UNIVERSITY